W9-DFA-744

laboratory manual in
the science of
biology

for the fourth
text edition

paul b. weisz
professor of biology, brown university

laboratory manual in the science of biology

for the fourth text edition

mc graw-hill book company
new york st. louis san francisco dusseldorf johannesburg kuala lumpur london mexico montreal new delhi panama rio de janeiro singapore sydney toronto

Laboratory Manual in the Science of Biology

07-069126-6

4567890 HDHD 7654

*This book was printed on permanent paper and bound by McGregor & Werner Graphics, Inc. The designer was Elliot Epstein.
The editors were Thomas Adams and Barry Benjamin.
John F. Harte supervised production.*

preface

To provide an appropriate fit with the fourth edition of "The Science of Biology," the sequence of exercises in this manual has been altered somewhat and the references to the text have been changed as necessary. However, the overall contents of the manual are the same as for the third edition of the text.

As before, the eight parts of the manual again correspond to the eight subdivisions of the text. The exercises in the first part are designed to be scheduled for virtually any stage of the course. Some instructors prefer to being the laboratory year with animal dissection (the choice of either the frog or the fetal pig being offered here), others defer this type of study to a later phase, and still others omit it altogether. Similarly, the exercise on taxonomy can be programmed for nearly any point of the course.

Part 2 now includes—in line with the topics of the corresponding subdivision of the text—the exercises on the chemistry, physics, and biology of cells, on tissue and organ structure of plants and animals, and on ecology. Sequence changes have not been necessary in the remaining parts. Thus the possibilities for selecting exercise assignments in many different ways remain unaffected. Indeed, to provide such choices, the manual includes nearly twice as many exercises as can be assigned in a year-course. In many cases it will also not be desirable to assign all parts of a given exercise.

Each exercise again consists of four segments: a listing of equipment needed (with references to an expanded Appendix containing notes on reagents and supplies); an introductory statement about the objectives of the exercise; a detailed set of directions on the work to be done (including illustrations where warranted as well as pertinent text references); and an Analysis section consisting of questions relating to the laboratory work and intended to aid in discussion, self-study, and examination. Basically each exercise is again designed to serve for one weekly unit of laboratory work. Exceptions occur in two or three cases, and these are so noted in the introductory segments of the exercises.

Paul B. Weisz

contents

laboratory manual in the science of biology

for the fourth text edition

part 1 the study of life

exercise 1 the frog [I]

I materials

Each Student

frog, freshly killed or preserved
dissecting pan, pins
dissecting instruments
hand lens

II introduction

In this and the following exercises, the anatomy of the frog will be examined in some detail. The frog is a vertebrate, which means that many or most aspects of its structural organization are shared in common with all other vertebrates, man included; in a general way, a study of frogs is also a study of man. Thus, as a first leading theme in these exercises, ask yourself, for every structure observed in the frog, if an equivalent structure exists in your own body; and if so, where that structure is located.

As a second leading theme, pay particular attention to the RELATIONSHIPS among organs and groups of organs. Structural parts are not "just there," in random locations. Their specific layout within the body contributes to making certain functions possible. Therefore, for every structure seen, determine what organ system it is part of; how it is connected up with other components of that and of different organ systems; what general function this structure serves; and how its shape, form, and specific position within a larger pattern of shapes and forms contribute to the execution of its general function.

To make a good, or informative, dissection, one needs good dissection technique. A first essential here is to know one's TOOLS and their limitations. Familiarize yourself with these three fundamental dissecting tools: SCISSORS, PROBE, FORCEPS. Ideally, you should have available two pairs of scissors, a small pair for fine work and a larger one for gross work. Either should be SHARP and should cut without much pushing and pulling. In dissecting the frog, scissors will serve adequately for all cutting jobs. Not only is a scalpel not needed, but scissors are safer, for both you and the frog; scissors are much less likely to botch your dissection than the unfamiliar scalpel. Your probe should be BLUNT. This instrument serves as an extension of your fingers, and is used to LIFT tissues, to PUSH tissues aside so that underlying structures become visible, and to FEEL for tissues which cannot be immediately seen. Never use sharp-pointed instruments here. Both ends of the probe can and should be used. The blunt forceps handle also makes an excellent probe; and where possible use your fingers—they are the most sensitive probes. Ideally you should have available two forceps—a narrow-tipped one for close work and a broad-tipped one for gross work. Forceps are used to hold and lift tissues. They should be used for lifting WHENEVER scissors are used for cutting. Never cut anything without raising the part to be cut; otherwise underlying parts might be destroyed.

Dissecting does not primarily mean "cutting up"; it means "exposing to view." Hence never cut more than is absolutely necessary to expose a part. Keep in mind that the more that is cut apart, the more the structural relationships among parts will be destroyed—and you want to preserve organizational patterns as much as possible. Moreover, where cutting cannot be avoided, make sure you have fully IDENTIFIED and studied the structural connections of a part before you cut it. It may be valuable to make a quick labeled sketch of a region before part of that region must be cut.

In summary:

1. READ the directions carefully before you begin to dissect, and obey them word for word.
2. IDENTIFY structures to be cut before cutting them.
3. LIFT structures to be cut.
4. CUT only what is absolutely necessary.
5. Then use probes and fingers to EXPOSE structures to view.
6. Proceed to STUDY them.

Following is a glossary of anatomical terms. These terms are used frequently in anatomical work, and you will do well to become thoroughly familiar with them (see also Fig. 1.1).

dorsal: near or toward the back
ventral: near or toward the belly
lateral: near or toward the sides, right or left
median: near or toward the middle
anterior: near or toward the head end
posterior: near or toward the hind end
caudal: near or toward the tail end
superficial: on or near the surface
deep: some distance below the surface
sagittal: relating to the mid-plane which bisects left and right

Fig. 1.1 A few of the commonly used anatomical designations. (Courtesy of Carolina Biological Supply Co.)

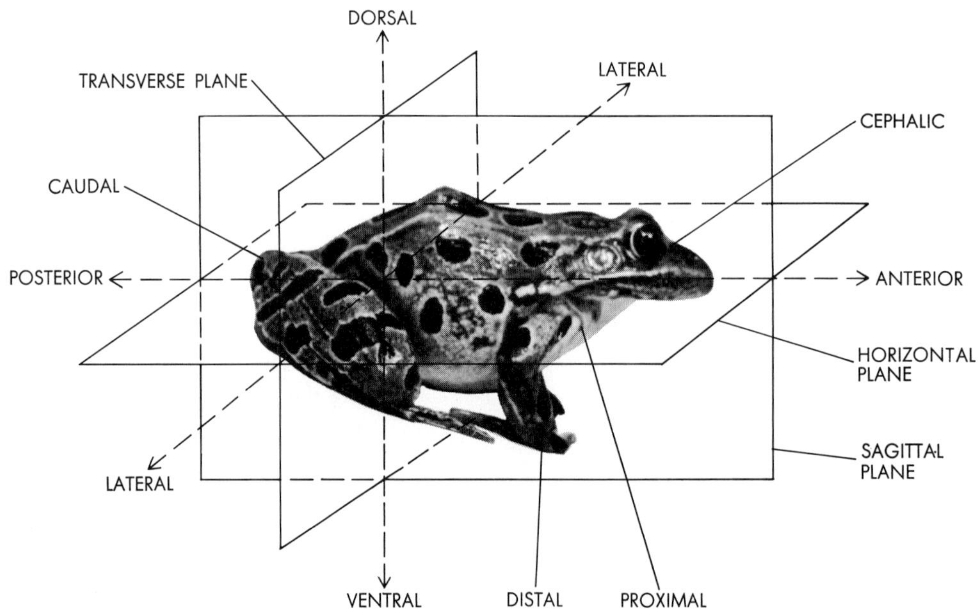

transverse: relating to a plane separating anterior and posterior
horizontal: relating to a plane separating dorsal and ventral
proximal: near to a point of reference
distal: far from a point of reference
pectoral: relating to the chest and shoulder region
pelvic: relating to the hip region

III directions

A. external anatomy

1. Trunk and Limbs

a. The principal body divisions are HEAD, TRUNK, and LIMBS. Frogs are without neck or tail. The SKIN is smooth, moist in the living animal, and thin; it is an important breathing organ. Slit the skin of the back and verify its thinness. Verify also the comparatively loose attachment of the skin to underlying body parts. In the living animal LYMPH fills the spaces underneath the skin. Note the COLORATION of the skin, that is, pale ventrally and greenish with dark spots dorsally. To some extent a frog may change the depth of the greenish dorsal color according to the illumination of the background environment. The skin contains mucus-secreting glands, concentrated particularly in the two DERMAL FOLDS running longitudinally from behind each eye along the back to the base of the hind legs. Locate the ANUS at the posterior end of the trunk. Just in front and to each side of it along the back, pulsations of a pair of lymph vesicles may sometimes be observed in the living animal.

b. The front legs consist, as in man, of UPPER ARM, LOWER ARM, WRIST, HAND, and FINGERS. How many of the latter are present? During the breeding season (April–May), the inner finger of male frogs develops a black, swollen NUPTIAL PAD, used in holding the female during mating. In the hind legs, identify THIGH, SHANK, ANKLE, FOOT, and webbed TOES. How many toes are present?

Cut through the skin around the top of one thigh and, using judicious force, pull the skin off the leg in one piece. Examine the leg musculature; move the leg and note how the muscles change shape and length. With a blunt probe, carefully loosen and separate individual thigh muscles from one another and locate the thigh bone, or FEMUR. Along it lies the white SCIATIC NERVE, the principal nerve of the leg, and the ILIAC ARTERY, the principal blood supply to the leg. Trace nerve and artery as far as the knee. In the shank, the largest muscle is the spindle-shaped calf muscle, or GASTROCNEMIUS. Loosen it away from other muscles and note its ORIGIN at the knee and its INSERTION on the foot. Insertion is achieved by the prominent ACHILLES' TENDON, which passes behind the heel and spreads fanwise over the sole of the foot. Pull on the gastrocnemius and observe the resulting motion of the foot.

2. Head, Mouth, and Pharynx

a. The head bears three pairs of prominent sense organs, namely, eyes, nose, and ears. The bulging EYES are equipped with a more or less nonmovable UPPER LID, a nonmovable LOWER LID, and a transparent fold, the NICTITATING MEMBRANE. The latter is attached to the inside of the lower lid and can be moved up over the eye. A frog can close its eyes altogether by retracting them deep into their sockets, a process which also brings the upper and lower lids together. Near the tip of the snout are the nostrils, or EXTERNAL NARES. They can be closed by valves, and they lead into nasal chambers. The latter communicate with the mouth cavity via a pair of INTERNAL NARES. Pass a fine flexible wire into a nostril and by this means locate the internal nares in the roof of the mouth. Behind each eye locate the coppery circular eardrum, or TYMPANUM; outer ears are not present in frogs. In the center of the tympanum a slightly raised spot marks the attachment of the interior COLUMELLA, the single middle-ear bone transmitting sound waves to the inner ear (there are three middle-ear bones in mammals).

b. Put the frog ventral side up in your dissecting pan and pin down hands, feet, and upper jaw. With scissors cut through the angles of the jaws on each side, so that the lower jaw can be folded back to expose the MOUTH CAVITY. On the floor of this cavity is the fleshy TONGUE, attached at its ANTERIOR end to the lower jaw; a frog hurls its sticky tongue out hind end first. Along the rim of the upper jaw feel with your finger for the small TEETH, PREMAXILLARY teeth along the middle, MAXILLARY teeth along the sides. Another set, called VOMERINE teeth, is present just behind the

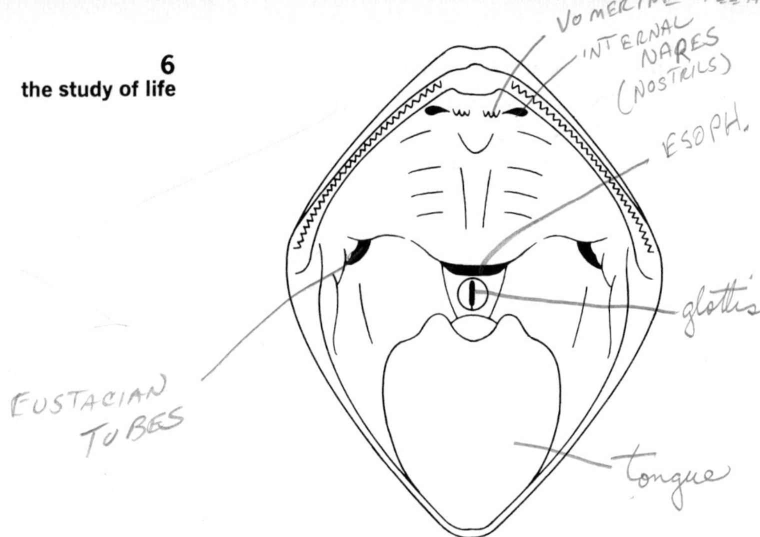

Fig. 1.2 Label this sketch of the mouth cavity.

mid-portion of the upper jaw along the roof of the mouth, attached to skull bones called VOMERS.

Reidentify the internal nares, and note the PHARYNX, the space behind the mouth cavity proper and toward the throat. Depress the floor of the mouth and probe carefully into the pharynx until you find a median projection with a longitudinal slit. The projection marks the position of the LARYNX (voice box), and the slit is the GLOTTIS, through which air passes into and out of the larynx (and from there directly to and from the lungs, a windpipe being absent in frogs). Probe between the larynx and the roof of the pharynx along the midline of the body and find the opening into the ESOPHAGUS, the alimentary tube leading into the stomach. In the angles of the jaws, on a level with the esophageal opening, locate the opening of the EUSTACHIAN TUBE on each side, on the roof of the pharynx. These tubes communicate with the middle-ear cavities. Verify this by slitting and gently removing one of the eardrums. Note again the columella. Ventral to it is the beginning of the eustachian tube. Pass a fine wire into this canal and determine where it emerges in the pharynx.

Label Fig. 1.2.

B. internal anatomy

1. The Coelom

a. Close the mouth of the frog and pin both jaws down. Lift the ventral trunk skin with forceps or needle, and with scissors make a longitudinal slit through the skin along the midline. Extend this slit forward into the lower jaw and backward to the end of the trunk. Make lateral cuts to each side, one set in front of the forelegs, another near the base of the hind legs, and pin the resulting skin flaps to the side. Note the ventral BODY-WALL MUSCLES and, along the mid-ventral line, the VENTRAL ABDOMINAL VEIN. Lift the muscles near the posterior end of the trunk and make a longitudinal incision through the muscles slightly to the left side (your right) of the vein. Then (always lifting the parts to be cut to prevent damage to underlying structures) continue the incision forward to the level of the forelegs, where you will encounter the transversely placed bones of the PECTORAL GIRDLE. Raise the girdle with forceps (do not be afraid to exert reasonable force) and continue your incision by cutting through the STERNUM (breastbone). Now make lateral cuts through the body wall to each side, one set of cuts immediately behind the pectoral girdle, another set at the posterior end of the trunk incision. Fold to the side and pin down the resulting flaps of body-wall muscles. Also fold to the side the left and right portions of the cut pectoral girdle; if necessary make additional cuts through these bones near the bases of the forelegs.

b. The COELOM, or principal body cavity, and most of the internal organs are now exposed. Note the shiny PERITONEUM lining the inner surface of the body-wall muscles. This thin membrane also covers and holds in place all other internal organs. Those peritoneal portions that fold around and hold such organs are called MESENTERIES.

If your specimen is female, much of the coelomic cavity is likely to be filled by a pair of large, transparent OVARIES, each containing hundreds of black and white eggs (up to 1,500). Gently lift the left ovary with forceps and find its place of attachment. Cut through the attachment and remove the ovary in one piece. If the other ovary still obstructs your view, it too may be removed altogether, or it may be lifted out of the body cavity as far as possible and pinned down.

In freshly killed specimens one or both LUNGS may be highly inflated with air and appear as elongated, reddish, semitransparent sacs. If so, make a slit in each lung to let the air out and to reduce its size. If the lungs are not inflated, they will be partly hidden under the LIVER, the large, prominent, dark brown organ in the mid-ventral portion of the trunk.

2. The Heart

If necessary, lift or shift the liver gently until you locate the HEART, along the midline at a level between the forelegs. On each side of the heart is a lung. The heart lies in a special part of the coelom, the fluid-filled PERICARDIAL CAVITY. This space is separated from the remainder of the coelom by the membranous PERICARDIUM. Lift the pericardial membrane with forceps and slit it open ventrally to expose the heart fully. This organ may still be beating if the frog has been freshly killed. Identify the single thick-walled, triangular VENTRICLE, and the two more anterior, thin-walled ATRIA. Lift the APEX of the heart and snip the slender strand of tissue that connects the atria to the dorsal wall of the pericardium. In this dorsal atrial region, well underneath the ventricle, locate the SINUS VENOSUS, a thin-walled, membranous sac which collects all the blood coming to the heart from the veins of the body (Fig. 1.3). More specifically, three large veins enter the sinus venosus: the POSTERIOR VENA CAVA along the midline and an ANTERIOR VENA CAVA laterally on each side. The sinus venosus itself empties into the right atrium (even though it appears to connect to both atria). The left atrium receives blood returning from the lungs via the pulmonary veins. These lie dorsal to the sinus venosus and will be difficult to see at this stage. Let the heart fall back to its normal position and locate the TRUNCUS ARTERIOSUS, a single wide arterial vessel emanating from the ventricle and passing ventrally over the right atrium. Follow it forward to where it divides into two branches. Make notes and sketches of the heart region for reference in the next exercise, when the circulatory system will be studied in detail.

3. The Alimentary System

Examine the liver; it is composed of three lobes. One lobe lies on the right side of the frog. A large left lobe consists of two sublobes; verify this by lifting the more ventral sublobe and note its basal attachment to the other sublobe. Between the right and left lobe find the saclike, bile-storing GALL BLADDER, greenish in color. The third liver lobe is small and lies dorsal to the gall bladder. Lift the left liver lobe and identify the STOMACH, whitish and roughly J-shaped. Anteriorly the stomach connects with the esophagus, posteriorly, with the SMALL INTESTINE. Slit the wall of the stomach and note its contents and the nature of the stomach wall. Carefully pass a blunt probe forward through stomach and esophagus into the pharynx. In the small intestine, the first portion is the DUODENUM, a section looping forward, parallel to the stomach and forming a U with it. In this U loop lies the diffuse yellowish tissue of the PANCREAS, an important digestive gland secreting pancreatic juice into the duodenum. This portion of the small intestine also receives bile from liver and gall bladder. The BILE DUCT from the gall bladder passes through the tissue of the pancreas, where small PANCREATIC DUCTS open into the bile duct as well. The duodenum thus receives both bile and pancreatic juice through the same duct. This connection may be verified readily in freshly killed frogs; slit the duodenum open along its entire length and squeeze the gall bladder, forcing bile out. Where the small intestine turns posteriorly again, the duodenum ends and the ILEUM begins, without obvious demarcation. Along this coiled section note some of the MESENTERIES referred to earlier. Each is a double membrane carrying blood vessels and nerves. Held by mesenteries near the posterior end of the stomach is the SPLEEN, a small, reddish, round organ that is not part of the alimentary system but is allied to the circulatory system. At its posterior end the small intestine (ileum) connects with the wide but shorter LARGE INTESTINE. The hind portion of this part of the alimentary tract is covered

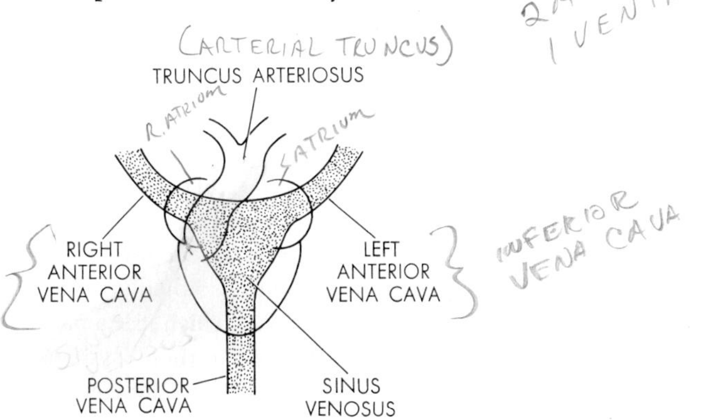

Fig. 1.3 ***Some of the vessels carrying blood to and from the heart.***

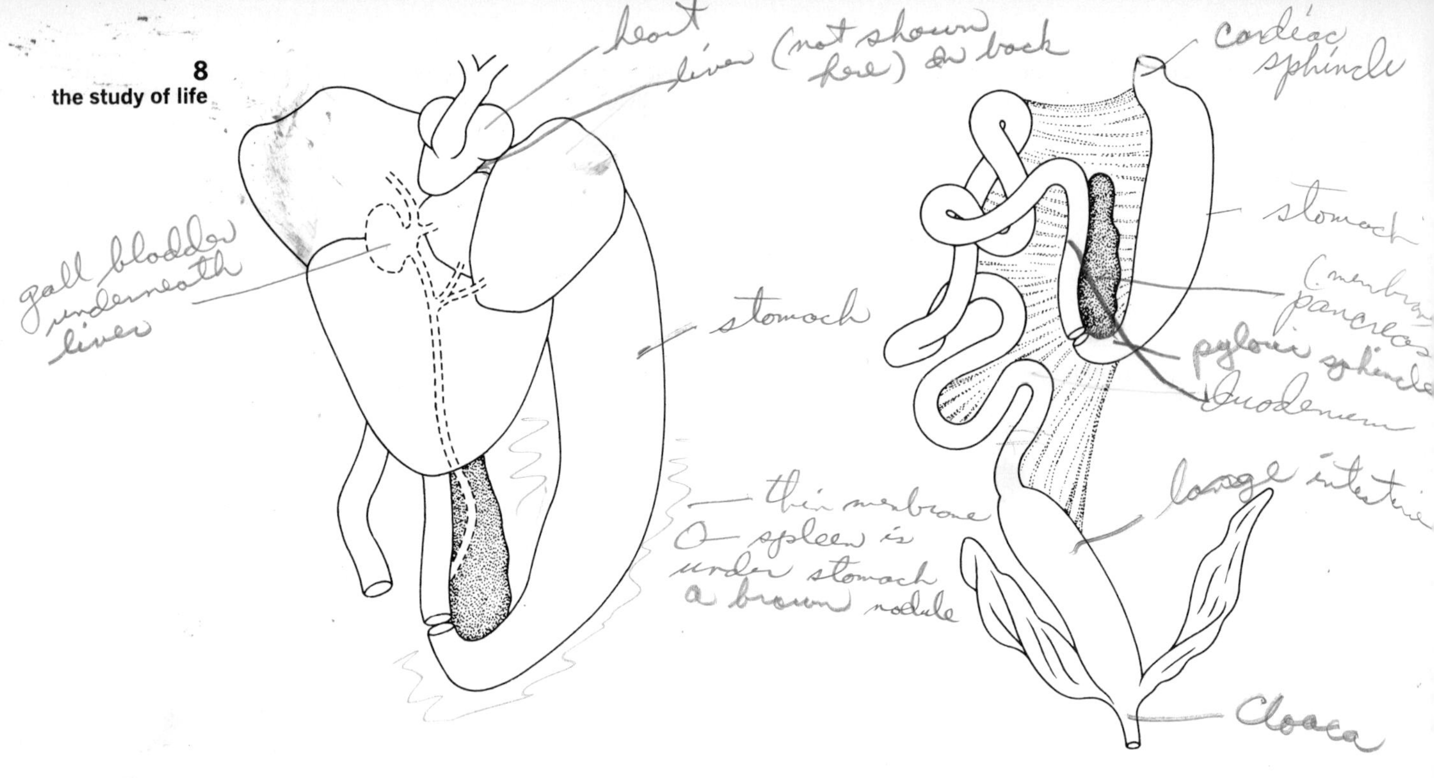

Fig. 1.4 Label this sketch of alimentary organs.

Fig. 1.5 Label this sketch of alimentary organs.

ventrally by the URINARY BLADDER, a thin-walled, double-lobed sac. The large intestine opens posteriorly into the CLOACA, which in turn opens to the outside via the ANUS. The cloaca will be examined in the next exercise.

Review the entire dissection, label Figs. 1.4 and 1.5, and make notes as desired or instructed. Then dispose of the frog as directed.

IV analysis

1. List the parts of the alimentary system of the frog, in sequence from the anterior end. Outline the functions of each structure listed. Which of these organs or body parts occur equivalently in man, and which do not?

2. For each organ or structure (other than alimentary ones) you have studied in this exercise, name the organ system of which it is a part. Name other organs belonging to these systems. How many organ systems are there altogether? What are they?

3. List five organs or body parts that differ in basic structure in frogs and in man. Outline the nature of the differences and show how the evolutionary transition from the amphibian to the mammalian condition is believed to have occurred.

4. List five organs or body parts of a frog that appear to you to be specific adaptations to the particular way of life of the animal. Show in what ways these structures appear to be adaptive.

5. List as many asymmetrical structures of your own body and that of a frog as you can. Indicate whether such a structure is on the left or the right or what other condition produces a left-right asymmetry.

6. On your own body, point to the exact location of liver, stomach, kidneys, and spleen. Look up the function of the spleen.

7. If a cross section were made through the thigh of a frog, what structures would be seen at the cut surface and in what arrangement? (If possible verify your answer by making such a cross section.)

8. If a cross section were made through the trunk of a frog at the level of (*a*) the heart, (*b*) the small intestine, what principal organs would

be seen at the cut surface and in what arrangement? Sketch your answers. Draw in the position and extent of (*a*) the pericardium, (*b*) the peritoneum.

9. Based on your dissection, make a sketch of a sagittal section through the anterior part of the body of a frog to show the positional relations of the components of the alimentary and the breathing systems. Superimpose on this sketch the position of nasal passages, eye, ear, and eustachian tube.

10. Define coelom, cloaca, truncus arteriosus, gastrocnemius, tympanum, vomer. Is (*a*) a tadpole, (*b*) an adult frog, herbivorous, carnivorous, or omnivorous? Review some of the structural and functional changes taking place during the metamorphosis of a tadpole into an adult frog.

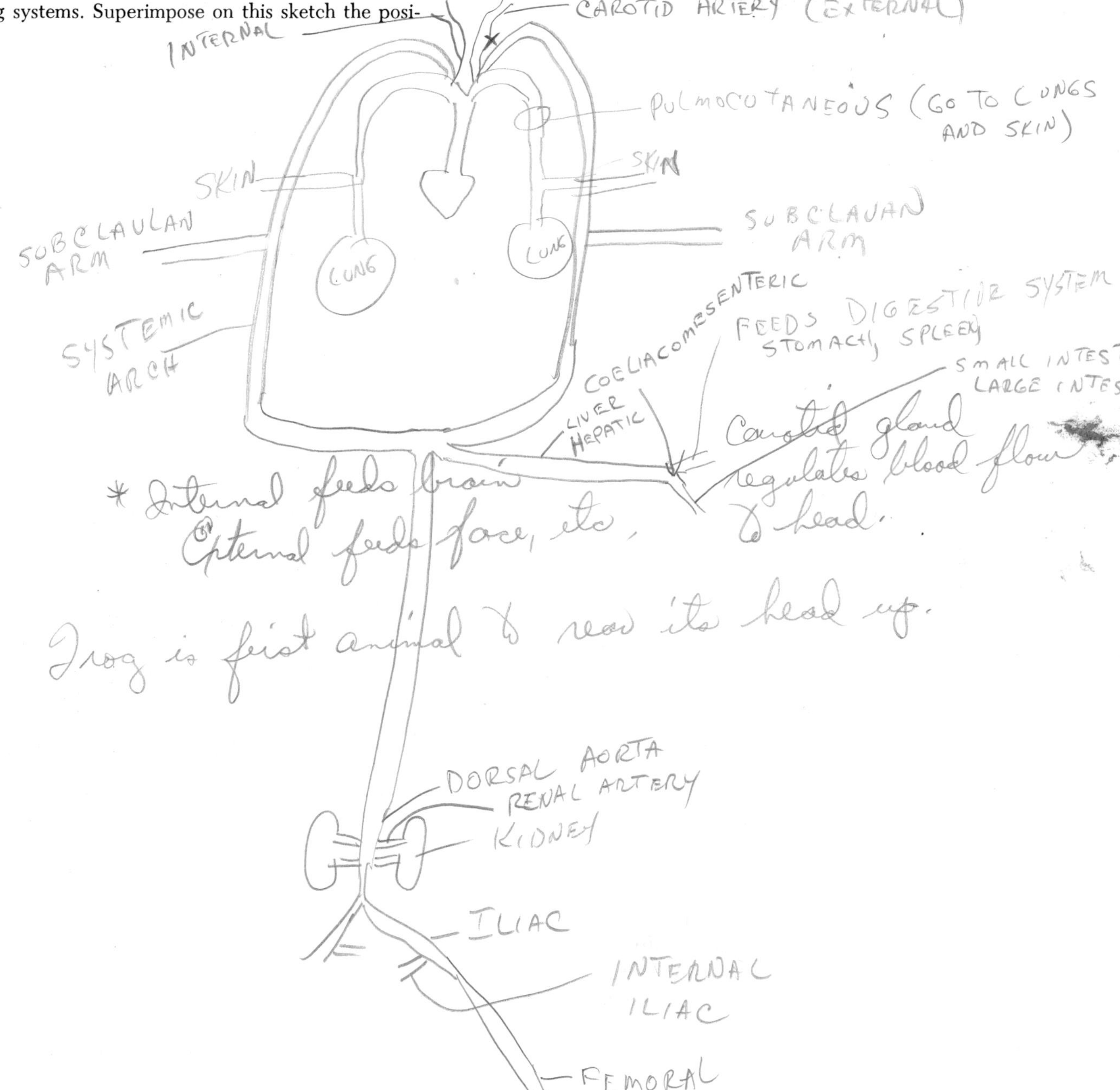

exercise 2 the frog [II]

I materials

Each student

fresh whole beef hearts
frog, freshly killed or preserved and single- or double-injected
dissecting pan, pins
dissecting instruments
hand lens

II introduction

In this exercise the study of frog anatomy will be continued. More specifically, you will examine the CIRCULATORY and the UROGENITAL (that is, EXCRETORY and REPRODUCTIVE) systems. The following exercise will deal with the skeletal system, and in a later context the nervous system will be studied.

Observe the rules of good dissection even more closely than in the preceding exercise; you will be searching for very fine blood vessels and ducts that are difficult or impossible to see unless you pay strict attention to the directions. If your dissection specimen has been freshly killed, arteries can usually be distinguished from veins by their color: arteries tend to be pale or orange red, veins, dark or purplish red. If your specimen is preserved, the instructor will inform you whether it has been single-injected (arteries only) or double-injected (both arteries and veins). The injection material is a pigmented rubber or plastic compound that makes blood vessels not only easier to see but also sturdier and less brittle. The arterial injection is usually made directly into the heart via a small incision in the chest region, which means that this organ may be damaged to a greater or lesser extent. You may therefore find your notes from the previous exercise very useful.

III directions

A. the heart

1. To serve at least 10 or more students, put a fresh beef heart into a dissecting pan. Locate the oblique groove across the ventricular muscle. A CORONARY ARTERY and VEIN travel in this groove. Orient the heart so that the groove runs from your upper right to the lower left. In this position the left chambers of the heart will be on your right,

as they would appear in a ventral dissection of the body. Now make a long and fairly deep incision on each side of the heart, starting anteriorly and ending posteriorly at the apex. The aim is to open the left chambers with a single cut and the right chambers with another.

2. The mammalian heart is composed of four chambers, a right and left ATRIUM (also called AURICLE in mammals) and a right and left VENTRICLE. Compare the thickness of the WALLS in auricle, right ventricle, and left ventricle. What is the functional significance of the differences you observe? Examine the GRAIN of heart muscle. Compare the internal VOLUME CAPACITY of the auricles, the right ventricle, and the left ventricle. Keep in mind that this heart is neither contracted nor distended. Examine the AURICULOVENTRICULAR VALVES, found where the auricles join the ventricles. How many flaps does the right valve contain? How many the left? From this, which is the BICUSPID (or MITRAL) valve, and which the TRICUSPID valve? Examine the CHORDAE TENDINEAE, strands of tissue attached at one end to the edges of the valve flaps and on the other to the inner surfaces of the ventricles. What is the function of these chordae? Examine the SEPTUM of the heart, the partition separating the left side from the right. On the outer surface of the heart, trace the path of the CORONARY blood vessels. Determine where they originate and where they terminate. What is their function?

Each of the four heart chambers connects with a large blood vessel. In each chamber of the beef heart, find the opening of this vessel and probe outward to identify the path of the vessel in external view. From the left ventricle leaves the thick-walled AORTA, one of the widest vessels in the body. From the right ventricle emerges the PULMONARY ARTERY, also large and thick-walled. Where aorta and pulmonary artery leave the ventricles, find the EXIT VALVES. What is their function? Into the right auricle opens the VENA CAVA, thinner-walled than the arteries but very wide nevertheless. The vena cava is formed by the junction of two vessels, the SUPERIOR (or ANTERIOR) VENA CAVA coming from the head region and the INFERIOR (or POSTERIOR) VENA CAVA coming from the hind region of the body. Can you find the stumps of these two vessels in the beef heart? Into the left auricle opens the PULMONARY VEIN, carrying blood from lungs to heart. Now trace the course of blood as it is pumped through the living heart, paying attention to the position of the valves, the state of contraction of auricles and ventricles, and the flow of arterial (oxygenated) and venous (nonoxygenated) blood.

3. Put your frog into a dissecting pan, pin it down, and open the ventral skin just as you did in the preceding exercise. Again as in the previous exercise, open the coelom by means of a longitudinal incision just to the left (your right) of the ventral abdominal vein. Also make a similar incision to the right of the vein, so that the latter remains intact throughout subsequent operations in a strip of ventral body-wall muscle. Very carefully cut through and pin back the pectoral girdle and expose the heart; DO NOT DAMAGE ANY BLOOD VESSELS IN THIS PROCESS! If your specimen is female, remove the left ovary if it obstructs your view.

Open the pericardial cavity and review your notes and sketches on the heart made in the preceding exercise. Unless your frog is injected and the heart is badly damaged, it will probably be advantageous to restudy this heart and the vessels entering and leaving it.

B. the main veins

1. Ventral Abdominal

Carefully trace this vein backward as far as possible, into the bases of the thighs. It is formed by the union of two PELVIC VEINS coming from the base of each thigh dorsally (see also Fig. 2.1). Follow the vein forward and note its entry into the liver, near the gall bladder. In the liver the vein breaks up into capillaries. Near the liver cut through the strip of body wall containing the ventral abdominal vein and pin the flap back.

2. Hepatic Portal

Lift the stomach forward and note that small veins from all parts of the intestine drain into a large vein which passes through the tissue of the pancreas. This is the HEPATIC PORTAL VEIN. Trace it through the pancreas into the liver, where it breaks up into branches to various lobes. In the liver lobes these branches capillarize. (Note that veins beginning as capillaries and ending in capillaries are usually called PORTAL veins. Thus, the hepatic portal begins in gut capillaries and ends in liver capillaries.)

3. Hepatic

Cut transversely through the stomach and through the large intestine. Lift this cut portion of the alimentary system out of the body cavity, and noting or making sketches of any arteries seen for future reference, remove the gut by cautiously snipping through the mesenteries where necessary. Remove also the pancreas but leave the liver in place. Lift the whole liver well forward, and near its attachment, try to locate the right and left HEPATIC VEINS that emanate from the liver and enter a very large vein right near the posterior tip of the sinus venosus. Blood collected from the liver by the hepatic veins is ultimately returned to the heart.

4. Renal Portal

Locate the left KIDNEY, an elongated, reddish organ along the roof of the body cavity. On its ventral side lies a yellowish band of tissue, the ADRENAL GLAND, a component of the endocrine system. Along the lateral edge of the kidney will be found the reasonably conspicuous RENAL PORTAL VEIN. It enters the kidney and capillarizes there. The renal portal is one of the branches of the large FEMORAL VEIN, the principal vein of the hind leg. Near the base of the leg the femoral splits into the renal portal and a pelvic vein, which, as noted above, joins the pelvic vein of the other side and becomes the ventral abdominal vein. The renal portal subsequently unites with a SCIATIC VEIN from the leg and passes to the kidney. Thus, follow the renal portal posteriorly till you find the juncture with the sciatic vein. The sciatic runs along the medial side of the leg and enters the body cavity dorsally near the cloaca. Posterior to this juncture find the union of the renal portal with the pelvic vein, and then locate the femoral vein in the leg.

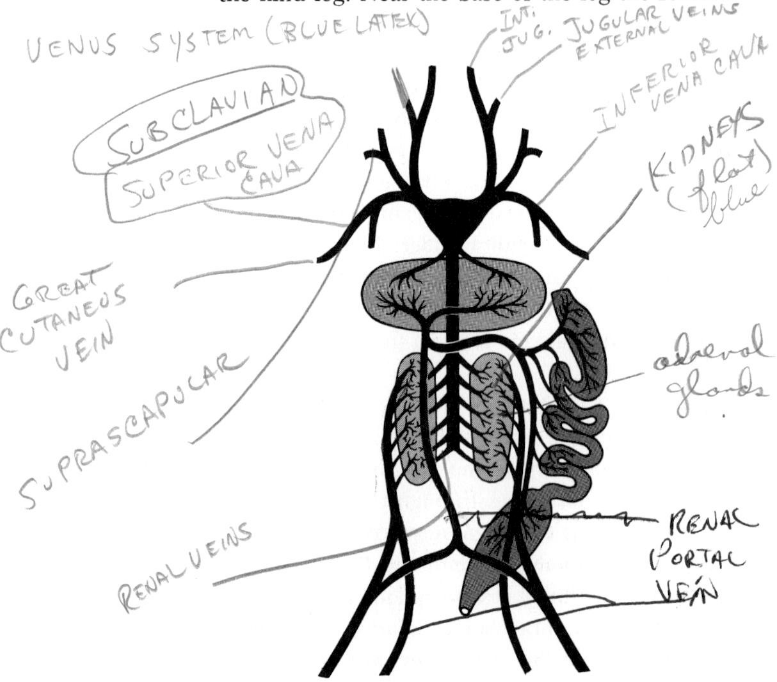

Fig. 2.1 The main blood vessels of the venous system. Label.

5. Posterior Vena Cava

In the midline of the body between the two kidneys lies the largest of all veins, the POSTERIOR VENA CAVA, or POSTCAVAL VEIN. Small UROGENITAL VEINS enter it from the kidneys and the reproductive organs. Follow the postcaval forward. For a short part of its course it is embedded in the liver. Lift the liver forward and note the point of entry. Find also the point of exit, very near the sinus venosus. As noted, the hepatic veins from the liver join the postcaval in this region.

Very carefully snip through all attachments of the liver and remove this organ. Exercise great caution so as not to damage other structures.

6. Pulmonary

Relocate the left atrium and find the LEFT PULMONARY VEIN. It passes from the anterior edge of the left lung to the atrium. Does it carry arterial or venous blood? Just before its entry into the atrium it joins the RIGHT PULMONARY VEIN from the right lung.

7. Anterior Vena Cava

Relocate the sinus venosus and note the large vein entering it laterally on each side. Each of these relatively short veins is an ANTERIOR VENA CAVA, or PRECAVAL VEIN. It is formed on each side by the union of three veins. The most posterior of these is the readily identifiable SUBCLAVIAN, which drains blood from the foreleg. More anteriorly lies the INNOMINATE VEIN, itself formed by the union of two branch veins near the angle of the jaw. One of these branches, the INTERNAL JUGULAR, brings blood from the head. The other, smaller branch is the SUBSCAPULAR, coming from the dorsal shoulder region. The third and most anterior of the three veins that form the precaval is the EXTERNAL JUGULAR. It receives blood from the mouth region and the lower jaw.

Review the venous system, label Fig. 2.1, and make notes as desired or instructed. The arterial system is best examined after the urogenital system has been studied.

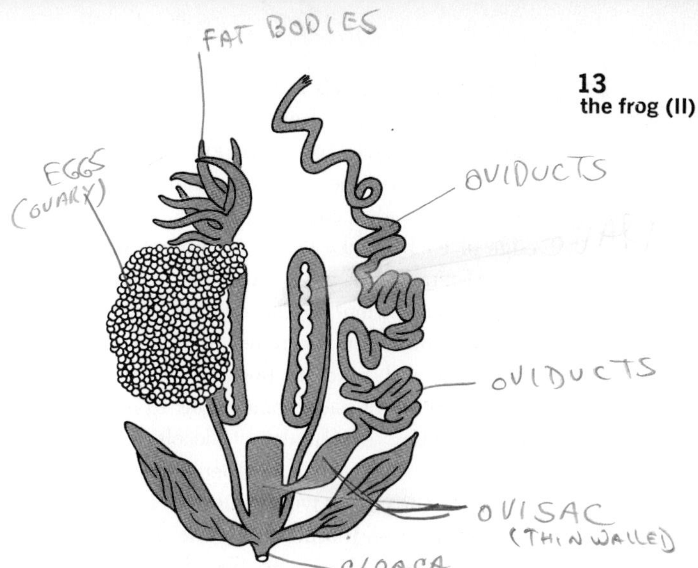

Fig. 2.2 The female urogenital system (parts of which are sketched only on one or the other side, though the parts are paired). Label.

C. the urogenital system

Unpin the hind legs, carefully pass the lower blade of your strong scissors through the cloaca into the stump of the large intestine, and cut along the midline through the muscles between the hind legs, the bone (PUBIC SYMPHYSIS) of the pelvic girdle, and the ventral wall of the cloaca. The urinary bladder will thereby be cut in half and the cloacal cavity will be exposed. If necessary, continue the cut to slit open the whole stump of the large intestine. Repin the legs.

Proceed to section 1 or 2, depending on the sex of your specimen. Afterward study the dissection of a fellow student whose specimen is of the opposite sex.

1. The Female System

Reexamine the remaining ovary, if not already removed, and find its attachment by mesenteries to the medial border of the kidney on that side. Attached to each ovary anteriorly is a FAT BODY, a yellowish bundle of fingerlike strands. This fat-storing organ varies in size seasonally, being largest in summer. Underneath each ovary (and already exposed if an ovary has been removed earlier) will be found the thick, whitish, highly coiled OVIDUCT (or MUELLERIAN DUCT). Trace the left oviduct forward to its beginning, well under and near the base of the lung. The anterior oviducal opening is the funnellike, ciliated OSTIUM. Ripe eggs are released from the ovaries into the body cavity all at one time during the breeding season, and the eggs then enter and pass through the oviducts. In these ducts jelly coats are secreted around the eggs. Near the posterior border of the kidneys each oviduct widens suddenly into a thin-walled, nonglandular OVISAC (often erroneously referred to as "uterus"), where descending eggs may be stored temporarily. Carefully separate the left half of the urinary bladder from its attachment to the left ovisac and examine the shape and extent of this sac. Posteriorly it joins the right sac along the midline, dorsal to the gut. The two sacs then open into the cloaca at two dorsal OVIDUCAL PAPILLAE, lying close together. Try to find these papillae with a hand lens.

Very carefully separate the left ovisac from its medial attachments to the right sac, lift it, and making sure that underlying structures are not being damaged, cut through it and remove the entire left oviduct. Along the posterolateral edge of the kidney now find a thin white tube. This is the MESONEPHRIC DUCT (or WOLFFIAN DUCT); it carries urine from the kidney. Trace the duct forward along the kidney as far as you can see it and backward to its termination dorsally in the cloaca. The urinary opening in the cloaca itself is usually too minute to be seen.

Label Fig. 2.2. Exchange your specimen with a male frog dissected by a fellow student and study the male system. Afterward reobtain your own frog.

2. The Male System

At the anteromedial end of each kidney lies a TESTIS, a rounded, yellowish organ. Attached to it anteriorly is a FAT BODY, a yellowish bundle of fingerlike strands. This fat-storing organ varies in size seasonally, being largest during the summer. Closely examine the dorsal surface of the mesentery that holds the testis to the kidney. Note the fine blood vessels and, between them, minute white ducts passing from testis to kidney. These are SPERM DUCTS, or VASA EFFERENTIA (sing., VAS EFFERENS); they conduct sperms into kidney tubules that also carry urine. Along the lateral edge of each kidney find a prominent wavy tube, the MUELLERIAN DUCT. This is a rudimentary oviduct, equivalent to the oviduct of the female but functionless in the male. Follow this oviduct backward and note its posterior expansion into a rudimentary ovisac (homologous to a large egg-storing ovisac in females). Closely attached to this ovisac medially is another duct, the MESONEPHRIC DUCT (or WOLFFIAN DUCT). It carries both sperms and urine from the kidney to the cloaca. Carefully separate this duct from its attachments to the rudimentary ovisac and trace it forward. Just behind the kidney it carries a pouchlike glandular enlargement, the SEMINAL VESICLE. This structure serves in temporary sperm storage, and it probably also produces a sperm-activating secretion during mating. Trace the mesonephric duct to its termination along the dorsal wall of the cloaca. The urinary pore in the cloaca itself is usually too minute to be seen, but it is sometimes marked by a pigment spot.

Label Fig. 2.3. Exchange your specimen with a female frog dissected by a fellow student and study the female system. Afterward reobtain your own frog.

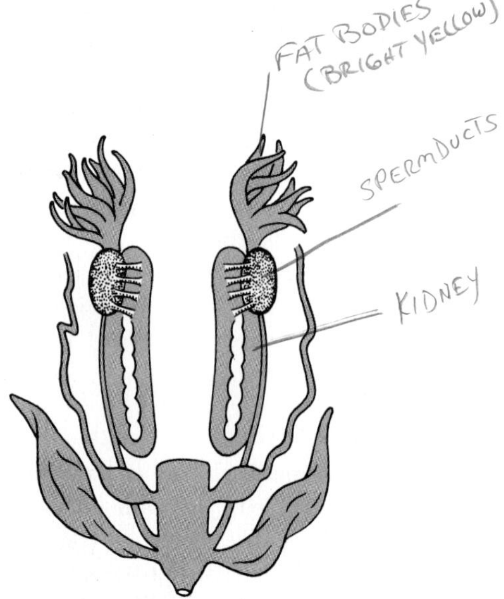

Fig. 2.3 The male urogenital system. Label.

D. the main arteries

Arteries are paler than veins by virtue of their thicker walls, and where arteries and veins lie together, the arteries are generally more dorsal. In frogs all main arteries emanate from the TRUNCUS ARTERIOSUS, which divides into two arterial trunks (called FUSED AORTIC ARCHES) inside the pericardial cavity. The arteries arising from these trunks have a bilaterally symmetrical arrangement, except for arteries to the gut, which are median.

Study and trace the left branch of the truncus arteriosus, carefully teasing away overlying muscles and membranes as necessary. The trunk soon divides into three main arteries: an anterior CAROTID ARCH, a middle, large SYSTEMIC ARCH, and a dorsolateral PULMOCUTANEOUS ARCH (see also Fig. 2.4).

1. Carotid Arch

This vessel branches a short distance after its origin into a smaller VENTRAL (or EXTERNAL) CAROTID and a larger DORSAL (or INTERNAL) CAROTID. The ventral branch passes anteriorly along the floor of the mouth and into the tongue; it lies alongside one of the branches of the external jugular vein. The dorsal carotid possesses a prominent swelling at its base, the CAROTID GLAND. This regulative structure aids in maintaining a sufficiently high pressure of blood flowing through the artery; the vessel leads into the dorsal regions of the head, including the brain.

2. Pulmocutaneous Arch

This dorsolateral vessel may be partly obscured by the large and more ventral systemic arch (and in prepared specimens it may not be injected completely). Pull the left lung back with forceps and tease away overlying tissue as necessary to expose the pulmocutaneous more fully. Very near its origin the vessel branches into two arteries, the PULMONARY ARTERY passing posteriorly into the lung and the CUTANEOUS ARTERY passing laterally toward the base of the foreleg (do not confuse it with the subclavian vein!). The cutaneous ramifies in the skin, which in frogs is a breathing organ equal in importance to the lungs. Trace this major artery as fully as you can.

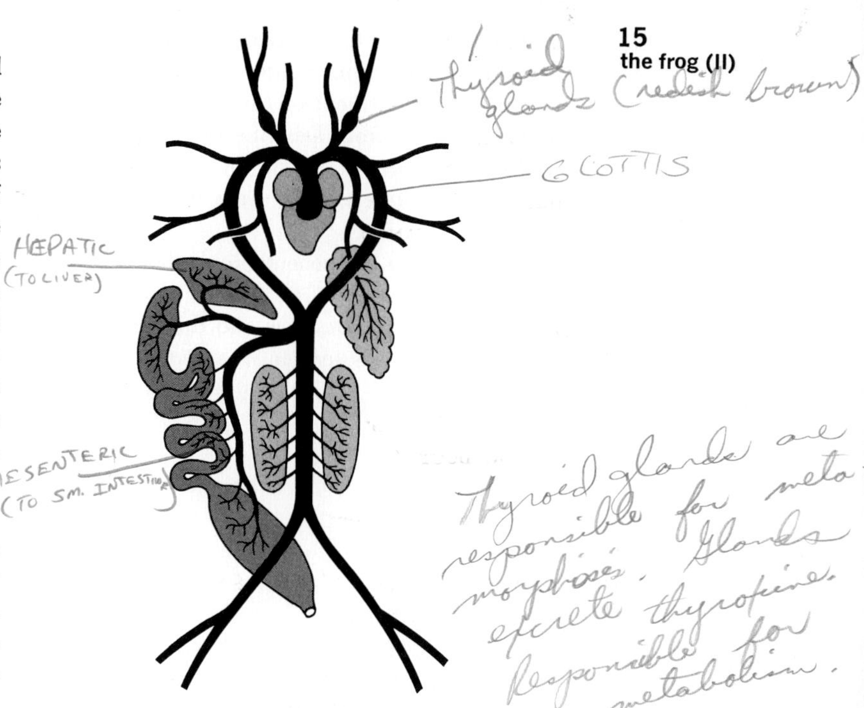

Fig. 2.4 The main blood vessels of the arterial system. Label.

3. *Systemic Arch*

This largest artery curves anterolaterally and dorsally, then passes posteriorly (and crosses the path of the cutaneous artery). As it reaches the roof of the body wall, the systemic arch gives off the OCCIPITOVERTEBRAL ARTERY, branches of which supply the dorsal regions of the head, the trunk, and the vertebral column. Just behind the occipitovertebral, the SUBCLAVIAN ARTERY arises from the systemic arch. The subclavian supplies blood to the foreleg. The systemic arch then curves toward the midline, where it joins the corresponding right arch, forming the joint, median DORSAL AORTA. Dissect the systemic arches fully.

4. *Dorsal Aorta*

Just where the systemic arches unite into the dorsal aorta, the COELIACOMESENTERIC ARTERY branches off. This vessel shortly divides into an anterior COELIAC ARTERY and a posterior MESENTERIC ARTERY. Both pass through mesenteries and supply parts of the alimentary system. Thus, the coeliac subdivides into GASTRIC, HEPATIC, and PANCREATIC arteries, and the mesenteric, into SPLENIC, ANTERIOR MESENTERIC, and POSTERIOR MESENTERIC arteries. These vessels are no longer present at this stage of dissection, but you have noted them before the alimentary tract was removed.

At the level of the kidneys the dorsal aorta gives off short, lateral RENAL and GONADAL ARTERIES to kidneys and reproductive organs, respectively. Along the lateral edge of a kidney cut through the peritoneum, which holds the kidney against the roof of the body cavity. Lift the kidney up and note the arteries.

Posterior to the kidneys the dorsal aorta divides into two ILIAC ARTERIES to the legs. Trace these vessels out of the coelom into the legs.

Review the arterial system, label Fig. 2.4, and make notes as desired or instructed. Then dispose of the frog as directed.

IV analysis

1. Compare the structure of the amphibian and mammalian heart, and trace the course of blood through it in each case. Name the vessels attached to each chamber of the amphibian and mammalian heart. Which type of heart is functionally more efficient? How so?

2. Describe the course of the (*a*) renal portal system, (*b*) hepatic portal system, in frogs. Make a summary sketch of all principal veins in the posterior part of the frog body, name the veins, and show by what pathways blood drains into the heart.

3. Make a summary sketch of all principal veins in the anterior part of the frog body, name the veins, and show by what pathways blood drains into the heart.

4. Describe the pulmonary circulation, both arterial and venous. Indicate for each vessel whether it carries arterial or venous blood.

5. Make a sketch of the arterial system of the frog body, name the arteries, and show by what pathways each organ system is supplied with blood.

6. Name the main arteries and veins that carry blood to and from the following body parts of a frog: brain, foreleg, hind leg, intestine, kidney, liver. Look up the basic pattern of blood circulation in man, and show in what principal respects (and in what principal vessels) the circulation

of amphibia differs from that of mammals.

7. Name the components and describe the anatomical arrangement of the reproductive system of a female frog. Describe also the parts of the female excretory system. In what structural ways do these systems differ from those of female mammals?

8. Name the components and describe the anatomical arrangement of the reproductive system of a male frog. Describe also the parts of the male reproductive system. In what structural ways do these systems differ from those of male mammals?

9. Contrast the functions of the Muellerian and Wolffian ducts in male and female frogs. Are such ducts present in man? Amplify your answer.

10. What are the functions and positions of (*a*) fat bodies, (*b*) seminal vesicles, in frogs? The frog kidney is a MESONEPHROS. From your text determine the nature of such a kidney and find out whether or not man too possesses such an excretory organ.

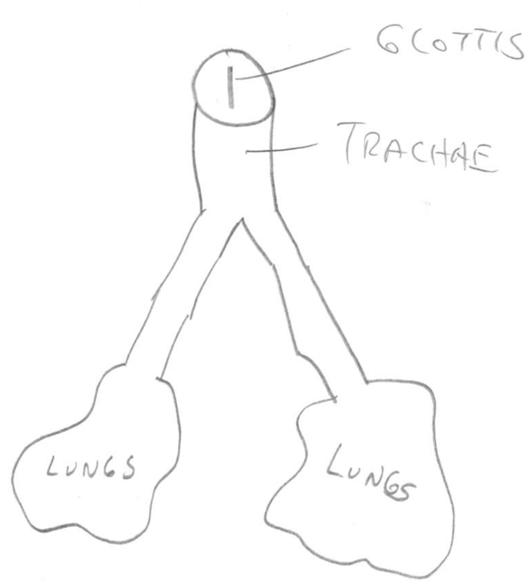

exercise 3 skeletons

I materials

Each 4 to 6 students

frog skeleton
cat skeleton

Class stock

human skeletons (as many as possible)
fish, reptile, bird skeletons (assorted, optional)

II introduction

This exercise is devoted to a COMPARATIVE study of the vertebrate skeletal system; frog, cat, and human skeletons will receive the main attention, and skeletons of other vertebrates will be examined optionally. One objective is to become familiar with the fundamental organization of the skeleton as such and with the structure and function of its component parts. A second, equally important objective is underscored by the word "comparative." All vertebrates are to greater or lesser degree interrelated in an evolutionary sense, and their skeletons reflect this relatedness. Thus, notwithstanding the many differences among frog, cat, and human skeletons, the most basic characteristics can be expected to be alike in all three.

Recall in this connection that two or more whole organisms or parts of organisms are said to be HOMOLOGOUS if they have similar structure and embryonic origin. They are said to be ANALOGOUS if they have similar function. If homology is established, close evolutionary relationship may be inferred. For example, regardless of the vastly different functions of primitive fish fins and human arms, or of primitive fish scales and human teeth, these pairs of structures are virtually identical in fundamental architecture and embryonic origin, and reasonably close evolutionary relatedness is therefore indicated. On the other hand, if only analogy can be established, then close evolutionary relationship does almost certainly not exist. For example, regardless of the very similar function of insect wings and bird wings, the structure and embryology of these wings are utterly different and these flight mechanisms therefore are at best related very distantly. Two or more structures may be both homologous AND analogous, as is the case in bird and bat wings, for example; and, of course, two or more structures may be neither homologous nor analogous.

In this exercise, therefore, study skeletons not only as components of given isolated animals, but also as components exemplifying important homologies and/or analogies among vertebrates generally; inasmuch as comparative degrees of homology are indices of corresponding degrees of historical interrelation, the exercise in effect represents a small study of vertebrate evolution.

III directions

A. frog skeleton

We may consider the vertebrate skeleton to consist of three subdivisions: SKULL, AXIAL SKELETON (the vertebral column), and APPENDICULAR SKELETON (limbs and limb girdles). Examine each of these divisions on the mounted skeleton of a frog (see also Fig. 3.1).

1. Skull

This portion of the skeleton consists of the CRANIUM, that is, the bones of the BRAIN CASE, and of the bones of the FACE and the JAWS. In the diagram below, the principal skull bones are labeled; identify each of them on the prepared skeleton. Insofar as possible, visualize which nonskeletal tissues and body parts of the head lie over, under, and around these bones. Which bones bear TEETH? Where is the ORBIT, or eye socket? Where are the ears located in relation to the skull bones? Locate the EXOCCIPITAL, the bone articulating with the vertebral column. Can you find the FORAMEN MAGNUM, the opening where the spinal cord emerges from the skull and passes into the vertebral column?

2. Axial Skeleton

The vertebral column of the frog consists of nine VERTEBRAE and a long posterior UROSTYLE, formed from several fused vertebrae. The first, most anterior vertebra is the ATLAS, which articulates with the exoccipital and supports the skull. Note that the atlas is without lateral projections. Such projections, called TRANSVERSE PROCESSES, are present on the other vertebrae, however; they represent the highly shortened and fused RIBS of the frog. The ninth vertebra is the SACRUM, to which the pelvic girdle is attached. Where is the spinal cord in relation to the vertebrae?

Fig. 3.1 The frog skeleton. Label the parts where indicated.

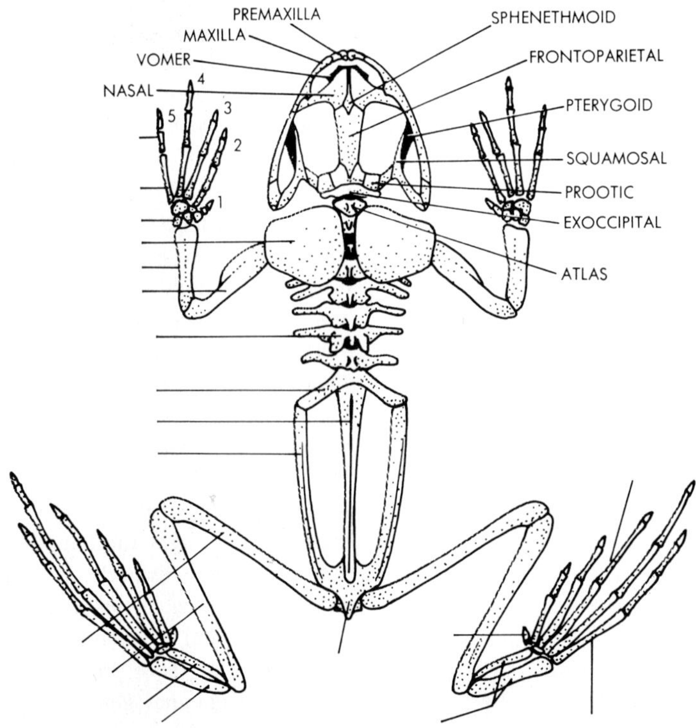

Vertebrae are often classified as CERVICAL (neck, between skull and pectoral girdle), THORACIC (chest), LUMBAR (between thoracic and pelvic girdle), SACRAL (supporting pelvic girdle), and CAUDAL (tail). The number of each can vary greatly even among closely related animals, and in frogs these divisions cannot be identified rigorously in view of the highly foreshortened and specialized axial skeleton of the animal. Which axial components correspond most nearly to the five divisions above? Label the parts of the axial skeleton in Fig. 3.1.

3. *Appendicular Skeleton*

a. The PECTORAL GIRDLE includes the STERNUM, or breastbone, much of it cartilaginous in frogs; the CLAVICLE, or collar bone; the CORACOID, a large strong bone just posterior to the clavicle; and the SCAPULA and SUPRASCAPULA, together representing the shoulder blade. Where the foreleg articulates with the girdle, the girdle bones form a socket called the GLENOID FOSSA.

Three pairs of fused bones compose the PELVIC GIRDLE. Attached to the sacrum of the vertebral column on each side is the long ILIUM. The ISCHIUM on each side is a small posterior projection, and the two ischia are fused along the midline. The PUBIS on each side is also small; it lies anteroventral, and the left and right pubic bones are again fused along the midline. The area of fusion is the PUBIC SYMPHYSIS. Where the hind leg articulates with the girdle, the girdle bones form a socket, here called the ACETABULUM.

b. The front and hind limbs are constructed according to a common basic pattern, which, indeed, is common to all vertebrates. The names of the bones in front and hind leg differ, but the bones themselves are entirely homologous. Identify these bones, named in the following list in sequence from the proximal to the distal end of the leg:

foreleg	*hind leg*
humerus (upper arm)	femur (thigh)
radioulna (lower arm)	tibiofibula (shin)
carpals (wrist, six small bones)	tarsals (ankle, two long bones, several small ones)
metacarpals (hand)	metatarsals (foot)
phalanges (fingers)	phalanges (toes)

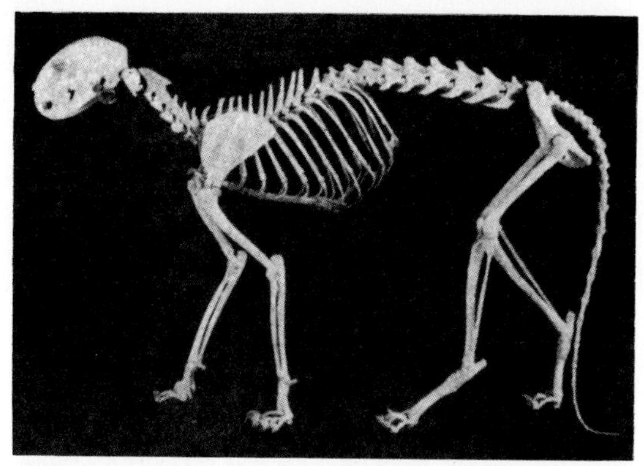

Fig. 3.2 The cat skeleton. Label the parts in as great detail as you can. (Courtesy of Ward's Natural Science Establishment, Inc.)

In Fig. 3.1, label all parts of the appendicular skeleton.

B. mammalian skeleton

Study the skeletons of the cat and of man. Do this in a comparative manner, and always include the frog in your comparisons.

It is best to carry out this examination simultaneously on equivalent parts of the skeletons, and to proceed bone by bone. For each type of bone compare shapes, relative sizes, position within the skeleton as a whole, and specific functions (see also Figs. 3.2 and 3.3). On the basis of this determine if the bones are homologous, analogous, or both. Keep in mind that frog, cat, and man pursue different ways of life and that equivalent bones may or may not serve different functions. Keep in mind also that the comparative structural PATTERN of given bones is more significant in an evolutionary sense than comparative sizes and shapes, but that differences of size and shape are significant from the standpoint of function and way of life.

1. *Skull*

Compare overall SHAPES and the relative sizes of BRAIN CASE and JAWS. In the brain case note the SUTURES between skull bones and the skull bones themselves: from the forehead back, FRONTAL BONES, PARIETAL BONES, OCCIPITAL BONE, and on each side of the brain case, the TEMPORAL BONE. Are any of these homologous to the bones

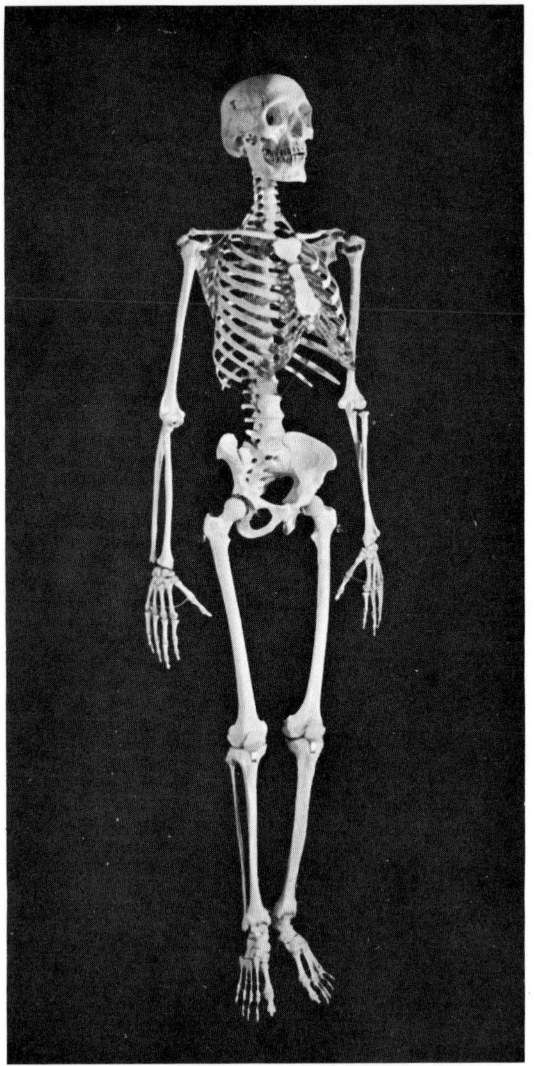

Fig. 3.3 The human skeleton. Label the parts in as detailed a fashion as possible. (Courtesy of Ward's Natural Science Establishment, Inc.)

in the frog skull? Compare the ORBITS (eye sockets); what are the differences here? Locate the AUDITORY MEATUS, a canal leading into the ear on each side of the head. In carnivore skulls note the TYMPANIC BULLA, a hollow bulging bone below the auditory meatus. Is such a bulla present in man? Examine the ZYGOMATIC ARCH, or "cheekbone," a horizontal bridge underneath the orbit. Which bones make up this arch? Find the NASAL BONES, and examine the upper and lower JAWS. How are the jaws articulated (that is, hinged together)? The lower jaw consists of two DENTARY bones, fused in front; the upper jaw on each side is formed by the PREMAXILLA and the MAXILLA. All these jawbones bear teeth. Observe how the teeth are set into bone.

Examine the TEETH. How many are there in each of the mammalian skulls? Determine the TOOTH FORMULA, that is, the number of INCISORS, CANINES, PREMOLARS, and MOLARS on one side of the head. Compare shapes and structure among these different teeth in the human skull. Relate shape with position in mouth and with function. Compare dentition in man and cat, tooth for tooth. What are the essential differences? How are these correlated with way of life? What is the tooth formula for baby teeth ("milk teeth") in man? Does a young cat develop milk teeth?

Examine the bones of the PALATE. Find the FORAMEN MAGNUM, the large opening back at the base of the brain case, where the spinal cord emerges from the skull. Along the sides of this foramen note bony humps which fit into depressions in the ATLAS, the first neck vertebra. The second neck vertebra is the AXIS, which bears a bony process projecting anteriorly into the ring-shaped atlas. Verify that these two vertebrae link the skull to the vertebral column and at the same time permit free movement of the head.

2. *Axial Skeleton*

Identify the following VERTEBRAE in the human skeleton: 7 CERVICAL (neck, including atlas and axis); 12 THORACIC (chest); 5 LUMBAR (waist); 5 SACRAL (hip); 4 COCCYGEAL (tail). Note that sacral and coccygeal vertebrae are fused together. The COCCYX of man is equivalent to the tail vertebrae of other mammals.

Examine the different types of vertebrae of man in a comparative sense. Relate the differences in shape and size to differences in function. Which are the sturdiest vertebrae? Which have NEURAL SPINES, bony processes projecting dorsally? What is the function of these processes? What is the tissue between adjacent vertebrae? Describe the manner of curvature of the whole vertebral column, and interpret adaptively.

Count the different types of vertebrae in the cat and compare with those of man. Compare the shapes of the cat vertebrae at different body levels, particularly in the cervical and lumbar regions, and contrast with those in man: relate the differences to the different problems of support in a tetrapod and a biped. Similarly compare the curvature of the whole vertebral column.

Study the RIB CAGE. Which vertebrae carry RIBS? Compare numbers of ribs in cat and man and in human males and females. Note the articulation of ribs with the STERNUM. TRUE RIBS are those which attach to the sternum independently; FALSE RIBS are either attached to preceding ribs or are FLOATING, that is, unattached ventrally altogether. How many of each type are there? Note the cartilaginous portion of each rib. What is the advantage of such nonbony parts in the rib cage?

Determine where the SPINAL CORD is situated relative to the vertebral column and where the SPINAL NERVES emerge.

3. *The Appendicular Skeleton*

Examine the PECTORAL GIRDLE, with CLAVICLE (collarbone) and SCAPULA (shoulder blade). How and where are these bones articulated with the axial skeleton? Compare the clavicle in man and in the cat: what is the adaptive significance of the pronounced difference? How are the FORELIMBS articulated with the pectoral girdle? In the forelimb of man identify HUMERUS, RADIUS, ULNA, the CARPAL (wrist) bones, the METACARPALS, and the PHALANGES (finger bones). How are radius and ulna joined to the humerus? Where do both ends of the BICEPS and TRICEPS muscles attach to the arm? Which of radius and ulna is on the thumb side? Count the number of carpal bones. How many joints are there in the fingers?

Examine the forelimb of the cat, and compare bone for bone with that of man. Is there a difference in the mobility of the shoulder joint? Where is the ELBOW of the cat? Where is the forefoot? Does the cat walk on the whole foot? Examine the PAWS and CLAWS; is there a bone-for-bone correspondence with the hand of man?

Examine the mammalian PELVIC GIRDLE, with three pairs of bones: PUBIS anteriorly, ISCHIUM laterally, ILIUM posterodorsally. All three bones are fused on each side. Which of these bones articulates with the sacrum, and so links pelvic girdle and axial skeleton? In the human skeleton, trace the path of the BIRTH CANAL in relation to the pelvic girdle. How does the HIND LIMB articulate with the pelvic girdle? In the hind limb of man identify FEMUR, TIBIA, FIBULA, the TARSAL (ankle) bones, the METATARSALS, and the PHALANGES. How are tibia and fibula joined to the femur? Which of tibia and fibula is the "shinbone"? Count the number of tarsal bones. How many joints are there in the toes? Are mammalian fore- and hind limbs analogous, homologous, neither, or both?

Examine the hind limb of the cat, and compare bone for bone with that of man. Is there a difference in the mobility of the hip joint? Where is the KNEE of the cat? Where is the HEEL? Observe that the elbow of the cat points backward and that the knee points forward; also that radius and ulna are crossed over each other when the forefoot points forward, but that tibia and fibula are parallel, not crossed over each other, when the hind foot points forward. In man, radius and ulna also cross when the hand is pointed forward, palm down. Can you think of an explanation of this crossing? Consider here that primitive vertebrate limbs originally jutted out horizontally from the side of the body (for example, more or less like the forelegs of frogs).

4. *Interpretation*

In man, can you tell the sex of the individual from its skeleton? What skeletal sex differences are there? Show how skeletal PROPORTIONS change from infancy to adulthood. Label Figs. 3.2 and 3.3.

Contrast the biped skeleton of man and the tetrapod skeleton of frog and cat from an engineering standpoint. For each type of skeleton show (*a*) where stresses and strains due to body weight and gravity, and frictional stresses due to movement of parts, are likely to be great; (*b*) what adaptive adjustments are in evidence, or are not in evidence, to accommodate such stresses; (*c*) how both rigidity and flexibility are provided; and (*d*) how problems of balance are solved in the rest position and in locomotion.

Finally, assess the evolutionary relationships between frog, cat, and human skeletons. Does each bone in one have an equivalent bone in the others? Of the bones in each skeleton (more than 200 in man), which, and roughly how many, are (*a*) homologous, (*b*) analogous, and (*c*) both homologous and analogous? From these percentage comparisons, which types among frog, cat, and man appear to be most closely related?

C. other vertebrate skeletons

If so directed by the instructor, study skeletons of FISH, REPTILES, and BIRDS, as available. Do this comparatively, and use the descriptions for amphibia and mammals above as a basis of reference. Examine each skeleton from two points of view. First, what features are unique for the type, and what adaptive role do these features play in the particular environment in which the animal lives? Secondly, what features can be homologized directly with parts of the amphibian, mammalian, and other vertebrate skeletons, and how close an evolutionary relationship is thereby suggested?

Pay particular attention to the following:

1. SKULLS. Comparative number and relative sizes of bones; degrees of fusion of bones; bones in gills and HYOID APPARATUS; jaw articulations.

2. DENTITION. Position and number of bones bearing teeth; manner of attachment of teeth; shapes and functional differentiations of teeth; number of teeth and number of sets of teeth; homologies of teeth with other structures (bills, beaks, etc.).

3. VERTEBRAE. Comparative total numbers; degree of structural differentiation at different body levels; tail architecture; variations in rib cage and in ribs; protective and locomotor functions of rib cage (for example, turtles, snakes); amount of vertebral fusion; articulation of vertebrae to one another, and of whole column with (*a*) head and (*b*) pectoral and pelvic girdles.

4. LIMB GIRDLES. Number of bones per girdle; amount of fusion; adaptively significant variations, particularly in pelvic girdles; articulation of girdles with (*a*) vertebral column and (*b*) limbs.

5. LIMBS. Locomotor functions and associated structural adaptations; homologies of bony elements; articulation with girdles, and position relative to body as a whole; number of digits and amount of digital fusion; types of limb joints and degree of mobility permitted; armature of limbs for locomotion and offense-defense; manner of walking.

6. OVERALL CONSTRUCTION. Specialized features of engineering in adaptation to swimming, flying, creeping, walking; relative sturdiness or lightness of skeleton; relative flexibility and mobility; relative length of neck; other unique or specialized features.

IV analysis

1. Describe the fundamental, common organization of the vertebrate skull. Then show how this organization differs for frog, cat, and man, and if you can, relate the differences to evolutionary change and to differences in ways of life.

2. Substitute "axial skeleton" for the word "skull" in item 1, above, and answer the question.

3. Substitute "pectoral girdle and foreleg" for the word "skull" in item 1, above, and answer the question.

4. Substitute "pelvic girdle and hind leg" for the word "skull" in item 1, above, and answer the question.

5. Name bones present in (*a*) amphibia but not mammals, (*b*) mammals but not amphibia. Then name bones present in (*a*) cats but not man, (*b*) man but not cats.

6. List skeletal parts of different vertebrates that are widely different in appearance and function, yet are homologous nevertheless. Are there any analogous skeletal parts in different vertebrates that are not homologous?

7. Review the internal structure of a bone, and ascertain from your text how a bone develops embryologically. How does cartilage differ from bone? What portions of the human skeleton remain permanently cartilaginous?

8. What is the general function of a skeleton? Contrast the functional efficiency of the vertebrate endoskeleton and the arthropod exoskeleton. In an animal like man, could a bony exoskeleton serve as well as the bony endoskeleton? Discuss.

9. Pronounced bony ridges are present in the occipital bones of carnivores but not of man; long neural spines are present in the cervical vertebrae of carnivores but not of man. Explain these differences in adaptive terms.

10. Well-developed clavicles are present in man but not in carnivores. Explain this difference in adaptive terms, by reference to the different ways of life of these animals.

11. Discuss comparative advantages and disadvantages of bipedal and tetrapodal posture and locomotion. Consider here not only physical factors such as balance and support, but also biological factors such as nervous and other control requirements.

12. Describe how the attachment of limbs to the body has changed during vertebrate evolu-

tion. From this, show why radius and ulna must cross over each other if the forefeet point forward.

13. Show how the following skeletal parts of primitive vertebrates have become transformed during later vertebrate evolution and to what mammalian or human structures they are homologous: gill bones; coracoid; atlas; tail bones; fin skeleton.

14. In what way is possession of a neck advantageous to a mammal; and in what way is absence of a neck advantageous to a frog? What structural adjustments in skeleton and other organ systems must necessarily occur during the evolutionary development of a neck? Do whales and dolphins have necks? Would you estimate the number of neck vertebrae in giraffes to be greater than, less than, or the same as in man?

15. In the fish skull there are some 60 bones, and in the human skull there are about 20. In the light of this, is it justifiable to describe evolution as a progression "from simple to complex," as is so often done? By what phrase COULD evolution be described correctly?

exercise 4 the fetal pig [I]

I materials

Each student

fetal pig, 11 to 13 in. long, arteries injected, embalmed or formaldehyde-preserved, with container
dissecting pan, pins
dissecting instruments
2 18-in. lengths of strong string
identification tag

II introduction

In this and the following exercises, the anatomy of the fetal pig will be examined in some detail. The pig is a mammal, which means that many or most aspects of its structural organization are virtually identical with those of all other mammals, man included; in a general way, a study of the fetal pig is also a study of man. Thus, as a first leading theme in these exercises, ask yourself, for every structure observed in the pig, if an equivalent structure exists in your own body; and if so, where that structure is located.

As a second leading theme, pay particular attention to the RELATIONSHIPS among organs and groups of organs. Structural parts are not "just there," in random locations. Their specific layout within the body contributes to making certain functions possible. Therefore, for every structure seen, determine what organ system it is part of; how it is connected up with other components of that and of different organ systems; what general function this structure serves; and how its shape, form, and specific position within a larger pattern of shapes and forms contribute to the execution of its general function.

To make a good, or informative, dissection, one needs good dissection technique. A first essential here is to know one's TOOLS and their limitations. Familiarize yourself with these three fundamental dissecting tools: SCISSORS, PROBE, FORCEPS. Ideally, you should have available two pairs of scissors, a small pair for fine work and a larger one for gross work. Either should be SHARP and should cut without much pushing and pulling. In dissecting the fetal pig, scissors will serve adequately for all cutting jobs. Not only is a scalpel not needed, but scissors are safer, for both you and the pig; scissors are much less likely to botch your dissection than the unfamiliar scalpel.

Your probe should be BLUNT. This instrument serves as an extension of your fingers, and is used to LIFT tissues, to PUSH tissues aside so that underlying structures become visible, and to FEEL for tissues which cannot be immediately seen. Never use sharp-pointed instruments here. Both ends of the probe can and should be used. The blunt forceps handle also makes an excellent probe; and where possible use your fingers—they are the most sensitive probes. Ideally you should have available two forceps—a narrow-tipped one for close work and a broad-tipped one for gross work. Forceps are used to hold and lift tissues. They should be used for lifting WHENEVER scissors are used for cutting. Never cut anything without raising the part to be cut; otherwise underlying parts might be destroyed.

Dissecting does not primarily mean "cutting up"; it means "exposing to view." Hence never cut more than is absolutely necessary to expose a part. Keep in mind that the more that is cut apart, the more the structural relationships among parts will be destroyed—and you want to preserve organizational patterns as much as possible. Moreover, where cutting cannot be avoided, make sure you have fully IDENTIFIED and studied the structural connections of a part before you cut it. It may be valuable to make a quick labeled sketch of a region before part of that region must be cut.

In summary:

1. READ the directions carefully before you begin to dissect, and obey them word for word.
2. IDENTIFY structures to be cut before cutting them.
3. LIFT structures to be cut.
4. CUT only what is absolutely necessary.
5. Then use probes and fingers to EXPOSE structures to view.
6. Proceed to STUDY them.

Following is a glossary of anatomical terms. These terms are used frequently in anatomical work, and you will do well to become thoroughly familiar with them (see also Fig. 1.1, Exercise 1).

dorsal: near or toward the back
ventral: near or toward the belly
lateral: near or toward the sides, right or left
median: near or toward the middle
anterior: near or toward the head end
posterior: near or toward the hind end
caudal: near or toward the tail end
superficial: on or near the surface
deep: some distance below the surface
sagittal: relating to the mid-plane which bisects left and right
transverse: relating to a plane separating anterior and posterior
horizontal: relating to a plane separating dorsal and ventral
proximal: near to a point of reference
distal: far from a point of reference
pectoral: relating to the chest and shoulder region
pelvic: relating to the hip region

III directions

A. external anatomy

1. Put the pig into a dissecting pan and identify the four divisions of the body: a large compact HEAD, a short NECK, a roughly cylindrical TRUNK with two pairs of appendages, and a small short TAIL. What does the tail correspond to in man? The trunk of the pig may be divided into the anterior THORAX and the posterior ABDOMEN. These two external regions correspond to two internal divisions of the trunk, the THORACIC CAVITY and the ABDOMINAL CAVITY, to be studied below.

2. In the head region observe the EYES, EARS, NOSTRILS, and MOUTH. Pry open the mouth and look for the TONGUE and TEETH. On the FORELIMB locate the ELBOW, the first joint below the shoulder. Find KNEE and HOCK JOINT on the HIND LIMB. What does the hock joint correspond to in man? In the posterior region of the trunk, locate the ANUS.

3. On the ventral side locate the pairs of NIPPLES. Search all along the trunk and determine the number of pairs. Since the pig is fetal, some structures are present that are not found in the adult. One such structure is the UMBILICAL CORD, extending from the ventral side of the body. Through it pass the vessels that carry nutrients and waste products between the fetus and the mother. Cut across the cord at a distance from the body and identify the vessels in the cut end of the cord. There are two small UMBILICAL ARTERIES, which have much thicker walls than the single large UMBILICAL VEIN. There is a fourth vessel, usually collapsed, the ALLANTOIC DUCT. Make a mental note of the location of these vessels; their connections will be examined later.

B. internal anatomy

1. Put the animal on its back in the dissecting tray. Tie one end of a string to the right forelimb at the ankle, pass the string underneath the tray, then tie the other end to the left ankle so that the legs are spread apart under tension. Repeat with the hind limbs. Using scissors and forceps, make a mid-ventral incision through the skin and the muscles of the body wall. Cut from the neck posteriorly, to the region of the umbilical cord (Fig. 4.1). Then cut around on each side of the cord and continue the incision as far as the pelvic region. Now, along the incision in the thorax, probe for the breastbone, or STERNUM. Carefully cut through its entire length and so deepen the incision already made in this region. Near the anterior end of your incision, at the level of the forelimbs, cut the body wall laterally to each side, at right angles to the mid-ventral cut. Make similar right-angle cuts at the posterior end of the mid-ventral incision, just anterior to the level of the hind limbs. Left and right flaps of body wall can now be turned out, exposing the thoracic and abdominal cavities. In the abdominal region, a strip of skin bearing the umbilical cord will still remain in its original place. Retie the strings attached to the limbs to take up any slack that may have developed while the pig was cut open.

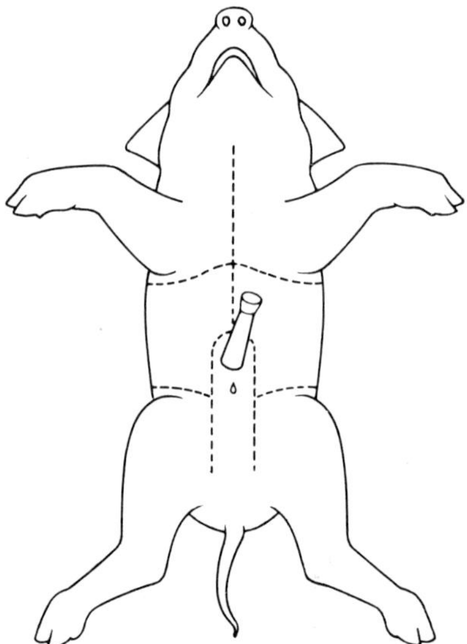

Fig. 4.1 Cut through the body wall of the animal as indicated here by broken lines.

2. Identify the DIAPHRAGM, a thin muscular partition separating the THORACIC CAVITY from the ABDOMINAL CAVITY. In the thorax, examine the cone-shaped RIB CAGE. Along its inner surface note the path of the RIBS, each accompanied by a small artery and a thin white nerve. Count the number of ribs. Identify the two PLEURAL MEMBRANES, thin, transparent tissues of which one lines the inner surfaces of the thoracic cavity and the other the outer surfaces of the lungs. If necessary cut through the pleural membranes to expose the LUNGS, lying on either side of the heart, in PLEURAL CAVITIES. Identify the HEART, situated ventrally along the mid-plane of the thoracic cavity. Note that the heart is enclosed in a thin membrane, the PERICARDIUM. This membrane bounds a PERICARDIAL CAVITY, a special portion of the coelom in which the heart lies.

3. In the abdominal cavity (Fig. 4.2), identify the LIVER, a large brown organ lying just posterior to the diaphragm. Note that a large vein extends from the base of the umbilical cord, on the inside of the median strip of body wall, to the liver. This is the UMBILICAL VEIN, already noted above; it originates in the placenta, passes through the umbilical cord, and leads into the liver. Cut through this vein. You will now be able to reflect the median strip of body wall posteriorly. Attached to it on the inside are two UMBILICAL ARTERIES, also noted above. These branch off the aorta, pass through the umbilicus, and capillarize in the placenta. Between the umbilical arteries, attached to the inside of the median strip of body wall, find the URINARY BLADDER. At one end it narrows into the ALLANTOIC DUCT which, as already noted above, passes into the umbilical cord.

Underneath the liver on the left and partly hidden by it is the STOMACH, a large whitish sac. The SPLEEN is the elongated red body lying along the greater curvature of the stomach. The SMALL INTESTINE is the long, convoluted tube which leaves the posterior end of the stomach and fills the right side of the posterior part of the abdominal cavity. The small intestine connects posteriorly with the LARGE INTESTINE, a wider, less convoluted tube filling nearly all the remaining space in the abdominal cavity. Without tearing anything, lift up the lateral loops of the intestine

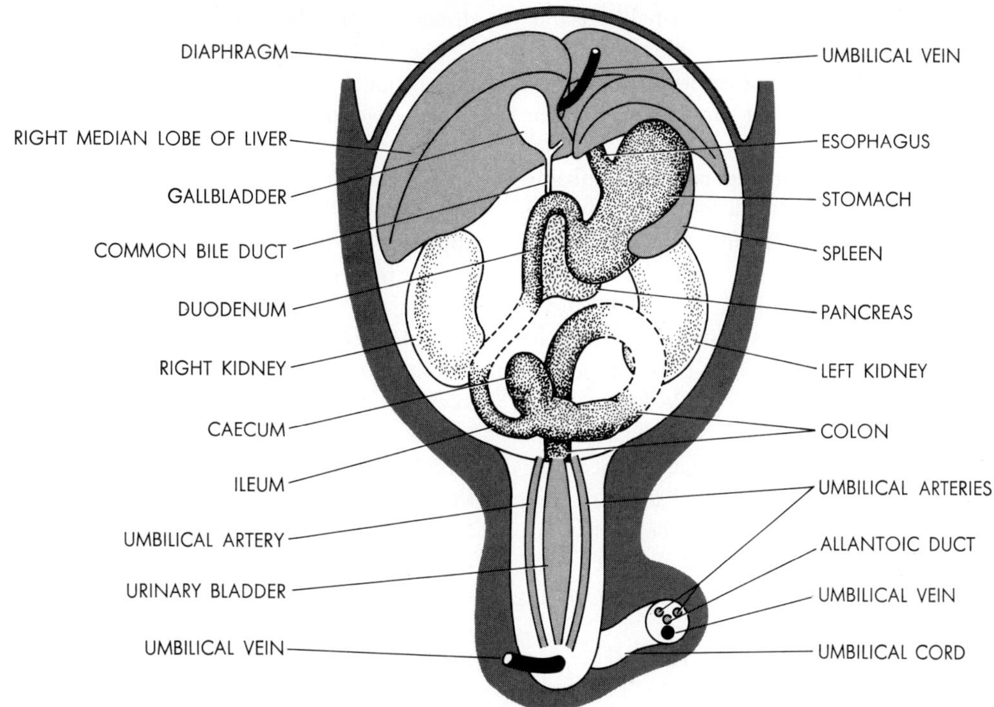

Fig. 4.2 The positions of some of the abdominal organs are sketched. For clarity the greater part of the intestine is not shown.

and find the KIDNEY on each side, a reddish bean-shaped organ partly embedded in fatty tissue. In various parts of the abdominal cavity identify the PERITONEUM, a thin glistening membrane which lines the whole cavity (COELOM) and covers the surfaces of all organs contained in it. Those portions of the peritoneum that fold around and hold in place the organs within the body cavity are called MESENTERIES.

C. the abdomen

1. Study the LIVER and its connections, lifting the organ forward and up as necessary. A fold of the peritoneum suspends the liver from the diaphragm and connects it to the ventral abdominal wall. This mesentery also folds around the liver LOBES. How many are there? Find the GALL BLADDER, a small greenish sac embedded on the underside of the liver (see Fig. 4.2). A small duct, the CYSTIC DUCT, leads from the gall bladder and unites with another duct, the HEPATIC DUCT from the liver, to form the COMMON BILE DUCT. The latter opens into the small intestine, a short distance below the lower end of the stomach. Try to find these ducts; they are small, but they can be seen with careful dissection. Remove the liver from the pig, without destroying adjacent structures. To do this, sever the peritoneal connections to stomach and diaphragm. As you cut between diaphragm and liver, note the large blood vessel. This is the INFERIOR VENA CAVA. It has joined here with the HEPATIC VEIN, which carries blood away from the liver. Note again that in the fetus the umbilical vein brings blood to the liver from the placenta. This blood is rich in food, and the hepatic vein transports this food-laden blood from liver to vena cava. From there it passes into the heart and is pumped throughout the body. In the adult, an umbilical vein is no longer present. But a HEPATIC PORTAL VEIN takes its place functionally; it brings food-laden blood from the intestine to the liver. The hepatic vein still drains the liver, as in the fetus.

2. Again locate the STOMACH, immediately below the diaphragm, and find the point where the ESOPHAGUS enters. This region of the stomach is the CARDIAC portion (why is it so called?). The large FUNDIC part of the stomach lies to the left of the cardiac part, and the PYLORIC part to the

right, where the stomach joins the small intestine. Find the PYLORUS, a ring-shaped sphincter muscle marked externally by a slight constriction between stomach and intestine. Slit the stomach open. What is the material present in the stomach cavity? Examine the opening of the esophagus and the pylorus from the inside, and note the FOLDS of the inner stomach surface. What is their significance?

3. Examine the SPLEEN along the greater curvature of the stomach. How is it attached? Is it part of the digestive system? Along the first portion of the small intestine, in the angle between intestine and stomach, find the PANCREAS, a not very compact, rather diffuse organ. Where the pancreas comes closest to the small intestine look for the PANCREATIC DUCT. It may be partly embedded within the pancreas itself, and it opens into the small intestine at a point close to the opening of the bile duct.

D. the intestine

1. Examine the SMALL INTESTINE. It consists of three parts. The DUODENUM is the first portion. It leaves the pylorus, turns sharply medially, and runs posteriorly a short distance. Then it turns forward, making a U-shaped loop. Without an external line of division, the small intestine now continues on as the JEJUNUM, much coiled and looped. Again without external demarcation, the jejunum merges with the ILEUM, the third and last section of small intestine. Starting at the pylorus, unravel the gut. To do this, you will have to cut in various places through the thin mesentery, that is, that portion of the peritoneum which envelops the intestine and holds it suspended from the dorsal body wall. Note the LOOPS of the gut and the radially arranged blood vessels traveling through the mesentery to the intestinal loops. The arteries among these vessels are branches of the MESENTERIC ARTERY, which arises from the dorsal aorta; the latter will be seen below in detail. The veins are branches of the hepatic portal vein, already referred to earlier, which collects blood from the gut and conducts it into the liver.

2. Examine the LARGE INTESTINE and unravel it as you do so. Find the juncture between ileum and large intestine. Note that the ileum joins some distance from the anterior end of the large intestine. This anterior portion thus forms a blind-ended pouch, the CAECUM. Is there an APPENDIX? Where would you expect to find it? Draw an imaginary line from your navel to the fold where your right leg meets your trunk; bisect this line: the point of bisection marks the position of the appendix in man. The portion of the large intestine posterior to the caecum is the COLON. In the pig, it extends through the left ventral part of the abdominal cavity, mainly in three close double-spiral coils. The colon merges with the RECTUM, the terminal portion of the large intestine. The rectum lies within the pelvis and is largely inaccessible in your dissection. Posteriorly, the digestive tract opens to the outside through the ANUS.

3. Cut through the small intestine at the pylorus and through the large intestine as far posteriorly as you can. Carefully remove the whole intestine in one piece, cutting blood vessels and other connections as close to the gut as possible. Measure the length of the gut, and determine how many times it is longer than the total body length from snout to tail base. On the basis of this ratio, how long do you judge your own intestine to be?

4. Review all structures seen so far and make sketches as desired. Then dispose of organs removed from the pig, tie the animal together, and deposit it in its preserving container.

IV analysis

1. List as many external anatomical features as you can in which pig and man differ. What features present in man are not present in the pig, and vice versa?

2. How many incisors, canines, premolars, and molars does the human adult possess? What is the particular function of each type of tooth? How many "milk teeth" does the human young have?

3. Do male and female pigs have the same number of nipples? Can you account for the presence of nipples in males, considering that these structures never serve a function?

4. List the parts of the alimentary system, in sequence from the anterior end. Describe the functions of each structure listed.

5. Review the structures seen in your fetal pig that are not present in the adult. Relate these

structures to prenatal functions. What happens to the umbilicus at birth? What adult structure bears witness of its earlier presence?

6. For each of 10 or more organs or structures you have examined in this exercise, name the organ system of which it is a part. Name other organs belonging to these systems. How many organ systems are there altogether? What are they?

7. List as many asymmetrical features of your body as you can. Indicate whether a structure is on the left or right, or what condition produces a left-right asymmetry.

8. On your own body, point to the exact location of liver, stomach, kidneys, and spleen.

9. Sketch a simplified diagram of a cross section through the abdomen. Draw in the position and extent of the peritoneum.

10. Outline the path of the colon on your own body. Is the length of the intestine of functional significance? How does relative intestinal length vary in different types of mammals?

11. Is the presence of a caecum of adaptive significance? Does a herbivorous mammal possess a caecum? Does a carnivorous mammal? Does a herbivorous mammal possess an appendix?

12. What principal organs or body parts are present in the mammalian thorax, and in what arrangement? Make a sketch showing what a cross section through the thorax would look like.

exercise 5 the fetal pig [II]

I materials

Each student

fetal pig from previous exercise
dissecting instruments
dissecting pan, pins

Class stock

fresh whole beef hearts
heart models
supply of string

II introduction

In this exercise the dissection of the fetal pig will be continued. Obtain your pig, tie it to the dissecting tray as in the previous exercise, and open the dissections already made.

III directions

A. mouth, nose, pharynx, and neck

1. Cautiously deepen and lengthen the mid-ventral incision in the throat region. Probe for the LARYNX, a white cartilaginous box. Carefully free the larynx from overlying skin, muscle, and connective tissue, and expose it fully. Just posterior to the larynx identify the THYROID GLAND, a pea-sized reddish body (see also Fig. 5.1). It lies ventral to the TRACHEA, which is a stiff tube leading from the larynx toward the lungs. Carefully loosen the connective tissue and muscle in the neck area, to expose the trachea to its full extent and to connect this dissection with the already opened thorax. Do not cut or tear any blood vessels passing through the neck. Push the trachea to one side to expose the ESOPHAGUS, a collapsed tube leading from pharynx to stomach. On either side of the trachea find the THYMUS bodies. They are loose lobes of tissue with irregularly grooved surfaces, found all along the neck and extending posteriorly to the heart.

2. Insert the tips of the scissors into the angle between upper and lower lips, and cut through the cartilaginous jaw. Repeat on the opposite side and lay back the jaw and tongue to expose the MOUTH CAVITY. The floor of the mouth is occupied by the TONGUE. Small elevations are scattered over its surface, which contains the taste buds. In fetuses almost ready to be born TEETH are present, which will be seen protruding from the GUMS of the upper and lower jaws. The roof of the mouth cavity is formed by the HARD PALATE anteriorly and the SOFT PALATE posteriorly. Note the numerous transverse ridges of the hard palate, on either side of a median furrow. The soft palate forms a sort of curtain which separates the mouth cavity from the cavity of the PHARYNX, posterior to the mouth.

3. A number of channels and passageways lead into or away from the pharynx. One of these can be found by gently probing behind the soft palate. This space is the NASOPHARYNX, a cavity continuous anteriorly with the NASAL PASSAGES. To examine the latter, cut transversely across the tip of the snout, about 1 in. back from the NOSTRILS. This will expose the nasal passages. Notice that they are separated by a sagittal partition of cartilage and bone, the NASAL SEPTUM. The floor of the passages is the hard palate. Along the lateral walls are large folds, the TURBINATE CARTILAGES. Insert the scissors into one of the nasal cavities, and cut posteriorly through the hard and soft palate. Probe along the length of this cut and examine the continuity between nasal passage, nasopharynx, and pharynx.

4. Depress the tongue where it is apposed against the roof of the pharynx. You will thereby expose the EPIGLOTTIS, a small, median cartilaginous flap over which food slides on its way from mouth to esophagus. Probe into the ESOPHAGUS from the mouth side, then lift up the lower jaw and examine the esophagus from your neck dissection to see if your probe is actually within the esophageal tube. Cut through the base of the epiglottis and note the GLOTTIS, a slitlike opening leading directly into the larynx. Probe into the larynx from the mouth side, and again check your position by lifting up the lower jaw and examining the neck dissection. Cut sagittally through the larynx. Observe the interior cavity and the location of the

Fig. 5.1 The principal arteries.

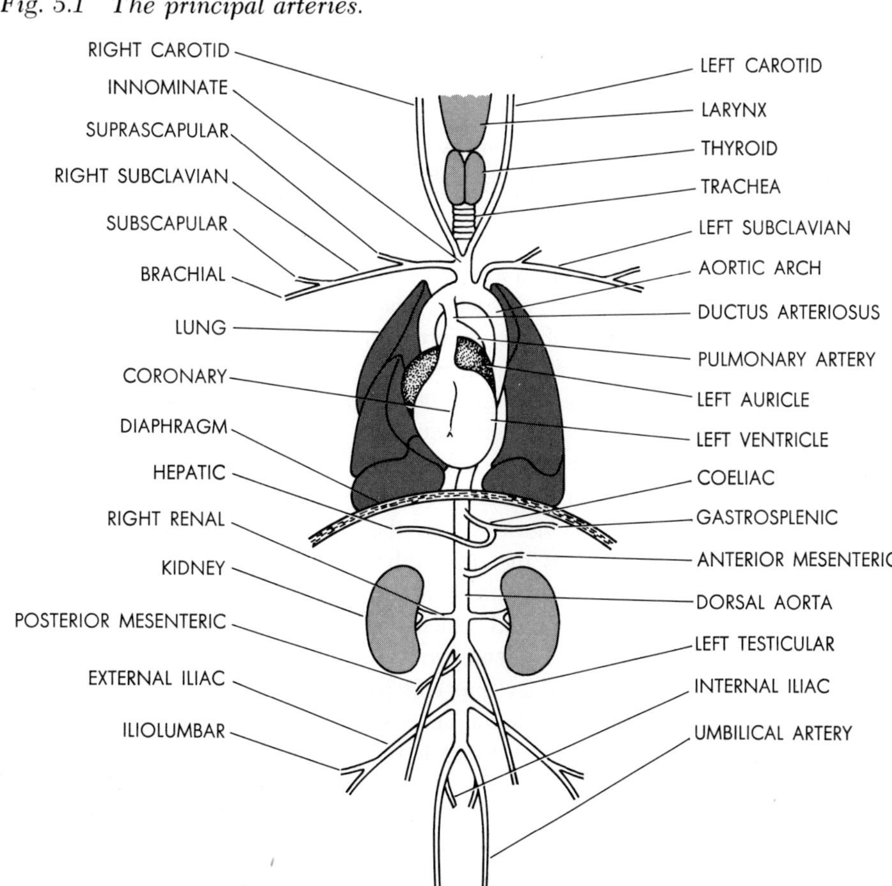

VOCAL CORDS. Probe from the larynx into the trachea. Observe the RINGS OF CARTILAGE which prevent the trachea from collapsing.

B. the heart

1. Study the ORIENTATION of the heart IN SITU (that is, as the organ appears in the thoracic cavity). Note the roughly cone-shaped bulk of the VENTRICLES and, anterior to them, the smaller AURICLES. Examine the oblique groove across the ventricular muscle. A CORONARY ARTERY and VEIN travel in this groove. The posterior tip of the heart is the APEX. Does it lie exactly in the sagittal plane? Describe. Make note of the large blood vessels connecting with the heart; they will be studied in detail below.

2. To serve at least 10 students, put a fresh beef heart into a separate dissecting pan and orient this heart exactly like that of the pig. The path of the coronary artery may serve as a valuable guide. In such an orientation, the left auricle and ventricle will appear to your right, the right auricle and ventricle to your left. Now make a long and fairly deep incision on each side of the heart, starting anteriorly at the auricle and ending posteriorly at the apex. The aim is to open the left cavities with a single cut and the right cavities with another, passing through the auricular and ventricular walls.

3. Compare the thickness of the WALLS in auricle, right ventricle, and left ventricle. What is the functional significance of the differences you observe? Examine the GRAIN of heart muscle. Compare the internal VOLUME CAPACITY of the auricles, the right ventricle, and the left ventricle. Keep in mind that this heart is neither contracted nor distended. Examine the AURICULOVENTRICULAR VALVES, found where the auricles join the ventricles. How many flaps does the right valve contain? How many the left? From this, which is the BICUSPID (or MITRAL) valve, and which the TRICUSPID valve? Examine the CHORDAE TENDINEAE, strands of tissue attached at one end to the edges of the valve flaps and on the other to the inner surfaces of the ventricles. What is the function of these chordae? Examine the SEPTUM of the heart, the partition separating the left side from the right. On the outer surface of the heart, trace the path of the CORONARY blood vessels. Determine where they originate and where they terminate. What is their function?

C. the anterior blood vessels

1. Each of the four heart chambers connects with a large blood vessel. In each chamber of the beef heart, find the opening of this vessel and probe outward to identify the path of the vessel in external view. From the left ventricle leaves the thick-walled AORTA, one of the widest vessels in the body. From the right ventricle emerges the PULMONARY ARTERY, also large and thick-walled. Where aorta and pulmonary artery leave the ventricles, find the EXIT VALVES. What is their function? Into the right auricle opens the VENA CAVA, thinner-walled than the arteries but very wide nevertheless. The vena cava is formed by the junction of two vessels, the SUPERIOR (or ANTERIOR) VENA CAVA coming from the head region, and the INFERIOR (or POSTERIOR) VENA CAVA coming from the posterior region of the body. Can you find the stumps of these two vessels in the beef heart? Into the left auricle opens the PULMONARY VEIN, carrying blood from lungs to heart. Now trace the course of blood as it is pumped through the living heart, paying attention to the position of the valves, the state of contraction of auricles and ventricles, and the flow of arterial (oxygenated) and venous (non-oxygenated) blood.

2. Transfer your attention to the heart of the fetal pig. By careful dissection, loosen the connective tissues which hold the large blood vessels as they emerge from the heart. Once separated one from the other, IDENTIFY each of the vessels, using the corresponding vessels of the beef heart for guidance.

3. In your pig, veins, with the exception of a few large ones like those entering the heart, cannot be easily studied; they are small, collapsed, and tear readily (but see Fig. 5.2). On the other hand, the rubber-injected arteries can be examined thoroughly. Using Figs. 5.1 and 5.2 for guidance, identify and trace the following arteries:

AORTA: it leaves the left ventricle, passes anteriorly for a short distance, then bends dorsally and to the left, and proceeds diagonally backward to the mid-dorsal line of the thoracic cavity.

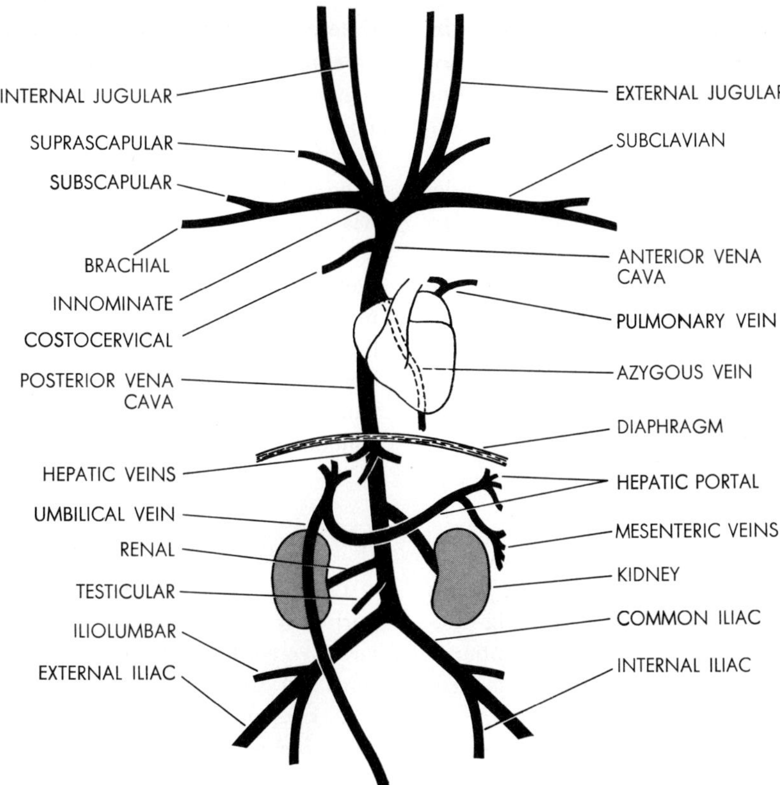

Fig. 5.2 The principal veins.

This path describes the so-called AORTIC ARCH, much of which is hidden behind the heart and will be seen later. Where the aorta leaves the heart, it gives off two small CORONARY ARTERIES.

PULMONARY ARTERY: it leaves the right ventricle, passes forward for some distance (dorsal or ventral to the aorta?), and divides into branches going to the lungs. Since your pig is fetal, the pulmonary arteries are still small and incompletely developed.

DUCTUS ARTERIOSUS: this is a short but wide vessel branching off the pulmonary artery and leading directly to the aorta. This vessel is found only in the fetus, in which it short-circuits blood around the still nonfunctional lungs: instead of going to the lungs, the bulk of blood from the right ventricle passes directly into the aorta, from where it is distributed throughout the body. At birth the ductus arteriosus shrivels (and at the same time an open passage between the right and left auricle of the fetal heart closes off). Thereafter all the blood from the right ventricle must go to the lungs, where it is oxygenated. The fetal condition is advantageous because the placenta, not the lung, supplies oxygen.

INNOMINATE ARTERY: follow the aortic arch; beyond its juncture with the ductus arteriosus, the first branch vessel is the large innominate (that is, "nameless") artery. It passes anteriorly and branches into three vessels: the RIGHT SUBCLAVIAN ARTERY, passing laterally and supplying the right forelimb; and the RIGHT and LEFT CAROTID arteries, passing anteriorly and supplying the neck and the head.

CAROTID ARTERIES: trace the path of the carotids forward through the neck. Where do they run in relation to trachea and esophagus? Press your fingers against the side of your neck and feel the pulse of the carotids. Feel the pulse at your temples; the arteries there are branches of the carotids. These vessels provide virtually the whole blood supply to the head.

LEFT SUBCLAVIAN ARTERY: unlike the right subclavian, which branches off the innominate artery, the left subclavian arises directly from the aorta, the second branch off this vessel. The left subclavian supplies the left forelimb. Subclavian arteries are so called because they travel "under the clavicle." Press your fingers under your collarbones and feel the faint pulse of the subclavian arteries. Trace the path of both subclavians into the forelimbs of the pig.

4. If desired or instructed, make a quick sketch of the blood vessels seen and label them.

D. the thorax

1. Cautiously cut through the large blood vessels near the heart (being careful that nothing else is cut), and remove the heart from the pig. Reidentify the AORTIC ARCH. This arch continues posteriorly as the DORSAL AORTA, the large median vessel just ventral to the vertebral column.
2. Study the BREATHING SYSTEM. First review the parts of this system in head and neck, already dissected in the previous exercise. Then trace the trachea posteriorly, to the point where it divides into the two BRONCHI. Follow each bronchus into the pleural cavity, to its entry into the lungs. For better observation, carefully scrape some of the lung tissue away where the bronchus enters. Note the BRONCHIAL BRANCHES, each passing into a lobe of the lung. Note also the PULMONARY ARTERIES entering and branching into the lungs. The LUNGS are made up of alveolar tissue capable of great distention when filling with air. Since breathing has not yet begun in your fetal pig, the lungs are still quite compact. Beginning at the anterior end of the pleural cavity and passing posteriorly, find three of the lobes of the right lung. A fourth lobe occupies a median position in the pleural cavity, somewhat dorsal to the heart. Note how the heart has shaped the medial surfaces of the lung. The left lung is divided into lobes also. How many lobes are on this side?
3. Remove the lung on one side by cutting through its ROOTS, that is, the region where bronchi and blood vessels enter. On the inner dorsal surface of the rib cage examine the INTERCOSTAL ARTERIES, small vessels branching off the aorta and running alongside each rib. Now cut through the trachea just behind the larynx and carefully remove this tube together with the remaining lung. Trace the ESOPHAGUS from the neck posteriorly. Follow it through the thorax and find the point where it pierces the diaphragm. Where does the esophagus lie in relation to the heart? Remove esophagus and stomach.
4. Review the whole dissection and make sketches as desired or instructed. (If extra time remains, proceed to the first section of the following exercise.) Then detach the strings from the legs, tag or otherwise identify your pig, tie the animal together, and deposit it in its preserving container.

IV analysis

1. Look deep into your own mouth with a mirror, or look into the mouth of a fellow student, and give correct technical names for all the structures and cavities you see.

2. Do YOU possess thymus bodies? Did you ever? Review what is known about these organs.

3. On your own body, feel the extent of your rib cage. How many pairs of ribs are present in man? Does the number differ for males and females?

4. Sketch the region of the pharynx in side view. With what cavities or spaces does the pharynx connect? Trace the path of air and the path of food through the pharynx.

5. Hold a finger against your Adam's apple (what structure is this technically?) and swallow. Describe what happens. See if you understand the events in pharynx and larynx when food is swallowed.

6. What is the adaptive advantage of the cartilage rings in the trachea? Would it be useful to have such rings in the esophagus also?

7. Is the greatly folded condition of the turbinate cartilages of adaptive advantage? Explain. List all passages leading into or away from the nasal chambers. What are sinuses?

8. What is the function of the diaphragm? Which groups of vertebrates do, and which do not, possess a diaphragm? In the latter, how is breathing accomplished?

9. Do the pleural cavities connect with other cavities or spaces? What structures lead into or out of the pleural cavities? Do any of these struc-

tures provide openings into or out of the spaces between the lungs and the pleural membranes? Is this structural organization of the chest significant functionally?

10. Name the structures that pass through the diaphragm.

11. List the parts of the breathing system, in sequence from the anterior end.

12. Describe or sketch the course of the adult blood circulation through the heart. Determine from your text the course of the fetal circulation through the heart; show what changes occur at birth.

13. Name two arteries that carry venous blood and two veins that carry arterial blood. Review the general course of circulation in adult and fetus from the standpoint of arterial and venous blood.

14. Name the main arteries supplying blood to the following body parts: thumb, brain, lung, heart muscle, ribs. From your text determine on which side of the body and how many aortic arches are present in birds, reptiles, amphibia, and fishes.

15. Define turbinate cartilage, epiglottis, tricuspid valve, chorda tendinea, ductus arteriosus, intercostal artery, vena cava.

exercise 6 the fetal pig [III]

I materials

Each student

fetal pig from previous exercise
dissecting instruments
dissecting pan, pins

II introduction

In this exercise, the dissection of the fetal pig will be concluded with a study of the remaining portions of the CIRCULATORY system and of the EXCRETORY and male and female REPRODUCTIVE systems. The vertebrate NERVOUS system is examined in a later context, and the SKELETAL system is dealt with in exercise 3 (page 15).

Obtain your pig, tie it to the dissecting tray as in the previous exercises, and open your dissection.

III directions

A. the dorsal aorta

Study the abdominal portion of the dorsal aorta and identify the following branches (see also Fig. 5.1, Exercise 5):

COELIAC ARTERY: it leaves the aorta just posterior to the passage of the aorta through the diaphragm. The coeliac carries blood to stomach, duodenum, liver, spleen, and pancreas.

MESENTERIC ARTERY: this is the second aortic branch in the abdomen, arising a short distance posterior to the coeliac artery. The mesenteric supplies the small and large intestine, by means of branches passing through the mesentery, already observed earlier.

RENAL ARTERIES: one of these goes from the aorta to each kidney. Leave this and all posterior regions intact, for the study below.

ILIAC ARTERIES: in the pelvic region the aorta splits up into EXTERNAL and INTERNAL iliac arteries, one of each on each side. The external iliacs supply the hind limbs. The internal iliacs enter the pelvis, carrying blood to the organs there, and continue directly as two large vessels running on either side of the urinary bladder and out through the umbilical cord. These are the UMBILICAL ARTERIES, already mentioned.

B. the urinary system

1. Examine the bean-shaped KIDNEYS, lying against the dorsal wall of the abdominal cavity. Tease away the membrane lying over the ventral side of one of the kidneys; this membrane is the peritoneum, and you will note that it does not envelop the dorsal side of the kidney. Expose the organ more fully by carefully teasing away the surrounding fatty material. Along the anterior portion of the kidney, on the medial border, find the ADRENAL GLAND, a narrow whitish body. It is part of the endocrine system. The depression on the median side of the kidney is the RENAL HILUS. Here the RENAL ARTERY enters and the RENAL VEIN leaves. The hilus is also the point where the URETER emerges from the kidney. Identify the ureter, a thin whitish duct, and trace it posteriorly for some distance along the dorsal wall of the abdomen (see also Figs. 6.1 and 6.2).

2. Remove one of the kidneys from the pig and cut it into longitudinal halves. On the cut surface note the RENAL PELVIS, the expanded end of the ureter; the RENAL CORTEX, the compact outer layer of kidney tissue; and the RENAL PYRAMIDS (or RENAL MEDULLA), the triangularly arranged tissues between cortex and pelvis. Relate these subdivisions to kidney function.

3. Make a preliminary identification of the sex of your fetal pig. To do this, carefully examine the body skin just behind the base of the umbilicus. If you find a small opening there (which may be more or less concealed by hairs), then your pig is male: the opening is the UROGENITAL ORIFICE of the PENIS. If such an orifice is not present, examine the body skin just ventral to the anus: a urogenital orifice will be found in this region if your pig is female.

In all the following, proceed with EXTREME CAUTION. Most of the structures to be studied are small and thin, and are easily destroyed if the dissection is not carried out with careful precision.

Feel for the PUBIC SYMPHYSIS, the mid-ventral juncture of bones of the pelvic girdle, between the hind legs. Precisely along the midline in this region, cut skin and muscle until the bony pubic symphysis is exposed. With strong scissors, cut through the pubic symphysis along the midline, making sure that underlying structures are not damaged. Carefully chip away small pieces of

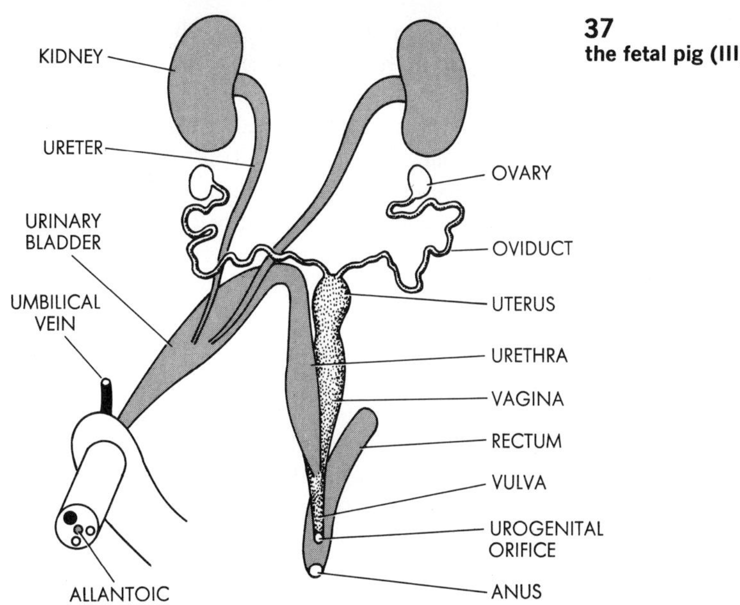

Fig. 6.1 The female urinary and reproductive systems.

bone (and only bone) to the right and left, so that a better view of underlying parts can be obtained; to this end, also, retighten the string which holds the hind legs apart.

4. Turn your attention once more to the ureters. Follow one of them posteriorly, and without cutting or tearing anything except transparent connective tissues, find the opening of the ureter into the URINARY BLADDER. This opening will be found near the base, that is, the posterior end, of the bladder. Carefully loosen the connective tissue that attaches the bladder to the strip of mid-ventral body wall. Follow the bladder anteriorly, and note once more how it narrows into the ALLANTOIC DUCT (see Figs. 6.1 and 6.2). The latter leaves through the umbilicus to the placenta. Cut transversely through the bladder (and only bladder) and examine the interior. In the fetus, urinary waste travels through ureter, bladder, and allantoic duct. After birth, the allantoic pathway is no longer available (how so?), and urine passes to the outside through other structures. These are still incompletely developed in the fetus, hence they are small. To find them, examine once more the base of the bladder. Just behind the opening of the ureters, the bladder will be found to narrow into a tube, which proceeds posteriorly along the midline underneath the pubic symphysis. This tube is the URETHRA. If your pig is female, the urethra will continue straight posteriorly and will terminate at the UROGENITAL ORIFICE, ventral to the anus. If the pig is male, the urethra will pass posteriorly for a distance of about 1 in., then will turn sharply anteriorly and ventrally, and will enter the PENIS. This is a firm strand of tissue running along the inside of the mid-ventral body skin. Push the bladder gently aside to see the penis. At its anterior end it is attached by means of membranes to the inside of the mid-ventral body skin, just behind the base of the umbilicus. At this point the urogenital orifice of the penis conducts the contents of the urethra to the outside. If necessary, sever the anterior attachment of the penis to the body skin, and trace the penis posteriorly to urethra and bladder.

5. As desired or instructed, sketch the parts of the urinary system. Make sure you understand the path of urine from the kidneys to the outside. Then proceed to section C or D, depending on whether your pig is female or male.

C. the female reproductive system

1. Locate the pair of OVARIES, small yellowish bodies suspended from the dorsal wall of the abdominal cavity, just posterior to the kidneys (see Fig. 6.1). The peritoneal mesentery which holds the ovaries in place is the MESOVARIUM. Mature eggs escape from the ovaries into the OVIDUCTS (or MUELLERIAN DUCTS). Examine these slightly coiled ducts. In the fetus they are still fairly small. Note that they do not connect directly with the ovaries; just short of the ovary, each oviduct ends in a fluted, funnel-shaped opening, the OSTIUM. Connective tissue envelops ovary and ostium, giving the superficial impression of direct continuity.

2. Trace the oviducts posteriorly, to their juncture with the UTERUS. This median structure consists of three parts. The posterior continuations of the oviducts are the uterine HORNS. The horns unite along the midline, forming the BODY of the uterus. This cylindrical tube continues posteriorly for a short distance, then constricts into the uterine CERVIX, or neck, the third part. Push the urethra gently to one side to expose the underlying VAGINA. This is an elongated channel into which the cervix of the uterus projects at the anterior end. Posteriorly the vagina unites with the urethra. The short, wide tube so formed is the UROGENITAL SINUS which opens to the exterior through the urogenital orifice, ventral to the anus. Note the LABIA, two rounded lips bordering the urogenital orifice laterally. Slit the urogenital sinus from the side: on its inner ventral surface locate the CLITORIS, a slight, rounded elevation. This structure is the equivalent of the penis in the male. A urogenital sinus, a structure also found in adult egg-laying and other primitive mammals, is not present in the adult female pig (or human being). During the later development of the fetus, the sinus reduces in size posteriorly, until the vagina and the urethra each acquires a separate opening to the outside, that is, the GENITAL ORIFICE and the URINARY ORIFICE, respectively. Thus, in the advanced adult female mammal, reproductive materials and metabolic wastes travel separate paths (a condition which differs from that in the adult male).

3. Make sketches as desired or instructed. Then team up with a fellow student whose pig is male. Exchange your pigs and examine in detail his dissection of the male system. You are required to study both systems even though you have dissected only one.

D. the male reproductive system

1. The TESTES are the sperm-producing organs, equivalent to the egg-producing ovaries of the female. Testes begin to develop in the abdominal cavity, posterior to the kidneys, in locations equivalent to those of the ovaries. But unlike ovaries, which remain in the abdomen permanently, testes migrate posteriorly as they mature (in pig and man alike), finally coming to rest in the SCROTAL SACS between the hind limbs. In looking for the testes, therefore, the age of the fetus must be taken into account. If your pig is near full term, the testes will be found in not very prominent scrotal sacs, one along the anteromedial side of each hind limb (see Fig. 6.2). Carefully slit the body skin medially, near the juncture of one of the hind limbs and the trunk, and look for an elongated, bulbous structure covered with a transparent membrane. Expose this structure fully. Note that is is attached anteriorly to strands of tissue: do not cut or damage these.

2. The testis is contained within the bulbous

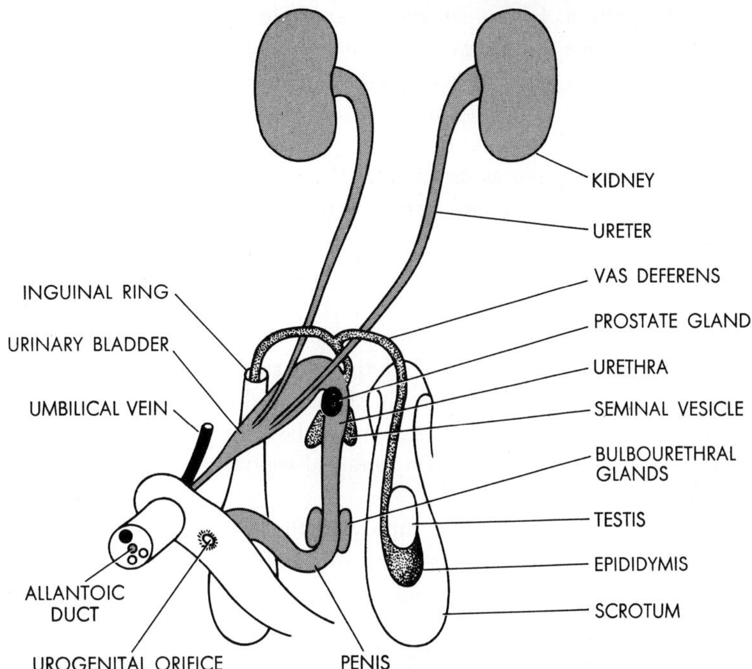

Fig. 6.2 The male urinary and reproductive systems.

structure. The covering membrane is the TUNICA VAGINALIS, a fold of peritoneum that has been carried into the scrotal sac along with the testis when the testis migrated out of the abdominal cavity. Slit the tunica open and find the oval testis. Note the irregular mass of highly coiled tubules. This is the EPIDIDYMIS. It is actually a single duct which originates at the testis and carries sperms from it. The coils serve for temporary sperm storage.

3. The epididymis continues anteriorly as the straight VAS DEFERENS. This tube is part of the SPERMATIC CORD, the white strand of tissue leading forward into the abdominal cavity. In addition to the vas deferens, the spermatic cord also contains blood vessels and nerves. Trace the vas deferens into the abdomen. Note that as it reaches the abdominal cavity it passes through a thin transverse strand of tissue shaped like a ring; this is the so-called INGUINAL RING. Note also that in the further course of the vas deferens it loops around the ureter on that side of the body. (The tissues here are very delicate; extreme care should be taken not to rupture anything. It may also be helpful to lift the testis, still attached to the spermatic cord, out from the scrotum into the abdominal cavity.)

4. Now carefully trace the vas deferens to its juncture with the anterior portion of the URETHRA, close to the point where the urethra itself emerges from the urinary bladder. The left and right vas deferens may unite in your pig and open as a single duct into the urethra. At the vas deferens–urethra juncture, on the dorsal side of the urethra, locate the PROSTATE GLAND, a small, rounded body. This gland may be partially concealed by the SEMINAL VESICLES, a pair of fairly large, lobulated glandular bodies, one lying along each side of the urethra. Both prostate and seminal vesicles secrete fluids which, mixed with sperms at this point, make up SEMEN. In the posterior, pelvic portion of the urethra, note the BULBOURETHRAL GLANDS, two elongated bodies, one on each side of the urethra. These glands secrete additional seminal fluid.

5. Trace the urethra once more into the PENIS, and follow the penis forward to the urogenital orifice behind the umbilicus. It should be clear from the structural arrangement that the urethra serves to conduct both urine and reproductive materials, though not both at the same time. This arrangement differs from that in the female, where separate ducts carry urinary and genital products.

6. Make sketches as desired or instructed. Then

team up with a fellow student whose pig is female. Exchange your pigs, and examine in detail his dissection of the female system. You are required to study both systems even though you have dissected only one.

7. Dispose of the pig as directed by the instructor, and clean your desk and dissecting pan.

IV analysis

1. Envisage an imaginary cross section made through your body at the level of the (*a*) neck, (*b*) chest, (*c*) abdomen. For each, sketch or describe the principal structures that would be seen at the cut surface, with attention to dorsal-ventral and left-right orientation.

2. Name the main arteries supplying the following structures: urinary bladder, gall bladder, reproductive organs, toes, duodenum, colon, kidneys.

3. Review the course of blood through the entire circulatory system in fetus and adult, taking into account all information obtained in the exercises on the pig.

4. Sketch or describe the path of urine through the urinary system, differentiating carefully between male and female and between adult and fetal anatomy.

5. What are the functions of the adrenal gland? What other endocrine organs have you dissected in the course of the exercises on the pig? Which endocrines have you not looked for by dissection, and where would you expect to find these?

6. Trace the path a mammalian sperm travels from the point of manufacture in the male to the point where it fertilizes an egg in the female.

7. Urinary and genital ducts exit through a single orifice at all times in the male mammal, but only during the fetal period in the female. What is the adaptive advantage of the separate exits of these ducts in the adult female?

8. Ovaries and testes are equivalent structurally and developmentally. Name other such male-female homologies in the reproductive system. Do they suggest anything to you regarding the embryonic origin of the sexual status of mammals?

9. From your text, determine the functional significance of testis migration during the early development of the male pig. Name mammals in which testis migration occurs seasonally in the adult. Name mammals in which such a migration occurs neither in the fetus nor in the adult.

10. List the organ systems of the mammalian body that you have examined wholly or partially in your pig dissections. Which organ systems have you not examined?

exercise 7 taxonomy and classification

I materials

Each student

hand lens
dissecting instruments

Each group of 10 *students*

whole or partial specimens, living or preserved, predissected and labeled if warranted, of the following:

Aurelia	*Cambarus*
Dugesia	*Romalea*
Mytilus	*Asterias*
Loligo	*Petromyzon*
Nereis	*Mus*
Lumbricus	

Class stock

10 or more types of "unknown" animal specimens, identified only by number, predissected and labeled if warranted, and representing the phyla here studied; living or preserved

II introduction

Since the time of Linnaeus it has been customary to label each living organism with two latinized names. Just as each person has a family name and one or more given names, so does each organism have a GENERIC name and a SPECIFIC name. Many frogs, for example, bear the generic name *Rana,* that is, these frogs belong to the same "group," or GENUS, of animals. Any one frog in addition has a name identifying its SPECIES, that is, the particular "kind" of frog it represents. For example, *Rana sylvatica,* the wood frog; or *Rana catesbiana*, the bullfrog. Generic names are capitalized, specific names are not; both names are underlined or are printed in *italic* letters.

A given genus (containing one or more species) is part of a FAMILY of organisms, which may contain other genera in addition to the one in question. For example, the family FELIDAE contains the genus *Felis* (cats), the genus *Panthera* (lions), and many other genera of catlike mammals. A family is part of an ORDER, which may contain several other families. An order similarly is part of a CLASS, and a class is part of a PHYLUM. At each level of this hierarchy subclassifications may exist, for example, subphylum, superorder, subfamily, sub-subspecies.

Distinctions between equivalent rank categories are based on permanent structural (less often functional) characteristics of organisms. Thus, different phyla represent broadly different body architectures and ways of life, and successive categories below phylum rank define distinctions of progressively finer detail. TAXONOMY is the name of the science dealing with living classification.

Taxonomic ranks also exist above the phylum level. Traditionally the largest, most inclusive rank is the KINGDOM, and since the time of Linnaeus two kingdoms have been recognized, namely, that of PLANTS and that of ANIMALS. Biological investigations during the last few decades have made it apparent, however, that a classification of organisms into just these two divisions is no longer adequate; numerous organisms exhibit both plant and animal traits simultaneously, and many others possess traits characteristic of neither plants nor animals. Accordingly, the "kingdoms" scheme can be supplemented today with alternative ones which fit the traits of actually existing organisms somewhat better. One useful scheme recognizes not two but four largest classification groups, the organisms in these being designated as the MONERA, the PROTISTA, the METAPHYTA, and the METAZOA. Figure 7.1 defines some of the identifying features of these four groups and the kinds of organisms included in each, and it also compares this classification scheme with that of the traditional kingdoms.

Note that in the newer scheme the designation "plant" is restricted to the organisms of the Metaphyta, that of "animal" to the organisms of the Metazoa. Note also that within the Metazoa, or animals, the largest subgroups are BRANCHES, classification ranks not encountered elsewhere. Indeed, several other uniquely animal ranks are interpolated between the main category and the phylum level. Figure 7.2 names and defines these intermediate animal ranks. Metazoa evidently encompass a more complex taxonomic hierarchy and many more phyla than any of the other three main groups of organisms.

That living organisms can be classified as above on the basis of structural similarities is of great theoretical and practical significance. Theoretically, the taxonomic hierarchy suggests the possibility of implying EVOLUTIONARY relationships among organisms; given degrees of structural similarity can be, and have been, taken to imply corresponding degrees of evolutionary relatedness. In many cases such inferences have been corroborated by independently obtained evolutionary evidence (for example, from fossils), and taxonomic pursuits have therefore become substantially more than mere mechanical card filing and indexing; in large measure such pursuits are also studies of past living history.

Practically, the advantages of taxonomic systems are many. An obvious one arises from the universal international use of taxonomic nomenclature. For example, "dogfishes" are common in many parts of the world, yet the fish so designated are rarely of the same type or species. International nomenclature clearly circumvents errors arising from local usage and linguistic habit. What other practical advantages would a taxonomic system provide?

This exercise will concentrate on the taxonomy of some of the more familiar metazoan phyla. Metazoa are selected for study because the choice of types is greater than in the other three main categories, and they can be examined without microscopes or other technical aids. The aim is to develop some familiarity with the universal taxonomic system generally and with the criteria used to define certain phyla, classes, and orders specifically. Note that a preliminary study of ways of life, adaptive features, and structural detail is an obvious necessity in an exercise of this kind. Keep in mind also that, although the attention is on Metazoa, the basic taxonomic principles under study apply as well to the Monera, the Protista, and the Metaphyta.

III directions

In one part of the laboratory, sets of 11 fairly familiar animals or parts of animals are set out. These are identified by popular, generic, and phyletic names, and some of the specimens, particularly the larger or more complex ones, may have been dissected by the instructor and their parts labeled. These animals represent the "knowns" which you will use to study some of the principles of taxonomic classification. Section

A below gives specific instructions, and section B provides the taxonomic descriptions on which this work is to be based. In another part of the laboratory, sets of "unknowns" are displayed which are to be classified later on the basis of information gained from a study of knowns. Section C and again section B are to be used in this phase of the exercise.

A. classification of knowns

1. The 11 knowns are: *Aurelia,* jellyfish; *Dugesia,* a flatworm; *Nereis,* a segmented worm; *Lumbricus,* an earthworm; *Loligo,* a squid; *Mytilus,* a clam; *Asterias,* a starfish; *Cambarus,* a crayfish; *Romalea,* a grasshopper; *Petromyzon,* a lamprey; and *Mus,* a mouse. These 11 represent 7 of the more familiar animal phyla. The whole exercise will concentrate on these 7.

2. Your first task is to examine each of the knowns carefully, using the descriptions given in section B (and, where desired, pertinent data from your text). The sequence of study is immaterial. Use a hand lens as necessary and, if so directed by the instructor, also dissecting instruments. In the course of this work, become thoroughly acquainted with the diagnostic features of the phyla here represented. For each animal studied, ask and answer questions such as the following:

What visible structures or organs can be identified, and what role do these structures play in the functioning of the animal?

What visible features place this animal into this particular phylum?

How is this animal (and this phylum) uniquely distinguished from animals in other phyla?

What features of animals in this phylum adapt them to particular ways of life?

Can the English translation of the phyletic name help in identifying the diagnostic characteristics of the phylum? (Make use of the glossary in your text here.)

3. After you have studied the phylum characteristics, proceed to become familiar with the diagnostic features of the subordinate rank categories, as described in section B. On the basis of this, place the animal you examine into the appropriate class and order. Here again determine carefully how classes and orders are distinguished, how technical names help in diagnosis, and why your animal belongs to a particular taxonomic category. Try also to name representative animals of all other listed rank categories within a phylum, and show in what ways animals in a particular class and order are adapted to a particular way of life.

B. description of taxonomic groups

The diagnostic features listed below for each of the seven phyla are by no means complete. They suffice however for present purposes. In most cases all taxonomic subdivisions within a phylum are not given.

1. Phylum Cnidaria

Representatives: *Aurelia.*

Radial symmetry. The three layers of the body are arranged into a sac with a single opening serving both as mouth and anus. A simple nerve net is located in the middle layer, the MESOGLOEA, an often extensive jelly tissue. A two-phase life cycle involving asexual, sessile POLYP and sexual, free-swimming MEDUSA stages is typical, and the relative dominance of these phases is the basis of subdivision into classes:

CLASS HYDROZOA—typically, medusae arise as buds from polyp colonies and free medusae then separate.

CLASS SCYPHOZOA—polyp phase temporary during development, free-swimming, flat-belled medusae dominant.

CLASS ANTHOZOA—medusa phase absent; digestive cavity of polyps divided by vertical partitions.

2. Phylum Platyhelminthes

Representatives: *Dugesia.*

Bilateral symmetry. Acoelomate, that is, mesodermal body cavity not present. No skeleton. Body flattened dorsoventrally. Digestive cavity with single opening, as in coelenterates. Nerve cord ventral, shaped like ladder, with head ganglia. No circulatory system. Ways of life and associated structural features form basis of subdivision into classes:

CLASS TURBELLARIA—free-living flatworms (planarians); body surface cellular and partly ciliated.

CLASS TREMATODA—parasitic flatworms (flukes); noncellular cuticle on body surface; one or more suckers.

Fig. 7.1 The principal phyla and larger groups of organisms, arranged according to traditional (left) and more recent (right) classifications. A few of the identifying traits of the four main categories at right are indicated. A subclassification of Metazoa down to the phylum level is given in Fig. 7.2.

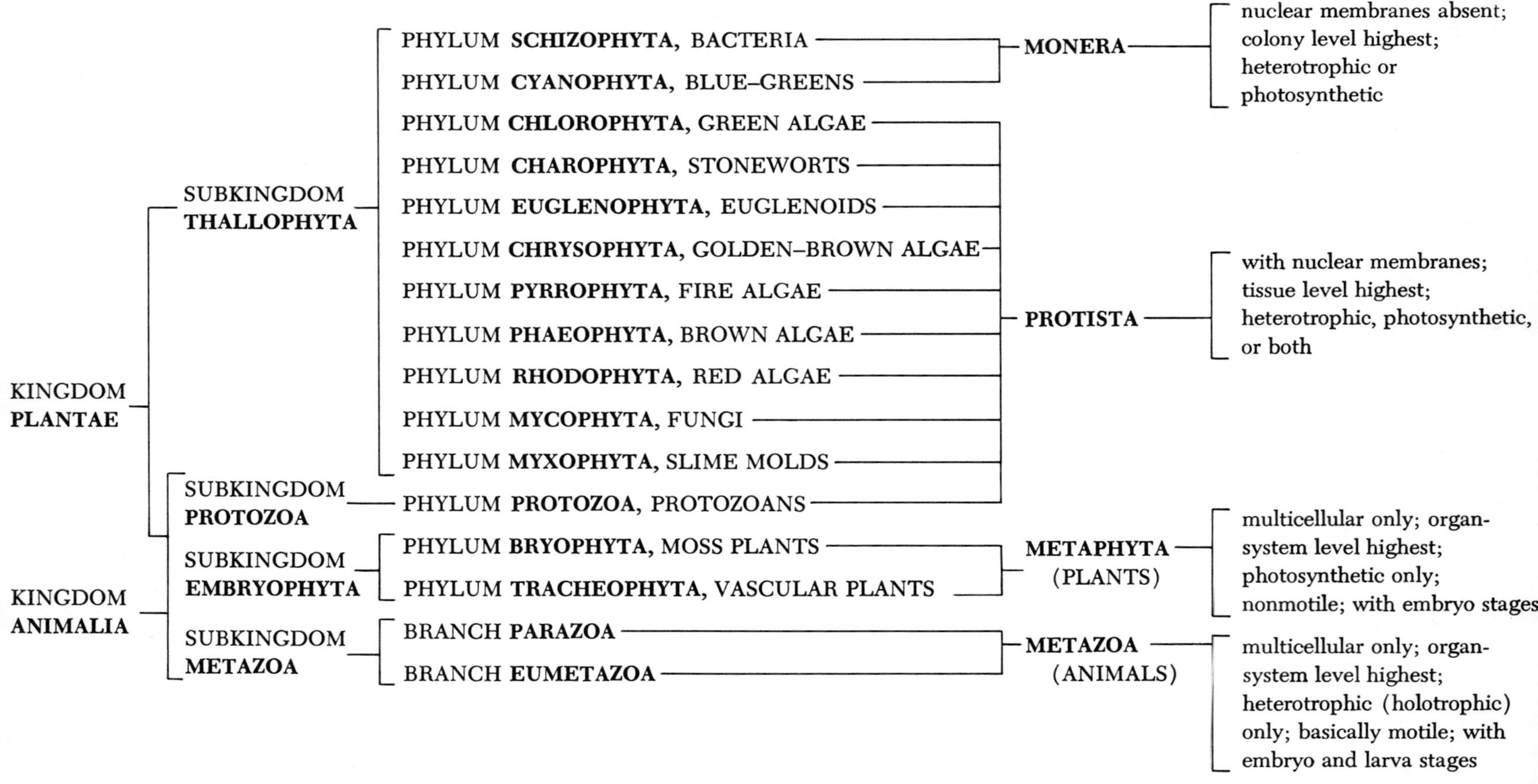

Fig. 7.2 ***The classification of Metazoa to the level of phyla.***

METAZOA, ANIMALS

- BRANCH **PARAZOA** — tissue level highest
  - PHYLUM **PORIFERA**, SPONGES
- BRANCH **EUMETAZOA** — above tissue level
  - GRADE **RADIATA** — organ level highest; radial symmetry primary
    - PHYLUM **CNIDARIA**, COELENTERATES
    - PHYLUM **CTENOPHORA**, COMB JELLIES
  - GRADE **BILATERIA** — organ-system level highest; bilateral symmetry primary
    - SUBGRADE **ACOELOMATA** — without body cavity, middle body layer (mesoderm) solid
      - PHYLUM **PLATYHELMINTHES** FLATWORMS
      - PHYLUM **NEMERTINA**, RIBBON WORMS
    - SUBGRADE **PSEUDOCOELOMATA** — body cavity not a coelom, but bounded by body wall (ectoderm) and alimentary tract (endoderm); mesoderm dispersed in body cavity
      - PHYLUM **ASCHELMINTHES**, SAC WORMS (ROTIFERS, ROUND WORMS)
      - PHYLUM **ACANTHOCEPHALA**, SPINY–HEADED WORMS
      - PHYLUM **ENTOPROCTA**, ENTOPROCTS
    - SUBGRADE **COELOMATA** — body cavity a true coelom, bounded entirely by tissues of mesoderm, usually by peritoneum

SUPERPHYLUM **LOPHOPHORATES**
coelom forms in various unique ways

- PHYLUM **PHORONIDA**, PHORONIDS
- PHYLUM **ECTOPROCTA**, ECTOPROCTS
- PHYLUM **BRACHIOPODA**, LAMP SHELLS

SUPERPHYLUM **SCHIZOCOELOMATES**
coelom forms by splitting of mesoderm layer

- PHYLUM **MOLLUSCA**, MOLLUSKS
- PHYLUM **SIPUNCULIDA**, SIPUNCULIDS
- PHYLUM **ANNELIDA**, SEGMENTED WORMS
- PHYLUM **ECHIUROIDA**, ECHIUROIDS
- PHYLUM **ONCOPODA**, ONCOPODS
- PHYLUM **ARTHROPODA**, ARTHROPODS (CRUSTACEANS, INSECTS)

SUPERPHYLUM **ENTEROCOELOMATES**
coelom forms by pouching out of mesoderm from endoderm

- PHYLUM **CHAETOGNATHA**, ARROWWORMS
- PHYLUM **POGONOPHORA**, BEARD WORMS
- PHYLUM **HEMICHORDATA**, HEMICHORDATES
- PHYLUM **ECHINODERMATA**, SPINY–SKINNED ANIMALS, ECHINODERMS (STARFISHES, SEA URCHINS)
- PHYLUM **CHORDATA**, CHORDATES (TUNICATES, AMPHIOXUS, VERTEBRATES)

CLASS CESTODA—parasitic flatworms (tapeworms); noncellular cuticle on body surface; life cycle includes formation of PROGLOTTIDS, that is, sections of worm filled with ripe eggs, constricted off body, and released.

3. Phylum Mollusca

Representatives: *Mytilus, Loligo*

Schizocoelomate, that is, body cavity a true coelom formed by splitting of mesoderm and lined by peritoneum. Size of coelom reduced in the phylum, restricted to region around heart. Body divided into HEAD (often reduced), ventral muscular FOOT, dorsal VISCERAL HUMP. Subdivision into classes based on structural features as follows:

CLASS AMPHINEURA—chitons; oval body; indistinct head; flat broad creeping foot; dome-shaped calcareous shell (exoskeleton) composed of eight overlapping plates and embedded in MANTLE; small gills in groove between mantle rim and foot.
CLASS GASTROPODA—snails; distinct head with tentacles and eyes; flat broad creeping foot; characteristically coiled calcareous shell.
CLASS PELECYPODA—clams; body compressed from side to side, enclosed by pair of dorsally hinged exoskeletal shells; head greatly reduced or absent; foot can be protruded between shells; gills large, platelike, ciliated, and used in filter feeding.
CLASS CEPHALOPODA—squids and octopuses; well-developed head and eyes, head surrounded by crown of tentacles; shells often reduced or absent; endoskeletal cartilage in some forms; mantle and muscular funnel used in jetlike type of locomotion.

4. Phylum Annelida

Representatives: *Nereis, Lumbricus.*

Schizocoelomate. Body segmented transversely, segments quite similar, large coelom within each segment. Mouth anterior, anus posterior. Ventral nerve cord with head ganglia. No skeleton. Circulatory system present, blood in dorsal aorta flowing toward head end. Relative abundance of bristles (CHAETAE) on body surface and ways of life form basis of subdivision into classes:

CLASS POLYCHAETA—marine annelids; numerous bristles arising in each segment from paired fleshy lobes called PARAPODIA; distinct head, with appendages and eyespots.
CLASS OLIGOCHAETA—land and fresh-water annelids (earthworms); few bristles; no parapodia; indistinct head.
CLASS HIRUDINEA—leeches; typically no bristles and no parapodia; fixed number of segments; anterior and posterior suckers.

5. Phylum Arthropoda

Representatives: *Cambarus, Romalea.*

Body segmented, segments not similar, each typically bearing paired, jointed appendages. Exoskeleton chitinous, hard, well developed. Body divided into distinct HEAD, THORAX, and ABDOMEN, head and thorax often fused as CEPHALOTHORAX. Ways of life and associated structural features form basis of subdivision as follows:

SUBPHYLUM CHELICERATA—without jaws or antennae; head appendages (CHELICERAE, PEDIPALPS) used in feeding; cephalothorax with eight segments, four of them bearing paired walking legs.
- CLASS XIPHOSURIDA—horseshoe crabs; marine; cephalothorax with prominent shieldlike cover (CARAPACE); abdomen with gill books; long spine (TELSON) posteriorly.
- CLASS PANTOPODA—sea spiders; long legs, abdomen reduced.
- CLASS ARACHNIDA—scorpions, spiders, mites, ticks; terrestrial; breathing by lung books or tracheal tubes.

SUBPHYLUM MANDIBULATA—jaws and antennae present; head formed from six fused segments.
- CLASS CRUSTACEA—largely aquatic; two pairs of antennae; breathing by gills.
  - SUBCLASS BRANCHIOPODA—fairy shrimps, brine shrimps, water fleas; trunk limbs lobed; some with carapace.
  - SUBCLASS COPEPODA—copepods; five or six thoracic segments with appendages; lateral compound eyes absent.
  - SUBCLASS CIRRIPEDIA—barnacles; adults sessile; carapace forms enclosure of body, often calcareous; abdomen very reduced.
  - SUBCLASS MALACOSTRACA—shrimps, sandhoppers, lobsters, crabs; typically eight thoracic segments, six abdominal segments; carapace usually prominent; compound eyes stalked.
- CLASS CHILOPODA—centipedes; terrestrial; trunk segments numerous, each with one pair of legs;

first thoracic appendages are poison fangs; breathing by tracheal tubes.

CLASS DIPLOPODA—millipedes; terrestrial; trunk segments numerous, most with two pairs of legs each; without poison fangs; breathing by tracheal tubes.

CLASS INSECTA—insects; largely terrestrial; one pair of antennae; thorax with three segments, each with one pair of legs; abdomen typically 11 segments, without appendages; breathing by tracheal tubes; adults largely winged.

SUBCLASS APTERYGOTA (AMETABOLA)—wingless; without metamorphosis.

SUBCLASS EXOPTERYGOTA (HEMIMETABOLA)—wings grow on exterior of larva; metamorphosis gradual, via several larval molting stages; compound eyes present in larvae.

ORDER ORTHOPTERA—grasshoppers, locusts, crickets, cockroaches; forewings narrow, leathery; hind wings membranous.

ORDER ISOPTERA—termites; wings similar, membranous.

ORDER ODONATA—dragonflies; wings similar, net-veined.

ORDER ANOPLEURA—sucking lice; body flattened, wingless.

ORDER EPHEMOPTERA—mayflies; wings membranous, folded up at rest, hind wings small.

ORDER HEMIPTERA—true bugs; forewings thickened basally, membranous terminally, crossed flat on body at rest; hind wings membranous, folded under forewings.

ORDER HOMOPTERA—plant lice, scale insects; wings tentlike at rest, forewings thickened or membranous.

SUBCLASS ENDOPTERYGOTA (HOLOMETABOLA)—wings grow internally in larva; metamorphosis abrupt; larval stages are caterpillars and pupae; compound eyes not yet present in larvae.

ORDER LEPIDOPTERA—moths, butterflies; wings membranous, scaly, horizontal at rest in moths, folded up at rest in butterflies; antennae feathery in moths, filamentous in butterflies.

ORDER DIPTERA—flies, gnats, mosquitoes; hind wings reduced to knobbed stalks.

ORDER SIPHONAPTERA—fleas; body compressed laterally, wingless.

ORDER COLEOPTERA—beetles, weevils; forewings horny, hind wings folded under forewings.

ORDER HYMENOPTERA—bees, ants, wasps; hind wings smaller than forewings, both pairs membranous.

6. *Phylum Echinodermata*

Representatives: *Asterias.*

Bilateral symmetry in larval stages, radial symmetry in adult phase. Enterocoelomate, that is, coelom formed by mesodermal pouches growing out from endoderm. Endoskeleton of calcareous plates bearing spines, located near surface of body. Locomotion by means of water-vascular system; usually, conspicuous tube feet. All marine. Structural features form basis of subdivision into classes as follows:

CLASS CRINOIDEA—sea lilies, feather stars; sessile or free-swimming; oral side directed upward; five feathery arms, with tube feet and ciliated food groove along each arm.

CLASS HOLOTHUROIDEA—sea cucumbers; oral-aboral axis horizontal, without arms; five sets of branching tentacles around mouth; tube feet often reduced or absent; skeleton reduced, body surface leathery.

CLASS ASTEROIDEA—starfishes; oral side directed downward; arms not sharply marked off from central disk; rows of tube feet on underside of arms, with ciliated food groove between rows.

CLASS OPHIUROIDEA—brittle stars, serpent stars; oral side directed downward; arms long and slender, highly mobile, sharply marked off from central disk; stomach blind-ended, intestine or anus absent; tube feet on underside of arms, food grooves absent.

CLASS ECHINOIDEA—sea urchins, sand dollars; body globular or discoidal, without arms; endoskeleton forms fused, rigid shell, with movable spines; tube feet in five sets of rows on body.

7. *Phylum Chordata*

Representatives: *Petromyzon, Mus;* classify also the following (to be examined in different contexts during various other exercises): *Sus,* the pig; *Squalus,* the shark; *Rana,* the frog; and *Homo,* yourself.

Enterocoelomate. Dorsal hollow nerve cord.

Blood in dorsal aorta flowing toward tail end. NOTOCHORD (endoskeleton) present at some stage of life cycle. Variations of endoskeleton form basis of subdivision into subphyla:

SUBPHYLUM UROCHORDATA—tunicates, sea squirts; notochord present only in tail of tadpole; otherwise no skeleton; head absent; not segmented.

SUBPHYLUM CEPHALOCHORDATA—amphioxus; notochord persists as such into adult; head absent; fish-shaped segmented body.

SUBPHYLUM VERTEBRATA—vertebrates; notochord usually replaced by vertebral column in adult; head and tail present; segmented; ways of life, reproductive adaptations, and associated structural features form basis of subdivision into classes:

CLASS AGNATHA—jawless fishes; aquatic; sucking mouth without jaws; notochord persists into adult, surrounded however by a cartilaginous vertebral column.

CLASS CHONDRICHTHYES—cartilage fishes; aquatic; jaws present; endoskeleton cartilaginous; skin with denticles.

CLASS OSTEICHTHYES—bony fishes; aquatic; endoskeleton bony; skin with scales.

CLASS AMPHIBIA—amphibians; aquatic larvae, adults often terrestrial; external fertilization (as in all previous classes); skin soft and glandular.

CLASS REPTILIA—reptiles; primarily terrestrial; internal fertilization; skin with horny scales.

CLASS AVES—birds; terrestrial; internal fertilization; skin with feathers; forelimbs typically adapted for flying; warm-blooded.

CLASS MAMMALIA—mammals; mammary glands present; nurse young; skin with hair; warm-blooded.

SUBCLASS PROTOTHERIA (Monotremata)—duck-billed platypus, spiny anteaters (echidnas); egg-laying mammals.

SUBCLASS METATHERIA (Marsupialia)—opossums, kangaroos, other marsupials; pouched mammals.

SUBCLASS EUTHERIA (Placentalia)—placental mammals; offspring complete development in uterus of female.

ORDER INSECTIVORA—shrews, moles, hedgehogs; arboreal and subterranean.

ORDER CHIROPTERA—bats; limbs and digits elongated, supporting wings formed from skin folds.

ORDER PRIMATES—lemurs, tarsiers, monkeys, apes, men; flat nails on digits; forelimbs usually grasping.

ORDER CETACEA—whales, dolphins, porpoises; secondarily marine.

ORDER RODENTIA—rodents; continuously growing single pair of upper incisors with enamel only on front face.

ORDER LAGOMORPHA—rabbits, hares; continuously growing two pairs of upper incisors with enamel on front and back faces.

ORDER CARNIVORA—cats, dogs, bears, walruses, seals; carnivorous; canine teeth long, others pointed.

ORDER PROBOSCOIDEA—elephants; thick-skinned; incisors are tusks; nose and upper lip form proboscis.

ORDER PERISSODACTYLA—horses, tapirs, zebras, rhinos; odd-toed ungulates, toes terminating in hoofs.

ORDER ARTIODACTYLA—pigs, camels, cattle, sheep, goats; even-toed ungulates, toes terminating in hoofs.

C. classification of unknowns

Ten or more unfamiliar animals or parts thereof (living or preserved, some dissected and with parts labeled) are set out and are identified only by a number. Your task is to study each animal carefully (the sequence is immaterial) and to classify it in as fine detail as the diagnostic descriptions in section B allow. All you know is that each animal belongs to one of the seven phyla studied above.

In your examination proceed as systematically as you can, that is, determine phylum characteristics first, class characteristics next, etc. In many cases, a single visible feature will identify the phylum or class; in such an event determine all other diagnostic features also, for added assurance and to become more familiar with the unifying features of the group as a whole.

RECORD your diagnostic observations in full on Data Sheet 1, page 259. (Data Sheets are perforated and may be torn out and placed next to the relevant text discussions.)

IV analysis

1. Check your classification of knowns and unknowns against the correct classification supplied by the instructor. He will also give the generic designation of the unknowns. Discuss and account for any discrepancies in classification.

2. Cite representative types of animals for every taxonomic category described in section B, particularly for categories where knowns or unknowns have not been studied as part of the exercise.

3. Review the diagnostic features of the seven animal groups studied, and determine which groups appear to be closely related and which appear to be relatively unrelated.

4. What structural features appear to be the fundamental criteria in distinguishing animal phyla? Determine the minimum number of diagnostic questions one must answer to place an animal uniquely into one of the phyla studied.

5. Cite as many diagnostic features as you can that distinguish vertebrate from invertebrate animals.

6. If you find a "worm," how would you go about classifying it? How many different phyla might it belong to? Do the popular words "bug" and "germ" have any taxonomic significance? Many persons classify the animal world into "people," "animals," "birds," "fish," "worms," "germs," and "bugs." What is wrong with this? Discuss.

7. Could a good, informative taxonomic system be established by classifying organisms on the basis of (*a*) alphabetical order, (*b*) body size, (*c*) habitat, (*d*) nutritional patterns? Discuss.

8. Are any of the taxonomic categories in section B defined solely on the basis of functional criteria? Why is structure more useful than function in defining a taxonomic group? What is meant by the phrase "natural system of classification"?

9. Evolution is "continuous"; that is, when one organism gives rise to another, many graded transitional types may occur between initial and terminal types. By contrast, taxonomy is "discontinuous"; that is, at least one sharp, clear-cut difference distinguishes any two taxonomic groups (particularly those of high rank). How "natural" therefore do you consider the taxonomic system to be? Discuss.

10. Name groups of mammals secondarily adapted to an aquatic existence. What distinguishes these from "fish," from terrestrial mammals, and from one another?

11. Chordates are sometimes classified as Acraniata and Craniata, and vertebrates are sometimes classified as (*a*) Anamniota and Amniota, (*b*) Agnathostomata and Gnathostomata. Determine the meaning of these terms, and from this, state which groups belong in each of these categories.

12. Many people often confuse the following: reptiles and amphibia; monkeys and apes; insects and spiders; salamanders and lizards; lampreys and eels; butterflies and moths; centipedes and millipedes; oysters and scallops; and many other such pairs. How can you prevent such confusion in your own mind?

13. From information in your text, ascertain the number of known species in all phyla of organisms. In terms of species number, which are the five largest phyla? What factors of structure, way of life, and evolutionary history would you guess to be reasons for the present diversity of these groups? How are the classes of vertebrates ranked on the basis of species numbers?

14. From information in your text, determine in a preliminary way how animal phyla not studied in this exercise are defined and distinguished from others. Ascertain also the name and appearance of representative types within such phyla.

15. From information in your text, determine in a preliminary way how the phyla within the Monera, Protista, and Metaphyta are defined and distinguished. For each such phylum ascertain also the nature of the large subgroups, if any, and the name of one or more representative types.

part 2 the levels of life

exercise 8 minerals and carbohydrates

I materials

Each group of 4 students

1 doz test tubes, with rack
2 medicine droppers
1 test-tube holder and brush
1 pipette, 10 ml
1 stirring rod
1 spot plate
2 stoppers for test tubes
1 bunsen burner plus stand, wire grid
1 flask, 100 or 150 ml
3 or 4 beakers, 50 to 250 ml
wax pencil
conc. HCl, in bottle (see Appendix, "Acids")
conc. NaOH, in bottle (see Appendix, "Bases")
50 ml Benedict's reagent (see Appendix)
20 mil IKI reagent (see Appendix)

Team or class stock

2% solutions of the following, approx. 10 ml per team:

$CaCl_2$	$MgSO_4$	glycogen
$FeCl_3$	Na_2HPO_4	glucose
Na_2CO_3	$K_4Fe(CN)_6$	fructose
$NaHCO_3$	oxalic acid	maltose
$CuSO_4$	citric acid	sucrose
$AgNO_3$	formaldehyde	lactose
$BaCl_2$	starch (boiled)	ribose (or arabinose)

Class stock

beef liver, fresh
potatoes, fresh
distilled water, stock
blendor
cheesecloth or wire strainers
crushed ice
dialysis tubing
95% ethyl alcohol (in refrigerator)
phenol reagent (see Appendix)
orcinol reagent (see Appendix)
0.5% NaF solution
red and blue litmus paper

II introduction

A detailed chemical analysis of living matter is a task of considerable technical and theoretical difficulty, especially when it is desired to determine not only what specific compounds are present but also precisely how much of each. However, if the analyst is not after detail and exact quantity but wishes merely to identify the general classes of cellular compounds, he can successfully employ a number of rather simple tests. Several such tests will be examined and used in this exercise and the three following exercises. The general objective will be to identify given known compounds, to isolate and demonstrate the presence of such compounds in biological materials, and to learn something about the chemical properties of the compounds. The biological source materials will be largely liver, potatoes, spinach, and yeast, but note that the procedures to be followed are equally applicable to other samples of living matter.

This is the first of a series of experimental exercises you will perform during the course. The word "experimental" points up an important lead theme, and a few words about your approach seem appropriate.

Doing experiments does not mean carrying out instructions mechanically. Keep in mind that experiments serve a FUNCTION (namely, they test hypotheses) and that hypotheses supported by experimental evidence increase UNDERSTANDING. The last is the reason why experiments are performed at all, whether in research or in your laboratory.

To increase your understanding of a biological process under experimental investigation, and thus to exploit these exercises fully, ask questions about the ADEQUACY of the experiments. What is intended to be tested? What is the hypothesis on which the test is based? How well is the test designed? Are the experimental controls fully adequate to provide incontestable answers, or does the test have loopholes? Can such loopholes be regarded as negligible in a given instance or are they critically significant? What do the results ACTUALLY show? Do they support or weaken the original hypothesis? Can I explain the significance of EVERY step of the experimental procedure? Considering the limited specificity and sensitivity of my tools and my technique, how reliable is the result I obtain?

Ask and answer such questions WHILE you carry out given experiments, and at all events when you come to interpret your work. Doing so clearly involves much more than a mere mechanical execution of the instructions; the added thinking is essential if you hope to gain understanding.

In this and in most other experimental exercises, groups of four students will work together as teams. Within each team divide the work, and rotate specific functions among the members from experiment to experiment. One team member should serve as protocol keeper, reading instructions to the team, seeing that the right experimental steps are performed, watching timing, and recording data. One member should serve as team assistant, preparing and readying solutions, supplying clean glassware, and performing other necessary operations auxiliary to the experiments. Two members should be experimenters, carrying out the tests, taking readings and measurements, and checking on each other's technique. After an experiment is completed, EVERY member of the team should record ALL observations and data for himself, and the whole team may discuss and interpret results as a group.

Unless the instructor directs otherwise, every experimental team will perform all the experiments of the exercise. On occasion time may be limited, in which case the instructor may assign some of the experiments to one team and the remainder to a second team. This division of labor notwithstanding, all members of both of such paired teams will be responsible for ALL data and interpretations.

III directions

Most of the work to be done involves the mixing of reagents in test tubes and observing the result—either the development of a characteristic color or the formation of a precipitate. Primarily to ensure the safety of personnel, secondarily to ensure the success of the experiments, a number of fundamental precautions MUST be observed:

1. TREAT ALL REAGENTS WITH THE GREATEST RESPECT, AS IF THEY WERE DANGEROUS. Many of them actually are—they may be strong acids, strong alkalis, biological poisons, they may be volatile and inflammable, or they may give off dangerous fumes. You will have to handle such materials throughout this and many other exercises. If you maintain CAUTION and COMMON SENSE at all times you will not have to worry. DO NOT SPILL any reagent on your hands, clothes,

or furniture. Pour out solutions slowly. If anything is spilled, WASH YOUR HANDS at once. Keep reagents AWAY FROM OPEN FLAMES AND HOT SURFACES. And keep your—and everyone else's—eyes and nose well away from reaction mixtures.

2. Unless the directions specify otherwise, heat solutions in test tubes not over open flames but by placing them in a beaker of boiling water. On occasion, direct heating over a bunsen burner does become necessary. In such cases, hold the tube slightly slanted, let the tip of the flame play over the length of the tube and not merely along the bottom, and POINT THE OPEN END OF THE TUBE AWAY FROM YOU OR ANYONE ELSE WHO MAY BE NEAR. When the solution begins to boil, BE DOUBLY CAUTIOUS: many reagents come to a boil suddenly and may spurt out explosively if the temperature becomes too high. Also, NEVER pour a cold solution directly into one that has just been boiled, or vice versa; otherwise explosive jets of reagent will burst out of the tube. Always see that solutions to be mixed are of approximately the same temperature.

3. Clean glassware BEFORE and AFTER each experiment. Use test-tube brushes, soap, and water, and use them routinely throughout the experiment. When the work is completed, make especially certain that all glassware is left scrupulously clean.

4. Always double-check the name of the reagent to be used (AND the reagent you are actually using). Reagent bottles must be LABELED; if one is not, notify the instructor AT ONCE. Reagent bottles must remain STOPPERED AT ALL TIMES, except when you actually pour solutions out of them. NEVER return leftover solution to a reagent bottle; what is poured out of a bottle should always be either used or discarded.

5. When you require small amounts of solution from a large stock bottle, NEVER pour from the stock bottle directly into the test tube. Decant from the stock bottle into a small beaker, and draw on the latter for your supply of solution. Use a medicine dropper if very small amounts of reagent are required.

6. When solutions put into a test tube are to be mixed thoroughly, DO NOT USE YOUR THUMB as a stopper. For gentle mixing, shake the tube carefully from side to side; otherwise use a stirring rod or stopper the tube with cork or rubber and shake.

7. The reagents you will require will be found either on your desk or on the table or shelf where class stocks are kept. Consult the materials list above for the location of specific items. DO NOT CARRY SOLUTIONS AWAY from their original place. If the reagent is class stock, draw what you require and bring only that to your working place.

A. preliminary operations

1. Liver Extract

Obtain a piece of beef liver roughly 2 in. square and ½ in. thick, and with a scalpel, scrape, shred, and cut this piece into about 75 ml of tap water in a beaker. Continue shredding the liver in the water to make as rich and concentrated a suspension as you can. Stir well and let the mixture stand for 2 to 3 min. Shred the sedimented larger pieces again, stir, and let the suspension settle once more. Then decant most of the fluid into a fresh beaker, taking care not to include any unshredded pieces. Boil this suspension gently for about 1 min; a coagulum will form at the bottom. Decant the clear fluid into a small flask or beaker and label it "liver extract," for use below.

2. Potato Extracts

Obtain approximately one-quarter of a medium-sized potato, peel it, and grind it in a blendor with about 75 ml of tap water. Run the resulting suspension into a beaker through a double layer of cheesecloth (or through a wire strainer). Let the filtrate stand for several minutes; white starch grains will slowly settle to the bottom. Then carefully decant the top fluid, but stop when still-suspended white grains begin to pour out. Let the decanted juice stand. Pour out the remaining fluid and discard it. At the bottom of this beaker will be found a thin white layer of starch grains. Add 25 ml of tap water to it, stir to suspend the grains, and, while continuing to stir, heat this suspension till it boils. On cooling it will form a thick, viscous mass. Label this beaker "potato starch," for use below. Return now to the previously decanted potato juice. Carefully decant the top half of it again, making sure not to include any starch grains that may have settled to the bottom by now. Label this decanted portion "potato extract," for use below.

3. *Other Procedures*

Bring a 250-ml beaker half-filled with water to boiling, and maintain such a water bath at a slow boil throughout the laboratory period; add more water from time to time as necessary.

Ascertain that a small amount of thoroughly iced 95% ethyl alcohol will be available to you for later use; if a class stock is not maintained, set a test tube half-filled with alcohol into a beaker of crushed ice (and away from heat sources).

Make sure your team stock of test tubes and other glassware is clean; rinse in water as a precaution.

B. mineral ions

1. Most of the biologically important inorganic ions can be identified in simple color or precipitation tests. For each of the ones examined here, record the result and work out the chemical equations underlying the test-tube reactions.

a. Calcium ion. To 2 ml of calcium chloride ($CaCl_2$) test solution add a few drops of (1) 2% oxalic acid ($H_2C_2O_4$), (2) citric acid.

b. Magnesium ion. To 2 ml of magnesium sulfate ($MgSO_4$) test solution add a few drops of 0.5% sodium fluoride (NaF). CAUTION: fluorides are poisons.

c. Iron and copper ions. To 2 ml of (1) ferric chloride ($FeCl_3$) test solution, (2) copper sulfate ($CuSO_4$) test solution, add a few drops of 2% potassium ferrocyanide ($K_4Fe(CN)_6$).

d. Carbonate and bicarbonate ions. To 2 ml of (1) sodium carbonate (Na_2CO_3) test solution, (2) sodium bicarbonate ($NaHCO_3$) test solution, add a few drops 10% HCl (dilute 1 ml of concentrated HCl with 2.6 ml distilled water). What is the gas bubbling out?

e. Chloride ion. To 2 ml of calcium chloride ($CaCl_2$) test solution add a few drops of 2% silver nitrate ($AgNO_3$). The same result is obtained with bromides and iodides.

f. Sulfate ion. To 2 ml of copper sulfate ($CuSO_4$) test solution add a few drops of barium chloride ($BaCl_2$).

g. Phosphate ion. To 2 ml of any phosphate salt (for example, Na_2HPO_4) test solution add a few drops of ferric chloride ($FeCl_3$).

2. Repeat these tests with liver extract and potato extract as test solutions. Record the results.

C. carbohydrates

1. *Reducing Sugars*

One of the most important methods of identifying sugars is the so-called Benedict's test. The Benedict reagent contains, essentially, copper sulfate in alkaline solution (see Appendix). If the reagent is heated in the presence of a reducing substance, the divalent copper, Cu^{++}, becomes reduced to monovalent copper, Cu^{+}. More specifically, cuprous oxide (Cu_2O) is formed, which appears as a colored precipitate. Depending on the concentration of the Cu_2O, the color of the precipitate varies from greenish at low concentrations to yellow, orange, bright red, brown-red, and brown at high concentrations. In living material, the only reducing substances of consequence happen to be compounds containing free aldehyde (—COH) or free ketone (—CO—) groups—in other words, principally sugars. Benedict's test can therefore be used specifically to demonstrate the presence of "reducing sugars."

Note that the test requires an alkaline medium; hence, if acid solutions are to be tested, they must first be rendered alkaline (for example, by addition of adequate amounts of NaOH).

a. To determine the range of applicability of Benedict's test, prepare 10 numbered test tubes and add to them 1 ml (approximately 10 drops) of the following (2% solutions for all tubes except the last three):

1: glucose
2: fructose
3: ribose (or arabinose)
4: sucrose
5: lactose
6: maltose
7: formaldehyde
8: liver extract
9: potato extract
10: potato starch

To each tube add 2 ml of Benedict's reagent, shake up, and put all tubes into the boiling water bath for 2 min. Observe and record the results, and interpret them on the basis of the chemical structure of the compounds tested (consult your text if necessary).

b. To determine the performance of Benedict's reagent with different concentrations of a test compound, prepare six numbered test tubes each containing 2 ml of one of the glucose solutions listed below. Use a pipette to measure quantities. Prepare the first solution in a separate test tube, pipette 2 ml of it into tube 1, and use the excess to prepare the second solution; pipette 2 ml of that into tube 2, and again use the excess to prepare the third solution; etc.

1: 0.4% glucose (1 ml 2% solution plus 4 ml distilled water)

2: 0.2% glucose [equal parts of (1) and distilled water]

3: 0.1% glucose [equal parts of (2) and distilled water]

4: 0.05% glucose [equal parts of (3) and distilled water]

5: 0.025% glucose [equal parts of (4) and distilled water]

6: 0.01% glucose [2 ml of (5) plus 3 ml distilled water]

Into the 2 ml content of each tube now pipette 2 ml of Benedict's reagent, shake, and place all tubes into the boiling water bath. For each tube record (*a*) the time taken for a precipitate to form and (*b*) the color and relative amount of precipitate formed.

2. *Ketoses, Pentoses*

a. Ketose sugars may be identified through their reaction with acidified phenol (hydroxybenzene, C_6H_5OH) or resorcinol (dihydroxybenzene, $C_6H_4(OH)_2$). The composition of these reagents is given in the Appendix. Put 3 ml of acid phenol reagent into each of three numbered test tubes. To tube 1 add 1 ml of 2% glucose solution; to tube 2, 1 ml of 2% sucrose solution; and to tube 3, 1 ml of 2% fructose solution. Heat all three tubes for exactly 1 min in the boiling water bath, then set them into a rack to cool. Note the development of color. Account for the result on sucrose (especially after you have performed the tests in section 4, below). Try the test on your liver and potato extracts.

b. Pentose sugars give a color reaction with acid orcinol reagent (orcinol is dihydroxymethylbenzene, $CH_3C_4H_3(OH)_2$; see Appendix). Put 3 ml of the orcinol reagent in a test tube and heat to boiling in the water bath. Remove the tube and immediately add 1 ml of 2% ribose (or arabinose) solution. Note the reaction. A precipitate forms frequently on standing. Try the test on the liver and potato extracts.

3. *Polysaccharides*

a. *Precipitation*. When polysaccharides such as starch or glycogen are in solution, they may be precipitated out with ethyl alcohol. Prepare four test tubes containing 2 ml amounts of the following:

1: 2% starch solution

2: diluted potato starch (dilute a little with an equal amount of water)

3: 2% glycogen solution

4: liver extract

Now add to each tube 4 ml of ice-cold 95% ethyl alcohol. Record results.

b. *Identification*. Many polysaccharides are readily identifiable by their reaction with "IKI" reagent (iodine, I_2, dissolved in potassium iodide, KI). A deep blue-black color is obtained with AMYLOSE, the straight-chain polysaccharide present in starch, a violet-brown to red-brown color is given by CELLULOSE, and a red-brown or russet color is developed by GLYCOGEN. The colors fade on heating but return on cooling.

To observe the reaction of cellulose, put a drop of IKI on a piece of filter or tissue paper and also on a piece of absorbent cotton. Then prepare five numbered test tubes containing the following, 2 ml in each:

1: 2% starch solution

2: diluted potato starch (dilute a little with 3 or 4 volumes of water)

3: 2% glycogen solution

4: potato extract

5: liver extract

Add a single drop of IKI reagent to each tube and record results. Then heat tubes 1, 2, and 3 and observe. Cool the tubes under the tap and again observe. Now add a drop of concentrated NaOH to each tube. Record and explain the result.

c. *Diffusibility*. The macromolecular nature of polysaccharides may be demonstrated as follows.

Obtain a length of dialysis tubing, tie it securely at one end to form a watertight bag, and fill it with a mixture made up from equal amounts of the 2% starch and 2% glucose solutions. Suspend the bag in a beaker containing just enough distilled water to cover about one-half to two-thirds of it. Let this assembly stand for about 1 hr or longer (and in the meantime do other sections of the exercise). Then carry out both the IKI and Benedict's tests on a little of the water surrounding the bag. Record and account for the results.

4. Hydrolysis

Polysaccharides can be decomposed into their constituent monosaccharide units by treatment with HCl. Such an acid hydrolysis is a gradual decomposition; that is, a few monosaccharide units at a time are split off a polysaccharide molecule. The latter so becomes smaller progressively, and oligosaccharides, disaccharides, and eventually monosaccharides are formed in this manner. By using the IKI and Benedict's tests in combination, the process of breakdown can be followed; in the course of acid hydrolysis, the IKI reaction should decrease and the Benedict's reaction should increase progressively.

Perform an acid hydrolysis on both the potato starch and liver extracts as follows:

a. Put about 5 ml of the potato starch into a test tube, add an equal volume of water, and shake thoroughly. To this solution add 3 ml of concentrated HCl, stir, and place the tube into the boiling water bath. With a medicine dropper, take a drop of solution from the tube, put it on a spot plate, and test it with IKI. Repeat the IKI test with successive drops taken from the tube at 30-sec to 1-min intervals. Note that the hydrolysis proceeds fairly rapidly; the time interval between successive drop tests will have to be gauged according to the concentration of your original starch extract. Try to obtain a succession of IKI tests showing a gradual change from the blue-black of unhydrolyzed starch to the violet or red-brown of the oligosaccharide dextrin (partially hydrolyzed starch) to the absence of a reaction with maltose and glucose (more or less completely hydrolyzed starch). After the IKI test is negative, pour about 2 ml of the test solution into a fresh test tube and alkalinize the contents by adding an equal amount (or more) of concentrated NaOH (check with litmus paper). Then carry out Benedict's test. You already know (from one of the tests in section 1a, above) how untreated starch reacts in such a test. What is the present result with hydrolyzed starch?

b. Inasmuch as untreated liver extract already reacts positively to Benedict's reagent, a hydrolysis test must be compared with a control test run in parallel. Put 3 or 4 ml of the liver extract into each of two test tubes; the quantities in each tube must be equal. One tube, labeled B, will be the control. To the other tube, labeled A, add 1 ml of concentrated HCl. Place both tubes into the boiling water bath for 15 min. Then remove the tubes, cool them under the tap, and add 1 ml of concentrated HCl to tube B (so that the total amount of fluid here will equal that in tube A). Now alkalinize both tubes by adding equal amounts of concentrated NaOH to each. Subsequently add 1 ml of Benedict's reagent to each tube and heat in the water bath. Compare and record (1) the time taken for a precipitate to form, (2) the color of the precipitate.

IV analysis

1. If in your experiments you tested for a substance and the test was positive, can you rightfully conclude that the substance was present? If the test was negative, can you conclude that the substance was not present? Discuss fully.

2. What have calcium, iron, and copper ions in common? What have carbonate, sulfate, and chloride ions in common? What have calcium, sulfate, carbonate, and copper ions in common?

3. Explain the results of Benedict's test on (*a*) formaldehyde, (*b*) sucrose. What monosaccharides is sucrose made of? Do these monosaccharides give a positive Benedict's test? In the light of this, draw conclusions about the chemical union of the monosaccharides in sucrose.

4. Review, or if not done previously, write out, the chemical reactions on which the tests for the mineral ions in this exercise are based.

5. If you were provided with a single sample of a solution too small to be divided up into several portions, and if this solution had to be tested for calcium, chloride, and sulfate, all three of which give a white precipitate, how would you proceed?

6. How could one demonstrate the presence of WATER in an unknown substance? How could the relative amount of water be measured quantitatively?

7. Review the nature of the chemical linkages between monosaccharide units in different polysaccharides. Describe the chemical differences between glycogen, cellulose, and starch.

8. On the basis of the data you obtained in section C1b, how sensitive do you judge the Benedict's test to be? How would you determine the sensitivity of the IKI test?

9. Explain your results of the diffusibility test in section C3c. Using the tests you have studied in this exercise, design a controlled experiment to demonstrate that sucrose consists of an aldose unit and a ketose unit joined together.

10. So far as your tests in this exercise have shown, how do liver and potato extracts differ in composition? What additional differences would you expect to be present?

exercise 9 lipids and pigments

I materials

Each group of 4 students

6 test tubes, with rack
1 test-tube holder and brush
1 stirring rod
1 medicine dropper
1 dropper drawn to capillary end
1 flask, 100 or 150 ml
3 or 4 beakers, 50 to 250 ml
bunsen burner plus stand, wire grid
wide-mouth jar with cork stopper (for example, pint milk bottle)
25 ml salad oil
conc. HCl, in bottle
conc. NaOH, in bottle
wax pencil
paper clips

Team or class stock

approx. 10 ml per team:

carbon tetrachloride
10% $CaCl_2$ solution
0.5% Sudan IV dye in 95% alcohol
egg white, diluted 10 times
2% Na_2CO_3 solution
2% bile salt solution
2% soap solution

Class stock

fresh spinach
other pigment sources (pine needles, carrots, etiolated plants, *Chlorella,* kelp, red algae)
blendor
cheesecloth
distilled water, stock
95% ethyl alcohol
acetone
petroleum ether
glycerol
$KHSO_4$, solid crystals
large filter papers
bars of soap
blank slides

II introduction

The objectives of this exercise are identical to those of the preceding one, even though different groups of compounds will be examined. Again observe correct chemical technique, and in this connection reread, if necessary, the pertinent sections of the previous exercise. Be especially careful with heated fats, for they have a tendency to spurt and splatter; do NOT mix hot fat and cold liquid. You will also be handling fat solvents of various kinds; most of them are highly flammable, hence keep them well away from open flames.

Groups of four students will again form individual teams. Within such a team, rotate and share the work as outlined in the preceding exercise.

III directions

A. lipids

1. Fats

a. Test the solubility of fats in water, ethyl alcohol, and carbon tetrachloride CCl_4; CAUTION: DO NOT INHALE THE FUMES). Use 1-ml quantities of salad oil for each test. Name several substances that are good fat solvents. Pour several drops of the fat-CCl_4 solution on a piece of paper toweling and let the CCl_4 evaporate; note the grease marks left. When fats occur in comparatively large quantities in a solution or suspension, a grease-mark test may be used to demonstrate their presence.

b. Similarly useful in demonstrating the presence of fats is a dye test, based on the ability of certain dyes to dissolve in fats specifically. Put a little of an alcoholic solution of Sudan IV dye into a test tube and add an equal amount of salad oil. Which fluid swims on top? Now shake the tube vigorously and let it stand for a minute. Which fluid contains the dye now?

2. Emulsification

Because fats do not dissolve in water chemically, they may be dispersed physically to form tiny colloidal droplets. Colloidal systems composed of liquids (for example, fats) dispersed in liquids (for example, water) are known as emulsions. A fat-water emulsion ordinarily is quite unstable; that is, the fat droplets coalesce rapidly and separate out as a continuous layer. However, by introducing a stabilizing agent into an emulsion, colloidal droplets may be prevented from coalescing. Such agents form a coating layer around the colloidal droplets, preventing their union; determine the detailed mechanism of action from your text.

Number five test tubes and add to each 5 ml of one of the five solutions listed below:

1: distilled water
2: 2% Na_2CO_3 solution
3: dilute egg-white solution
4: 2% bile salt solution
5: 2% soap solution

To each tube now add 5 (equal) drops of salad oil, and shake all tubes thoroughly for an equal length of time. Then carry out the following:

a. Rank the tubes according to the amount of foam produced. Record.

b. Shake up all tubes once more, and rank them according to the time required for a definite layer of unmixed fat to accumulate on top of the water. Record.

c. Put a drop of each of the five mixtures on a clean dry blank slide. Use a medicine dropper, and collect the drops not from the foamy top layers but from the watery bottom part of each tube. Examine the drops uncovered under the low power of your microscope. Record (1) in which mixtures the emulsions are most stable and in which they are least stable, and (2) in which mixture the finest, and in which the coarsest, emulsion is found.

d. Shake up all tubes, and put into each a few drops of 10% HCl (dilute 1 ml of concentrated HCl with 2.6 ml distilled water). Shake gently. What happens to the emulsions? Record and explain.

On the basis of these data generalize how an emulsion is formed, and how an emulsion can be stabilized. Draw conclusions, also, about the comparative emulsifying powers of the different agents tested.

3. Saponification

In a fat molecule, the ester links between glycerol and fatty acids may be broken by ALKALINE HYDROLYSIS; heating a fat with, for example, NaOH yields free glycerol and sodium salts of the fatty acids:

$$
\begin{array}{l}
\text{R-CH}_2 \\
\quad | \\
\text{R-CH} + 3\ \text{NaOH} \rightarrow 3\ \text{Na-R} + \\
\quad | \\
\text{R-CH}_2 \\
\text{FAT}
\end{array}
\begin{array}{l}
\text{CH}_2\text{OH} \\
\quad | \\
\text{CHOH} \\
\quad | \\
\text{CH}_2\text{OH} \\
\text{GLYCEROL}
\end{array}
$$

In this equation, R- symbolizes a fatty acid. Salts of fatty acids are called SOAPS, and a hydrolysis leading to the formation of a soap as above is known as a SAPONIFICATION.

a. Carry out a saponification as follows. To a small flask containing 20 ml of CONCENTRATED NaOH add 5 ml of salad oil. Bring the contents to boiling and let them boil vigorously for 10 min (or more, if necessary). At a certain stage you will note that the nature and rhythm of the bubbling in the flask has changed and that free-floating fat is no longer present. Instead, the contents of the flask have become evenly milky and viscous. Saponification is under way at that point. Continue the boiling for a minute or two longer and then let the flask cool. The material in it is now semisolid and will congeal altogether on cooling; it represents a soap. Also present is some of the alkali used, free glycerol, and any unhydrolyzed fat still left. Sodium soaps such as this are HARD soaps; if KOH instead of NaOH had been used, the potassium soap formed would have been SOFT.

Transfer the mass in the flask to a double layer of cheesecloth over a beaker, and pour water over it several times to wash it as free of contaminants as possible. As you do so, spread the material around on the cloth with a scalpel. Clean it further by transferring it to a double or triple layer of paper toweling and pressing it free of fluid with the scalpel. Then scrape off the cleaned mass and keep it on fresh paper toweling for the following tests.

b. To verify the identity of the material as a soap, put a small amount of it into a test tube, add some water, and shake these contents vigorously. What familiar characteristic of a soap is apparent? Test the emulsifying and emulsion-stabilizing powers of the material by adding some untreated salad oil to the tube and shaking vigorously. (Run a control by preparing another tube with commercial soap solution and oil.)

If the material is indeed a sodium salt, the sodium should be replaceable by other atoms. For example, calcium should be able to replace the sodium and produce a white, hard calcium soap. Take 3 ml of commercial soap solution and add 3 ml of 10% $CaCl_2$ to it; shake, and verify the appearance of a curdy precipitate of calcium soap. Now repeat this test with an aqueous solution of a little of your saponification product.

The sodium should also be replaceable by hydrogen, yielding free fatty acids. Such a replacement can be accomplished by treatment with strong acids. Into each of two test tubes put 2 ml of concentrated HCl and 4 ml of water. To one tube add soap flakes scraped off a bar of commercial soap, and to the other some of your saponification product. Heat both tubes to boiling. Note the dissolution of the commercial soap and the appearance of an oily surface layer of free fatty acids. What is the result in the other tube? Work out the equation for this reaction.

Cool the tubes, add to each a few drops of alcoholic Sudan IV dye, and stir. Can the dye test be used to distinguish between whole fats and fatty acids? Save the tubes for the tests below.

c. Fat hydrolysis yields not only fatty acid salts but also glycerol. This compound can be identified by decomposing it in the presence of potassium acid sulfate to ACROLEIN, a substance giving off pungent, acrid, and tear-producing fumes:

$$
\begin{array}{l}
\text{CH}_2\text{OH} \\
\quad | \\
\text{CHOH} + 2\ \text{KHSO}_4 \rightarrow \\
\quad | \\
\text{CH}_2\text{OH} \\
\text{GLYCEROL}
\end{array}
$$

$$
\begin{array}{l}
\text{CH}_2 \\
\quad \| \\
\text{CH} + 2\ \text{KOH} + 2\ \text{H}_2\text{SO}_4 \\
\quad | \\
\text{CHO} \\
\text{ACROLEIN}
\end{array}
$$

Put a few crystals of solid $KHSO_4$ into a Pyrex test tube, add 2 or 3 drops of glycerol, and heat over a direct flame. Smell the fumes—do not inhale them directly, but wave your hand so that some of them will be wafted to you.

Repeat the test with a few drops of salad oil. Would you expect the acrolein test to be useful in identifying soaps and fatty acids? Check your answer by carrying out the test with some of the soaps and the fatty acids you prepared earlier.

d. Consider item 5 in the Analysis section below. With the concurrence of the instructor and if time permits, carry out the test suggested in that question.

B. pigments

Among the many different pigments of living organisms, several important groups have a distant chemical relation to lipids, and they are also soluble in fat solvents. Included here are the tetrapyrrols and the carotenoids. Plants and algae usually possess both kinds; the most conspicuous tetrapyrrols are CHLOROPHYLLS of several chemical varieties, and the carotenoids include CAROTENES of various types as well as XANTHOPHYLLS of various types (for example, LUTEIN is a yellow xanthophyll, FUCOXANTHIN, a brown xanthophyll). When chlorophylls and carotenoids occur together, as is most often the case, the green color of the chlorophylls more or less masks the colors of the other pigments. However, the presence of several pigments may be verified by a process called CHROMATOGRAPHY, through which the individual pigments become isolated from one another. Actually, the chromatographic technique is applicable not only to pigments but also to many other kinds of mixed compounds.

The technique makes use of the circumstance that different compounds are absorbed or adsorbed with different degrees of ease to given agents. For example, paper (cellulose) might be used as an adsorbing agent, and if a mixture of compounds is placed on one end of a strip of paper, the compounds will diffuse toward the other end. But depending on the inherent physical and chemical properties of the compounds, different ones will be adsorbed to the paper to different degrees. As a result, the compounds will move at different rates and become spread out along the paper. If the compounds are pigments, they will therefore become separated from one another visibly; and if they are not pigments, they can be treated directly on the paper with specific color-producing reagents and can be visualized in that manner.

In the following tests, the pigments of plants and algae will be isolated and visualized through just such PAPER CHROMATOGRAPHY.

1. *Pigment Extraction*

While you have been carrying out the tests in section A, the instructor will have prepared class stocks of pigment extracts in the following manner.

A quantity of spinach leaves (or other pigment source, see below) is homogenized in a blendor with 95% ethyl alcohol. The mixture is filtered, and the filtrate is then boiled until the alcohol has nearly or completely evaporated. The pigments remaining are subsequently redissolved in petroleum ether to make a concentrated solution. This is the extract you will be using.

In addition to a spinach extract, the instructor will have prepared analogous extracts of several other plants or plant parts (for example, pine needles, carrots, dark-grown etiolated plant leaves) and of several algae (for example, *Chlorella,* seaweeds, red algae). As specified by him, use such extracts in parallel tests.

2. *Chromatograms*

Obtain a wide-mouth jar fitted with a cork stopper. To the underside of the stopper fix a paper clip, and into this clip fasten an approximately 1¼-in.-wide strip of filter paper. Cut such a strip from a large piece of filter paper. Square off one end of the strip, and approximately 1 in. from this end, draw a VERY FINE pencil line across the strip. At the other end, cut the strip to a length such that, when it is clipped to the stopper and the latter is pressed tightly into the

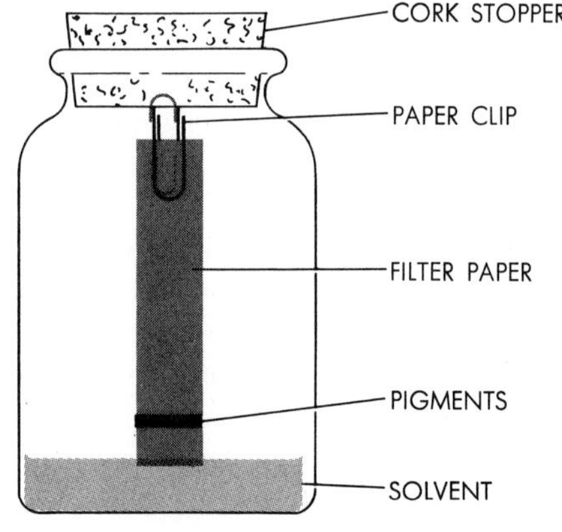

Fig. 9.1 Assembly of the chromatographic test system.

jar, the lower end of the strip is about ½ in. away from the bottom of the jar. With a wax pencil, mark on the jar the level to which the lower end of the strip actually extends (see Fig. 9.1).

Now obtain about 1 ml of the pigment extract, and with a medicine dropper that has been drawn out to a fine capillary end, deposit a NARROW band of extract along the pencil line on the strip of filter paper. Then let the extract dry THOROUGHLY. While you wait, prepare and add to the jar a pigment solvent composed of acetone and petroleum ether in a ratio of 1:9. Pour in only enough to let the level come just over the wax-pencil mark on the jar.

When the pigment on the filter strip is quite dry, suspend the strip into the jar from the stopper and cork the bottle; the lower end of the strip should now just dip into the solvent and the latter should NOT reach to the pigment line. Solvent will be drawn up into the strip, and the pigments will presently be carried along in the solvent. Soon the different pigments will separate out as a result of moving upward at different rates. Just before the uppermost pigment front has reached the top of the strip, remove the cork and let the strip dry.

Chlorophyll *a* is deep blue-green, chlorophyll *b* is yellow-green, carotenes are yellow-orange, and xanthophylls are yellow-brown. Which pigments are present on the strip, in what order have they become separated out, and which pigment appears to be most abundant?

If a satisfactory chromatogram is not obtained the first time, repeat the procedure. Then prepare analogous chromatograms with the other pigment extracts available and compare the results. Ascertain from your text what varieties of chlorophyll and other pigments can be expected to be present in each of the extracts you are using.

IV analysis

1. Describe (*a*) the characteristics of an emulsion, (*b*) the mechanism of stabilization of an emulsion, and (*c*) the nature of action of the specific stabilizing agents you used in this exercise.

2. Review the chemical structure of a fat. Distinguish between esters, salts, and soaps. Account for the cleaning action of a soap.

3. In one of the tests of section A3b, you replaced the sodium of a soap with calcium. Could the reverse be achieved as readily? What is meant by the "hardness" of water and what undesirable properties does it have?

4. Write the equation symbolizing the alkaline hydrolysis of (*a*) a fat, (*b*) ethyl acetate. Can the acrolein test be used to demonstrate the presence of (*a*) fats, (*b*) fatty acids, (*c*) soaps? Explain your answers.

5. What would be the result of an ACID hydrolysis of a fat? Write out the appropriate equation, keeping in mind that water is always an important participant in a "hydrolysis." (If time permits, carry out such an acid hydrolysis with concentrated HCl.)

6. Are the fatty acids you isolated from salad oil soluble in water? Explain your answer, taking into account here the properties of polar and nonpolar materials (consult your text if necessary). Similarly explain the immiscibility of whole fats in water, but the high degree of solubility of glycerol and soaps and short-chain fatty acids such as formic and acetic acids.

7. Review the chemical structure of tetrapyrrols, carotenes, and xanthophylls, as well as the specific structure of chlorophyll and heme. What other major classes of pigments are encountered among living organisms?

8. If an organism is given radioactive substances, the organism will eventually produce different organic materials that are radioactive to various degrees. Design chromatographic tests that will show what kinds of materials under such conditions become more radioactive than others.

9. Describe the comparative differences of the chromatograms you obtained for different pigment sources. How many different types of chlorophyll and carotenoids did you obtain evidence for?

10. In what sense are the pigments you examined in this exercise related chemically to lipids? What other lipid-derived or lipid-related compounds are found in living organisms, and what is the structure of such compounds?

exercise 10 proteins and nucleic acids

I materials

Each group of 4 students

6 test tubes
1 test-tube holder and brush
1 stirring rod
2 medicine droppers
1 pipette, 10 ml
1 flask, 100 or 150 ml
3 or 4 beakers, 50 to 250 ml
bunsen burner plus stand, wire grid
wax pencil
filter papers
conc. HCl, in bottle
conc. NaOH, in bottle
20 ml 10% NaCl solution
25 ml 15% trichloracetic acid
30 ml diphenylamine reagent (see Appendix)
red and blue litmus paper

Team or class stock

approx. 10 ml per team:

conc. H_2SO_4
conc. HNO_3
10% $CuSO_4$ solution
ninhydrin reagent (see Appendix)
Millon reagent (see Appendix)
5% RNA in 10% NaCl
5% DNA in 10% NaCl
0.1% phenol solution
2% alanine solution
2% tyrosine solution
2% tryptophane solution

Class stock

beef liver, fresh
eggs, fresh
blendor
casein, powdered
distilled water, stock
crushed ice
bromcresol green indicator solution
NaCl, solid
urea, solid
$HgCl_2$, saturated solution
NH_4OH, full-strength reagent
$(NH_4)_2SO_4$, saturated solution
5% lead acetate solution
95% ethyl alcohol (in refrigerator)

II introduction

If warranted, reread the introductory statements of exercise 8 to familiarize yourself again with the general objectives of the tests to be carried out and with the precautions to be observed in chemical manipulations. Also, if you have not yet studied the sections on proteins and nucleic acids in your text, it will be advisable that you at least read these sections through once before you begin the work of this exercise.

Four students will operate as a team, as in the preceding weeks of laboratory.

III directions

A. preliminary operations

1. Liver Extracts

For section B below, prepare a liver extract just as you did in exercise 8. However, after you have macerated the piece of liver in water as well as possible, simply let the mixture stand for a while and then decant the top fluid for use without any further treatment. In other words, do NOT boil the suspension but use it "raw."

For section C below, a more finely ground liver preparation should be used. It will be made ready by the instructor as class stock. He will homogenize some liver and water in a blendor to form a rich, thick suspension. Stir this suspension well when you pour off some of it for your tests.

2. Other Procedures

One fresh egg may be used to prepare enough egg-white solution for several teams in the class. Crack the egg and separate the albumen into a beaker. Dilute this egg white with 2 to 3 volumes of DISTILLED water, stir well, and let the mixture settle. Then draw off about 50 ml from the top for use by one team.

Heat a 250-ml beaker half-filled with water and maintain this water bath at boiling throughout the period; add water from time to time as necessary.

Ascertain the availability of ice-cold 95% ethyl alcohol, kept either as class stock in the refrigerator or as team stock in a test tube set into crushed ice.

B. proteins

1. Nitrogen and Sulfur

All tests in this section should be performed in parallel with egg-white solution and liver extract; both will be referred to simply as "protein solution."

a. To demonstrate the presence of nitrogen in proteins, put 2 ml of protein solution and 1 ml of concentrated H_2SO_4 into a test tube. Place the tube into the boiling water bath for 15 min (and in the meantime proceed to sections b and c below). The acid here destroys the protein such that the carbon is converted mainly to CO_2, the hydrogen to H_2O, and the nitrogen to ammonium sulfate, $(NH_4)_2SO_4$. If subsequently the mixture is made alkaline and heated, ammonium sulfate will react with the alkali and ammonia, NH_3, will be liberated. Free ammonia in turn can be detected by its ability to turn red litmus paper blue.

Thus, after the boiling period, cool the tube under the tap and, with a medicine dropper, add concentrated NaOH until a test with red litmus paper shows that the solution is thoroughly alkaline. Then reheat the tube in the water bath (CAUTION: the contents foam up and spurt out if they boil too strongly). As soon as the first signs of boiling are apparent in the tube, remove the flame from the water bath and, with forceps, immediately hold a fresh piece of red litmus paper well into the mouth of the tube (do not let the paper touch the glass, however!). If a slight bluing does not take place at once, bring the tube to boiling again and repeat the litmus test. Not enough NH_3 will be liberated to be smelled.

b. To verify the presence of nitrogen in another way, put 2 ml of protein solution into a test tube and add an equal amount of 10% NaOH (made up in a separate test tube by mixing 1 part of concentrated NaOH with 3 parts of water). Wipe the inner rim of the tube dry, bend a red litmus paper into a U shape, and place the bottom of the U into the mouth of the tube. Then heat the tube gently. Ammonia will be liberated, which will turn the litmus paper blue.

The reaction proves the presence of AMIDE groups, —$CONH_2$. Such groups form from free carboxyl groups, —COOH, present in some of the amino acids of most proteins. Amino groups, $—NH_2$, often replace the —OH group of —COOH, yielding amides. The latter react with NaOH, and NH_3 is then liberated.

c. To demonstrate the presence of sulfur, put 5 ml of protein solution into a test tube and add a few drops of concentrated H_2SO_4. Moisten a piece of filter paper with lead-acetate solution and crumple the paper loosely into the mouth of the tube. Then heat the tube gently and note the change in the filter paper. Explain the chemistry of the reaction.

2. Precipitation

a. Heat, alcohol, heavy metals, strong acids. Carry out parallel tests on egg-white solution and liver extract as follows.

Heat 2 ml of protein solution to boiling over a free flame. Note the formation of a coagulum and explain the nature of this change.

To different 2-ml amounts of protein solution add, drop by drop:

(1) an equal amount of 95% ethyl alcohol
(2) a few drops of 10% $CuSO_4$ solution
(3) a few drops of saturated $HgCl_2$ solution
(4) a few drops of 15% trichloracetic acid
(5) a few drops of concentrated HCl and, in fresh samples, concentrated nitric and concentrated sulfuric acids. To the tube with HCl, now add 2 or 3 ml of concentrated HCl and shake. What happens to the precipitate?

Account for the results obtained. Note that trichloracetic precipitation is frequently used in biochemical analyses of protein-containing materials (see also below).

b. pH and the isoelectric point. Shake up a scalpel-tip amount of powdered casein in a few ml of distilled water. Note the turbid condition of this suspension, as a consequence of the insolubility of the protein. Put 2 ml of the suspension into a test tube and add 3 ml of concentrated HCl. Most of the protein will dissolve on shaking; complete the dissolution by shaking while warming the tube gently (boiling will NOT be required). Cool thoroughly under the tap. Now add, a few drops at a time, concentrated NaOH and shake after each addition. Before long a precipitate will form in the region where the NaOH is added, but this precipitate will disappear again when the tube is shaken up. As more alkali is then added, a point will be reached when the precipitate will not disappear on shaking.

Continue adding alkali nevertheless. Note that soon the precipitate will disappear in the region where NaOH is added but will reappear when the tube is shaken. If alkali then continues to be added, a point will be reached when the precipitate will disappear permanently. After this point has been attained, reverse the alkalinization by adding 10% HCl to the tube, drop by drop (make up this acid in a separate test tube by mixing 4 ml of concentrated HCl with 10 ml of distilled water). Does a distinct precipitate reappear and remain after shaking? Explain and account for the results of the entire procedure.

Now repeat the whole process with a fresh sample of casein in water, but after adding concentrated HCl at the start, also add 2 or 3 drops of bromcresol green solution to the tube. This is an indicator dye giving a yellow color below pH 3.8 and a blue color in solutions above pH 5.4. From the color changes you obtain during the test and from the comparative amounts of acid or alkali required to produce color changes, estimate the pH of the isoelectric point of casein.

In analogous fashion, determine the isoelectric point of egg white. In this instance, however, start with 2 ml of your egg-white solution and add alkali until the solution is entirely clear. Then add a few drops of bromcresol green indicator and begin to acidify dropwise with 10% HCl. After a precipitate has formed, continue the acidification with CONCENTRATED HCl.

3. Color Reactions

Carry out parallel tests on egg-white solution and liver extract as follows.

a. The xanthoproteic test. Put 2 ml of protein solution into a test tube, add 1 ml of concentrated nitric acid, and warm gently over a free flame. Note the yellowing of the coagulum. Cool under the tap, and then add an excess of NH_4OH solution until a brilliant orange-yellow color develops.

Such a result is given not only by proteins, however. Repeat the test with 0.1% phenol solution and with 2% solutions of the amino acids alanine, tyrosine, and tryptophane. From the chemical structure of phenol and the amino acids, infer which atomic grouping appears to be responsible for the color reaction.

b. The Millon test. Put 2 ml of protein solution into a test tube and add 2 ml of Millon's reagent (see Appendix for composition). Warm gently to boiling. Note the color development, mainly on the precipitate but also in the solution.

Repeat the test with another sample of egg-white solution, but add a pinch of solid NaCl and shake briefly before adding the Millon reagent. Compare the result here with that on the liver extract. What can you conclude about the effect of salt in this test?

Repeat the test on 2 ml of (1) 0.1% phenol solution, (2) 2% tyrosine solution. What can you conclude regarding the specificity of Millon's test?

c. The ninhydrin test. Put 2 ml of protein solution into a test tube and add 2 ml of ninhydrin reagent (see Appendix for composition). Heat the solution in a boiling water bath for 2 or 3 min and then let it cool. Note the development of color.

Repeat the test with each of the amino acids available to you and also with NH_4OH to which a little concentrated NaOH has been added. In the latter case, however, do not heat the solution at first and let color develop at room temperature. Then heat and observe what happens to the color. On the basis of all results obtained, conclude (1) what substances the ninhydrin test appears to be specific for, (2) the atomic grouping probably giving rise to the color reaction, and (3) the range of colors produced by the reaction.

d. The biuret test. This is a very sensitive and important test for proteins and for polypeptides generally. To 2 ml of protein solution add 3 or 4 ml of concentrated NaOH and shake well. Then add several drops of 0.5% $CuSO_4$ (make up in a separate test tube by mixing ½ ml of the 10% stock with 9.5 ml of distilled water). A pale violet color will develop. If the concentration of the added copper solution is greater, a deeper violet will be obtained (for example, try the test again using a few drops of a 5 or 10% $CuSO_4$ solution).

The biuret test should always be accompanied by a control test in which distilled water instead of protein solution is used, every other step being identical. Note that a positive result for proteins is a distinctly VIOLET color; a blue color is NOT indicative of proteins. Polypeptide molecules smaller than those of whole proteins give a pale PINK or ROSE biuret reaction (see below). Repeat the test with a sample of an amino acid solution.

This test is named after the compound BIURET, formed by the union of two molecules of urea (hence "biurea," or biuret):

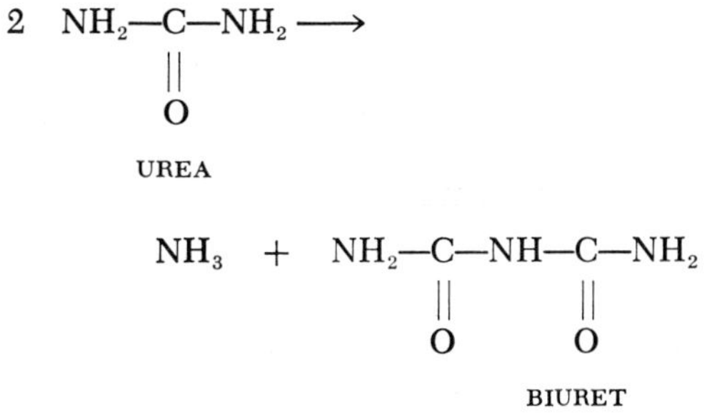

$$2\ NH_2\text{—}\underset{\underset{O}{\|}}{C}\text{—}NH_2 \longrightarrow$$

UREA

$$NH_3 + NH_2\text{—}\underset{\underset{O}{\|}}{C}\text{—}NH\text{—}\underset{\underset{O}{\|}}{C}\text{—}NH_2$$

BIURET

The color of biuret appears to be due specifically to the atomic grouping $\text{—}\underset{|}{N}\text{—}\underset{\underset{O}{\|}}{C}\text{—}$, hence the biuret test will be positive for compounds containing such groupings. This is the case for proteins, which contain peptide links, —CO—NH—. Can you therefore account for the negative result on individual amino acids? Actually the biuret test is sensitive only for polypeptides larger than dipeptides.

Urea itself contains a —CO— group next to nitrogen atoms and should therefore react positively. Melt a few crystals of urea in a dry Pyrex test tube and continue heating until ammonia can be clearly smelled. Cool the tube under the tap and add a few drops of distilled water. Then carry out the biuret test by adding NaOH and dilute $CuSO_4$.

Note that ammonia and ammonium ions interfere with the biuret reaction. To 2 ml of 10 times diluted egg-white solution add 1 ml of SATURATED ammonium sulfate. Run a control test with the diluted egg-white solution and distilled water. Then carry out the biuret test on both tubes. A blue cupric-ammonium ion complex forms in the experimental tube, which masks the biuret color.

4. Hydrolysis

Like carbohydrates, proteins may be decomposed by acid hydrolysis into smaller polypeptides and individual amino acids. Carry out the following procedures in parallel for egg-white solution and liver extract.

To two test tubes labeled A and B add, with a pipette, 4 ml of protein solution, and to a tube labeled C add 4 ml of distilled water. Into tube A also pipette 2 ml of concentrated HCl and boil the contents in a water bath for 15 min. Thereafter cool this tube under the tap and filter the contents into a clean test tube (again labeled A). Then pipette 2 ml of concentrated HCl into tubes B and C, shake well, and filter the contents of tube B into another clean test tube (also labeled B). Alkalinize the filtrate in tube A by adding concentrated NaOH from a pipette until the solution gives a strongly basic reaction to litmus paper; note the amount of NaOH added. Then pipette an exactly equal amount of the alkali into tube B and also into tube C (and verify the alkalinity of the result with litmus paper). Add now an equal number of drops of dilute $CuSO_4$ to all three tubes.

Compare and account for the results of the biuret reactions you obtain; explain also all steps of the above procedures.

C. nucleic acids

1. Isolation

You already know from previous tests that when a complex biological mixture such as liver extract is treated with trichloracetic acid, the proteins precipitate out. Nucleic acids too are carried down into the coagulum. Proteins and nucleic acids may then be separated from one another by treating the coagulum with NaCl; the proteins stay precipitated but nucleic acids go into solution. From such a solution the nucleic acids can be precipitated with ethyl alcohol.

Put 10 or 15 ml of finely ground liver homogenate (from the class stock) into a small beaker and add an equal volume of 15% trichloracetic acid. Stir well, then filter. Decant a little of the filtrate into a test tube marked A and discard the rest of the fluid. Transfer the coagulum on the filter paper to a small beaker containing 15 ml of 10% NaCl solution. Stir well and place the beaker into the boiling water bath for about 10 min. Then let the contents cool and filter them into a test tube or small flask marked B.

Pour a little of the filtrate in B into a separate test tube and, with a medicine dropper, carefully layer over it about 1 ml of ice-cold 95% ethyl alcohol; let the alcohol flow down the side of the inclined test tube. Note the milky precipitate forming slowly at the alcohol-water interface. Then add enough alcohol so that the tube contains about twice as much alcohol as water. Shake up, and if necessary keep the tube in crushed ice for 2 or 3 min. A floccular or milky precipitate will become apparent. The latter consists of nucleic acids.

2. Identification

To verify the nucleic-acid nature of the precipitate, perform first an analogous alcohol precipitation with known 5% RNA and DNA solutions (the prepared solutions on your desk have been made up in 10% NaCl). Compare results.

Then identify the nucleic acids through their color reactions with acid diphenylamine reagent (see Appendix for composition). Diphenylamine reacts with the sugar portion of nucleic acids and is particularly sensitive to deoxypentoses. After boiling with the reagent, RNA is indicated by a greenish color, DNA, by a violet or purple-bluish color. The color reaction can usually be improved by subjecting a crude nucleic acid source to acid hydrolysis before testing with diphenylamine. Accordingly, run seven tests in parallel, using the following solutions:

1: solution A, prepared above

2: filtrate B, prepared above

3: filtrate B treated with an equal volume of concentrated HCl in a boiling water bath for 15 min

4: 5% DNA solution

5: 5% DNA solution hydrolyzed in acid like (3)

6: 5% RNA solution

7: 5% RNA solution hydrolyzed in acid like (3)

To 2 ml of each of these materials in test tubes then add 3 or 4 ml of the diphenylamine reagent. Put all tubes in the boiling water bath for 15 min. Thereafter let the tubes stand and cool for 10 min or longer and note the development of color. If necessary, contrast the color in a given tube with a sample of UNBOILED test solution plus diphenylamine reagent. Which nucleic acid appears to be more abundant in the liver extract?

IV analysis

1. Distinguish between native, denatured, and coagulated proteins. Is the native form of a protein chemically different from its coagulated form? Just what changes when a protein is coagulated?

2. List the many categories of agents that coagulate proteins. How can these different categories have the same general effect? Review the methods of demonstrating the presence of nitrogen and sulfur in proteins. How could you demonstrate the presence of carbon?

3. Explain fully how your procedure in section B2b demonstrated the characteristics of isoelectric points. Describe these characteristics. Which classes of organic compounds other than proteins have isoelectric points? How are such points related to pH?

4. Could a knowledge of isoelectric points be used to separate individual proteins from a mixture of different proteins? Explain why addition of a few drops of concentrated HCl coagulates proteins whereas addition of larger quantities of this acid dissolves proteins.

5. Review the chemistry of the biuret test. Discuss the comparative specificities of the Millon and ninhydrin tests, and indicate which atomic groups are responsible for producing the colors of these tests.

6. Explain each step of the procedure you followed in the acid hydrolysis of proteins, and show how the results proved the actual occurrence of hydrolysis. Write the equation symbolizing an acid hydrolysis of protein. Could proteins be hydrolyzed with alkali?

7. Review the structure of proteins and of nucleic acids. What types of bonds occur in proteins? In nucleic acids? Which nitrogen bases occur in which nucleic acids? Review the procedure you used to isolate nucleic acids.

8. Describe the results of your diphenylamine tests on nucleic acids. What was the objective of the test with tube 1? What range of color did you obtain with the other tubes, and what do these colors signify?

9. Suppose you were given a sample of (*a*) fresh steak, (*b*) a head of lettuce. Using all the information you obtained in this and the two preceding exercises, how would you proceed to analyze the qualitative composition of these materials?

10. Name classes of compounds present in living organisms not tested for in this and the two preceding exercises. Can you suggest ways in which three or more of the qualitative tests you studied could be made quantitative, that is, suited to show how much of a given compound is present in a given sample material?

exercise 11 enzymes and enzyme activity

I materials

Each group of 4 students

12 or more test tubes
test-tube rack and brush
stirring rod
pipette, 10 ml
5 beakers, 50 to 250 ml
3 medicine droppers
millimeter ruler
wax pencil
bunsen burner plus stand, wire grid
thermometer
spot plate
50 ml 2 *N* H_2SO_4 (see Appendix, "Acids")
100 ml fresh 3% H_2O_2
150 ml 1% $KMnO_4$ solution
IKI reagent, in dropping bottle
25 ml Benedict's reagent

Class stock

beef liver, fresh
potatoes, fresh
blendor
distilled water, stock
crushed ice, stock
buffers, pH 5, 7, and 9 (see Appendix)
0.2 *M* sodium azide
0.2 *M* sodium fluoride

Team or class stock

approx. 10 ml per team:

NaOH, conc.
2% tyrosine solution
2% glucose-1-phosphate solution
5% trypsin solution

II introduction

The experiments of this exercise will demonstrate the existence of enzymes, the nature of action of these catalysts, and some of the factors that influence their action. The sources of the enzymes to be studied will be potato and liver tissue, and the substrates on which the enzymes will act will come partly from these same tissues, partly from ready-made stocks of commercial chemicals. Groups of four students will again work in teams.

NOTE: the exercise contains too many experiments to be performed by one team during a single laboratory period. Accordingly, the instructor will specify how the work is to be divided up between two periods. Alternatively, if only one period is to be used, all tests up to and including those of sections D1 and D2 may be performed by all teams in the class, and the remaining tests may be assigned to various different teams.

III directions

A. preliminary operations

1. To obtain a preparation of liver enzymes, shred by hand or homogenize in a blendor a piece of fresh beef liver in water just as you did in exercise 8. Let the mixture stand for some minutes, then pour off the top fluid and mark it "liver enzymes."
2. From a piece of fresh potato, prepare "potato juice" and "potato starch" extracts just as you did in exercise 8. Also obtain a piece of untreated whole potato.
3. Set up a beaker with water as a boiling water bath. Set up another beaker with water maintained at 37°C. The temperature here should not be allowed to rise above 40°C; mix hot and cold water to produce a bath of fairly even temperature.

B. tyrosinase

This widely distributed enzyme catalyzes the oxidation of the amino acid tyrosine to dihydroxyphenyl alanine, and it also promotes the oxidation of the latter compound to an intermediate which, after further transformations, yields the end-product MELANIN. This is a black or brown pigment, the visible color depending on the melanin concentration.

The action of the enzyme can be demonstrated quite simply. Prepare three pieces of fresh potato small enough to be placed into test tubes, and put one piece into each of three numbered tubes. With a pipette, add plain water to tube 1 to cover the tissue well; note the amount added. To tubes 2 and 3 add half as much water, and boil the contents of tube 2 for 2 min over a direct flame. Cool the tube, then add to it and to tube 3 an amount of 2% tyrosine solution that will bring the total fluid content to the same level as in tube 1. Let all three tubes stand for an hour or longer; shake up their contents from time to time. Thereafter record all observed changes and account for them.

Note that the darkening or browning of cut potatoes or apples is apparently due to the action of tyrosinase and the resulting melanin formation. Note also that the potato juice extract you prepared is white or light pink when quite fresh but becomes increasingly red to brown on standing.

C. phosphatase

This ubiquitous enzyme catalyzes the dephosphorylation of phosphorylated carbohydrates. For example, the enzyme splits glucose-1-phosphate to free glucose and inorganic phosphate:

$$\underset{\text{GLUCOSE-1-PHOSPHATE}}{\begin{array}{c} HC{-}O{-}PO_3H_2 \\ | \\ (HCOH)_4 \\ | \\ CH_2OH \end{array}} \xrightarrow[H_2O]{\textit{phosphatase}} \underset{\text{GLUCOSE}}{\begin{array}{c} HC{=}O \\ | \\ (HCOH)_4 \\ | \\ CH_2OH \end{array}} + H_3PO_4$$

The reaction takes place when cells convert stored polysaccharides to monosaccharides. Actually, cells have two means by which such conversions may be achieved. One is enzymatic hydrolysis, that is, splitting of a polysaccharide with WATER, the catalysts here being enzymes such as amylase or other hydrolytic carbohydrases:

$$\text{polysaccharide, water} \xrightarrow[\textit{enzymes}]{\textit{hydrolytic}} \text{monosaccharides}$$

The other method is more roundabout but in fact produces monosaccharides far faster. It involves the splitting of polysaccharides by means of inorganic phosphates instead of water. The enzymes in this case are PHOSPHORYLASES, and the product is glucose-1-phosphate. The latter is then split in a second reaction to free glucose and inorganic phosphate, PHOSPHATASE here being the enzyme:

$$1: \text{polysaccharide} + H_3PO_4 \xrightarrow[ATP]{phosphorylase} \text{glucose-1-phosphate}$$

$$2: \text{glucose-1-phosphate} \xrightarrow[H_2O]{phosphatase} \text{glucose} + H_3PO_4$$

Note that this pathway of free glucose formation requires energy in the form of ATP. It also functions as a first step in numerous metabolic activities of cells (for example, respiration), for glucose-1-phosphate produced as above can (whereas free glucose cannot) enter such metabolic processes directly.

In the tests below, you will use potato starch as the polysaccharide substrate. The objective will be to demonstrate the action of phosphatase (and by implication also that of phosphorylase) both in potato juice and in liver extract. Whereas potato juice might well be expected to act on potato starch, liver juice too contains similar enzymes and thus should have similar effects on the starch. Such effects can be assessed readily with the IKI and Benedict's tests. Although the enzyme extracts already contain some reducing sugar from the start, there should be a distinct increase after starch has yielded free glucose through phosphatase activity.

Carry out three paired tests in numbered test tubes, one tube of each pair representing a control. To serve as substrate, dilute some of the potato starch 10 times with water. Use a pipette to measure quantities as follows:

1 and 2: 3 ml 2% glucose-1-phosphate + 3 ml liver extract

3 and 4: 3 ml diluted potato starch + 3 ml liver extract

5 and 6: 3 ml diluted potato starch + 3 ml potato juice

Put tubes 1, 3, and 5 into the water bath kept at 37°C. Bring tubes 2, 4, and 6 to boiling (CAREFULLY) over an open flame until the coagulation is completed. Then cool these tubes somewhat and add them to the tubes kept at 37°C.

Beginning 5 min after the start of this incubation and at successive 5-min intervals thereafter, put a drop of fluid from each of tubes 3 and 5 on a spot plate and make an IKI test. Continue the incubation until the IKI tests are negative. Then remove tubes 1, 3, and 5 and bring them CAREFULLY to boiling over an open flame, until the coagulation is completed. Cool. Thereafter treat all six tubes in the same way. Decant (or filter, if necessary) exactly equal amounts of the clear fluids into fresh tubes, alkalinize the contents by adding a drop or two of NaOH, and perform a Benedict's test on each using equal amounts of reagent in all cases. Compare and record the results (use Data Sheet 2, page 264). Account for all steps of the testing procedure and explain the results obtained. Does plain glucose-1-phosphate solution give a positive Benedict's? Make a test to check your answer.

D. catalase

Present in all cells and found in particularly high concentrations in liver and blood cells, this enzyme promotes the decomposition of hydrogen peroxide, H_2O_2, according to the following equation:

$$2\ H_2O_2 \xrightarrow{catalase} 2\ H_2O + O_2\uparrow$$

The role of catalase within cells is not too clearly known; it is believed that the enzyme prevents the accumulation of toxic peroxides which otherwise could form during respiration. A study of catalase is particularly instructive, for the effect of the enzyme lends itself readily to quantitative measurement.

1. *The Action of Catalase*

To familiarize yourself with the reaction to be studied, pour H_2O_2 into a test tube to a height of about 1 in. Then, with a medicine dropper, add several drops of liver extract. Observe and explain what is happening. Set the tube aside, for use below.

After catalase has acted on H_2O_2 for a given length of time and before the amount of action can be measured, the activity of the enzyme must be stopped. This is done with sulfuric acid. Put some of the acid into a beaker, and reserve a medicine dropper for exclusive use with the acid. Then mark a clean test tube with a wax pencil, placing one mark exactly 1 cm from the bottom of the tube and a second mark exactly 2 cm from the bottom. Put in sulfuric acid to the lower mark. Then add to the upper mark the enzyme-H_2O_2 mixture prepared above. Shake the acid mixture, and compare with the tube containing enzyme-H_2O_2 only. What is happening? Explain the enzyme-stopping effect of sulfuric acid.

A certain amount of H_2O_2, which the catalase has not had time to decompose, will now be present in the acid mixture. To determine this amount and thus to obtain a measure of the amount of H_2O_2 that WAS decomposed by catalase, potassium permanganate ($KMnO_4$) is used. This substance, in the presence of sulfuric acid, reacts with any H_2O_2 in solution as follows:

$$5\ H_2O_2 + 2\ KMnO_4 + 4\ H_2SO_4 \longrightarrow 2\ KHSO_4 + 2\ MnSO_4 + 8\ H_2O + 5\ O_2\uparrow$$

In other words, the more H_2O_2 there is in a solution, the more $KMnO_4$ will have to be added to make the reaction above go to completion. While the reaction is still incomplete, any $KMnO_4$ added will be decomposed as above, that is, the deep red color of permanganate will disappear. But once the reaction IS complete, any more $KMnO_4$ added will be excess and thus will no longer be decomposed, that is, the red color will persist. In practice, therefore, the amount of H_2O_2 in an acid mixture is determined by adding $KMnO_4$ until the red color no longer disappears and the whole mixture stays permanently just very faintly pink. The amount of $KMnO_4$ added to reach this endpoint is a direct measure of the amount of undecomposed H_2O_2 originally present.

Accordingly, pour some $KMnO_4$ into a beaker, and using a separate medicine dropper reserved exclusively for this, add $KMnO_4$ to the acid mixture already prepared. Squirt in the permanganate a dropperfull at a time and shake the acid mixture after each addition. Gradually decrease the amount of $KMnO_4$ added with each squirt. The red color will disappear more and more slowly, until a point is reached when the color will not disappear at all. Ideally, a single final drop of $KMnO_4$ should change a colorless mixture to one which becomes permanently very faintly pink. The column of fluid above the 2-cm mark now represents the total amount of $KMnO_4$ added. Measure this column to the nearest millimeter, and use the figure as an inverse index of catalase activity: the higher the column, the more H_2O_2 was still intact in solution and the less H_2O_2 has therefore been decomposed by catalase.

NOTE: (*a*) In all subsequent experiments, use only SCRUPULOUSLY CLEAN glassware. Catalase is an extremely potent enzyme, and if a test tube which contained it is not washed thoroughly, enough will adhere to the glass to make subsequent tests quite inaccurate. (*b*) Use reagents to as EXACT a measure as possible. The results in each experiment depend on comparing mixtures in several test tubes; and if the directions call for equal amounts of solution for different tubes, the amounts must really be as nearly equal as possible or else comparisons will be valueless. All test tubes used for these experiments should be of equal width, length, and shape. (*c*) Before you actually carry out any one experiment, READ through the pertinent instructions COMPLETELY. Make sure that you have all required materials on hand, that you understand the sequence of procedural steps, and that each member of your work team knows his assigned function.

2. The Time Course of Enzyme Activity

Number four test tubes 1 to 4 and mark each as in the preceding section, 1 and 2 cm from the bottom. Make sure the marks are at exactly equal comparative heights in the four tubes. Put H_2SO_4 into each tube to the 1-cm mark and set the tubes side by side in a rack.

On another tube labeled A, put wax-pencil marks exactly 5 and 6 cm from the bottom. Fill this tube with H_2O_2 exactly to the 5-cm mark. Then, noting the time to the nearest 10 sec, quickly add liver extract exactly to the 6-cm mark.

Precisely 1 min thereafter, the time now being recorded as zero time, fill tube 1 up to the 2-cm mark with solution from tube A. Shake tube 1, and measure the catalase activity in this tube with $KMnO_4$. At exact 3-min intervals after zero time, repeat this procedure with tubes 2, 3, and 4: in each case fill to the 2-cm mark with solution from tube A and measure catalase activity with $KMnO_4$. Then determine to the nearest millimeter the amount of $KMnO_4$ added to each tube. Record these figures on Data Sheet 2, page 264, and also plot the data on the graph on the same page.

From these results, describe the time course of enzyme action. Is the action increasing, decreasing, or constant over successive units of time? How can your result be explained in terms of reacting molecules in solution?

3. *The Effect of Enzyme Concentration*

Prepare three dilutions of the liver extract:

¾ strength: 3 ml extract, 1 ml water
½ strength: 2 ml extract, 2 ml water
¼ strength: 1 ml extract, 3 ml water

Then set up three tubes labeled 1 to 3 and marked 1 and 2 cm from the bottom as in the preceding tests. Put H_2SO_4 into each tube up to the 1-cm mark. Also set up three tubes A to C and mark them 5 and 6 cm from the bottom as in the earlier tests. Then, noting the time exactly to the nearest 10 sec, add to the 6-cm mark liver extract of ¾ strength to tube A, of ½ strength to tube B, and of ¼ strength to tube C.

Precisely 4 min thereafter, pour solution of tube A into tube 1 up to the 2-cm mark. Analogously add solution of tube B to tube 2 and solution of tube C to tube 3. Shake up, then measure catalase activity with $KMnO_4$. Record all data (Data Sheet 3, page 265). Use the 4-min reading of the preceding series (section 2, tube 2) as a determination for a full-strength enzyme effect. Draw conclusions about whether enzyme activity is proportional to enzyme concentration or about any other way in which activity and concentration appear to be correlated.

4. *The Effect of Substrate Concentration*

Prepare three dilutions of H_2O_2:

0.50: 1 part H_2O_2, 1 part water
0.10: 1 part H_2O_2, 9 parts water
0.05: 1 part H_2O_2, 19 parts water

Then carry out all procedures as in expt. 3, above, except that the three dilutions of H_2O_2 are used for tubes A through C in place of full-strength H_2O_2. Record all data (p. 265). Use the 4-min reading of the experiments in section 2 (tube 2) as a determination for a full-strength substrate effect. Draw conclusions about how enzyme activity and substrate concentrations appear to be correlated.

5. *The Effect of Temperature*

Prepare two clean test tubes exactly like tubes 1 and 2 in the preceding series. To each add H_2SO_4 up to the 1-cm mark. Set aside.

Now put 2 or 3 ml of the liver extract into one new test tube and 6 or 7 ml of H_2O_2 into another. Place both tubes into a beaker with crushed ice and allow them to be thoroughly chilled (this may be done ahead of time). Also prechill in ice a clean, newly marked test tube A (like tube A in the previous experiments). Read the temperature in the tube containing H_2O_2; the experiment should be performed at about 10°C.

When this temperature is reached, put cold H_2O_2 into tube A up to the 5-cm mark, and noting the exact time, add cold enzyme solution to the 6-cm mark. Immediately replace tube A in the ice. After exactly 4 min, pour solution of tube A into tube 1, up to the 2-cm mark. Shake, then measure catalase activity. Record the result (Data Sheet 3).

Repeat the whole procedure for a high temperature level. Into the water bath held at 37°C place one test tube containing liver extract, one containing H_2O_2, and one marked like tube A above. When the solutions in the tubes are at a temperature of 37°C, mix in tube A, note the time, and replace that tube in the water bath. Four minutes later test for catalase activity, using tube 2, already prepared. Record the result (Data Sheet 3).

Use the 4-min reading of the experiments in section 2 as a test at room temperature, and compare this with the tests at 10°C and 37°C. From these data, conclude how temperature affects enzyme action.

6. *The Effect of pH*

Prepare three clean test tubes exactly like tubes 1, 2, and 3 in the preceding series. Add H_2SO_4 to each up to the 1-cm mark and set aside.

Label three clean test tubes A, B, and C, and mark each at three points, namely, 2½, 5½, and 6 cm from the bottom. Put H_2O_2 into each up to the 2½-cm mark. Then, up to the 5½-cm mark in each case, add buffer of pH 5 to tube A, of pH 7 to tube B, and of pH 9 to tube C. Shake.

To tube A now add liver extract up to the 6-cm mark and note the exact time. Four minutes later determine catalase activity, using tube 1. Repeat this procedure for tubes B and C, using tubes 2 and 3, respectively, for the activity determinations.

Record and compare the results, and conclude how pH affects enzyme action.

7. The Effect of Inhibitors

Set up four clean test tubes numbered 1 through 4 and marked 1 and 2 cm from the bottom. Add H_2SO_4 to the 1-cm mark and set aside. Also prepare four tubes labeled A through D and mark them 3 and 5 cm from the bottom. Put H_2O_2 into each up to the 3-cm mark. Then prepare the following mixtures:

a. 1 part liver extract + 1 part water.

b. 1 part liver extract + 1 part 5% trypsin solution; incubate in water bath at 37°C for ½ hr or longer, then cool.

c. 1 part liver extract + 1 part 0.2 *M* sodium azide (CAUTION: POISON).

d. 1 part liver extract + 1 part 0.2 *M* sodium fluoride (CAUTION: POISON).

Noting the time in each case, add to the 5-cm mark solution *a* to tube A, solution *b* to tube B, etc. After 4 min in each instance, test for catalase activity using tubes 1 through 4. Record and account for the data (Data Sheet 3).

NOTE: at the end of the lab period or on direction by the instructor, clean all glassware you have used as thoroughly as possible, with soap, water, and test-tube brushes.

IV analysis

1. Describe and explain the results of your tyrosinase tests. Review the chemical process in which the enzyme participates and give the formulas of the substrates (consult your text if necessary).

2. Describe the design and the results of the phosphatase experiments. Why were IKI tests performed during the incubation? What other tests might be carried out (*a*) to demonstrate the role of phosphorylase and phosphatase, (*b*) to differentiate between the action of these enzymes and the action of hydrolytic ones such as amylase?

3. Define enzyme, coenzyme, substrate, catalysis. Review the theory of enzyme action. What is enzyme specificity and what is its cause? Illustrate the specificity of the enzymes you dealt with in this exercise.

4. Discuss the results of expt. D2. Is the action of catalase constant with time? Does your result agree with theoretical expectations? Explain the basis of the theoretical expectations.

5. Explain the theoretical basis of the effect of enzyme concentrations on catalysis. Do your results agree with theory?

6. Account for the results of your tests on substrate concentrations. What results should be expected on theoretical grounds?

7. How does enzyme action vary with (*a*) temperature, (*b*) pH? What are the theoretical reasons for such variations?

8. What is the action of trypsin and in what sense is it an enzyme inhibitor? What is trypsin itself? Where is it produced and what is its normal function?

9. Describe the effects of azide and fluoride on catalase activity. Through what property does each of these compounds become a reaction inhibitor? Does each inhibit an enzyme directly? What properties make the compounds poisons?

10. In list form, summarize the various general conditions necessary for effective enzyme action. Are these conditions specifically the same for each enzyme?

11. Explain the inhibiting effect of sulfuric acid on catalase. What other factors or conditions would have a like inhibiting effect? Why?

12. What is a buffer? How does it work? Explain the requirement of buffers in expt. D6. Would the other experiments of this exercise have been improved if buffers had been used there, too?

13. Why would an accumulation of H_2O_2 in cells be toxic? Should not catalase be expected to MAKE H_2O_2 as well as decompose it? Does this happen in cells? Discuss.

14. The enzyme invertase catalyzes the reaction: sucrose → glucose + fructose. How would you design a set of experiments to study the action of invertase?

15. How would you design an experiment to show how much faster H_2O_2 decomposes in the presence of catalase than without the enzyme?

exercise 12 physical processes

I materials

Each group of 4 students

12 test tubes
test-tube rack and brush
stirring rod
3 to 4 beakers, 50 to 250 ml
2 beakers, 400 ml
rubber bands
wax pencil
bunsen burner plus stand, wire grid
thermometer
medicine dropper
paper clips
dissecting pan, pins, instruments
1 small funnel
4 small (3-ml) test tubes, prefilled with alkaline agar gel (see Appendix, "Agar")
frog Ringer solution, in 500-ml flask (see Appendix)
25 ml isotonic ethylene glycol solution (see Appendix)
10 ml 0.9% NaCl solution

Class stock

distilled water, stock
frog Ringer solution, stock
crushed ice, stock
blank slides, cover slips
carmine particle suspension
jellied gelatin
dialysis tubing, presoaked
$KMnO_4$, crystalline
2 *M* sucrose solution
1 *M* sucrose solution
0.5% eosin solution
0.2% methylene blue, aqueous
0.4% methylene blue, aqueous
0.1 *N* HCl (see Appendix)
0.2 *N* HCl
frogs, living (1 per team)
pithing equipment
strong sewing thread
defibrinated mammalian whole blood (5 ml per team)

II introduction

Most of the physical phenomena occurring in living matter are consequences of two fundamental conditions: (1) cellular particles are in vibratory, oscillating MOTION, the more so the higher the temperature; and (2) cellular particles are partly of COLLOIDAL size. These two conditions produce a variety of effects, for example, diffusion, differential membrane permeabilities, osmosis, sol-gel reversals, Brownian movement, and others. Most of these phenomena play vitally important roles in the economy of living systems; life is as much a result of specific physical reactions as it is a result of chemical reactions. Many of the physical reactions lend themselves to demonstration and analysis in nonliving systems. Many of them can also be studied directly in the living system.

This exercise is devoted to an examination of some of these reactions as they occur in both living and nonliving systems. Before you begin your work, it might be well if you reviewed pertinent key terms such as solute, solvent, concentration, tonicity, colloid, diffusion, osmosis. You should also acquire at least a preliminary understanding of the actual physical processes denoted by terms such as diffusion and osmosis (consult your text if necessary).

The class will again form work teams of four students each. Read ALL the directions before you begin work. Where indicated, do preliminary operations sufficiently ahead of time, perhaps even as soon as the lab begins (for example, heating or chilling solutions).

III directions

A. diffusion

1. *The Process*

Fill a small beaker with water and drop into it a crystal of potassium permanganate ($KMnO_4$). Do NOT shake. Without disturbing the beaker in any way, let it stand for 2 hr. In the interval, do the other parts of this exercise.

Look at the beaker from time to time, and record the appearance of the water. What process does this experiment demonstrate? Explain this process as a physical reaction among molecular particles.

2. *Diffusion Rate*

Obtain four small test tubes (about 3-ml capacity) which have been previously filled completely with ALKALINE AGAR GEL (see Appendix for composition). Place the open ends of these tubes into dishes or small beakers containing the following solutions:

1: 0.2% methylene blue
2: 0.4% methylene blue
3: 0.1 *N* HCl
4: a mixture consisting of equal amounts of 0.2 *N* HCl and 0.4% methylene blue

Note the starting time, and at intervals specified in the data table on page 266 (Data Sheet 4), measure the position of the diffusion front in each tube to the nearest millimeter. Record and then plot the data, and calculate the rate of diffusion for each tube.

B. osmosis

Obtain a length of presoaked dialysis tubing and tie a knot at one end of it. Fill this bag with water to make sure that leaks are absent; empty the water. Now fill the bag with 1 *M* sucrose solution to which a trace of eosin has been added. Tie the open end of the bag over the wide end of a small glass funnel. Make sure the sucrose solution fills the funnel and projects a short distance into the tube portion of the funnel; make sure also that the bag is secured tightly. Attach a length of glass tube to the narrow end of the funnel, using a short piece of rubber tubing as a link. Fasten the whole system vertically to a stand and immerse the dialysis bag with the sucrose solution into a beaker of DISTILLED water. Mark the glass tube at 1-cm intervals with a wax pencil, and at four successive 15-min periods, measure the height of the sucrose solution within the glass tube.

Thereafter, replace the beaker containing distilled water with one containing a 2 *M* sucrose solution. Again measure and record the height of fluid within the glass tube at four successive 15-min periods.

C. colloid properties

1. *Brownian Movement*

Examine under the microscope a drop of carmine suspension on a slide. Observe the oscillation of the smaller dye particles. How many times larger than the smallest visible particles do you estimate the largest vibrating particles to be? Which of the particles do you judge to be in the colloidal size range? Compare small and large particles as to speed and extent of oscillation. Follow the path of individual particles for some minutes. Do these paths display any patterned regularity?

2. *Sol-Gel Reversal*

Put a piece of stiff gelatin jelly into each of two test tubes. Heat both tubes in a boiling water bath. What happens to the gelatin? Now dilute the gelatin in one of the tubes with 1 or 2 equal volumes of water, and cool both tubes in a beaker of ice. What happens in each tube? What does this test demonstrate?

D. permeability

The membranes used in this experiment will be the plasma membranes of mammalian red blood corpuscles. Some of the factors influencing their permeability may be studied by taking advantage of their osmotic properties. When dissolved particles present in an external water medium enter red corpuscles, osmotic pressure within the corpuscles will be raised and, as a result, water will move into the corpuscles. This will make them swell up; and when they attain a critical volume their membranes will burst, hemoglobin will escape, and the originally turbid suspension of corpuscles will become transparent rather suddenly. This phenomenon is called HEMOLYSIS. The time required for hemolysis to occur may be used as a measure of the rate with which the dissolved particles in the medium have entered the corpuscles, that is, as a measure of the permeability of the corpuscle membranes to given materials.

In practice, one puts into a test tube 5 ml of a solution containing the material to be tested and 3 drops of fresh blood. The time when the first drop is added is noted to the nearest second. This is zero time. The mixture is shaken quickly and the tube is put into a rack. The rack is placed in front of a light source, and a sheet of printed material (for example, newspaper) is placed behind the tube, between the tube and the light. At first the printing will be illegible, but once hemolysis begins the writing will become recognizable with rapidly increasing clarity. The time is noted when the printing becomes just visible enough to be identified. This end point is quite reliable; it represents about 75% hemolysis.

1. *The Effect of Tonicity*

Prepare five numbered test tubes containing the following:

1: 5 ml distilled water
2: 4½ ml distilled water plus ½ ml isotonic (0.9%) NaCl
3: 4 ml distilled water plus 1 ml isotonic NaCl
4: 3 ml distilled water plus 2 ml isotonic NaCl
5: 5 ml isotonic NaCl

Determine hemolysis time for each tube. Record the data on Data Sheet 4 and interpret them. How do you conclude permeability to be influenced by the tonicity of the medium?

2. *The Effect of Temperature*

Prepare three numbered test tubes each containing 5 ml of isotonic ethylene glycol solution. Put one into a water bath held at about 37°C, one into a water-ice assembly held at about 10°C, and keep one at room temperature.

When temperature equilibria are established in the tubes, determine hemolysis time for each. Record the data and interpret them. How do you conclude permeability to be influenced by temperature?

E. temperature and living processes

Before you begin the tests of this section, fill two 400-ml beakers with frog Ringer solution. Set one to chill in ice and let the other become very hot over a bunsen burner. Whenever in preparations below you need Ringer solution of given temperature, mix some of the hot and cold solutions together until the required temperature is obtained.

1. *Heartbeat*

Pith a frog (brain and spinal cord; see directions for brain pithing in exercise VI.7) and carefully expose the heart by dissection. NOTE: the instructor may carry out these procedures for you or will give you directions for them.

Count the number of beats per minute. Cautiously sever all structural connections of the heart, but BE CAREFUL TO LEAVE THE ENTIRE HEART INTACT. Remove it from the body and put it into a small marked beaker containing Ringer solution at room temperature. Allow several minutes to elapse, and when the heart beats at a fairly constant rate, determine this rate and the temperature of the medium.

By judicious mixing of hot and ice-cold Ringer solutions, prepare small beakers containing solutions at 30, 20, 10, and 0°C. Place the heart into each of these successively (starting at 30°C), and record the rate of beat. In each case, wait a few minutes before making measurements to allow for temperature equilibration.

Return the heart to Ringer at room temperature. After a few minutes, put a thermometer into the solution and SLOWLY warm by adding hot Ringer. Keep stirring as you do so. Determine the highest temperature at which the heart will still beat. Return the heart to Ringer at room temperature, and find out if it will resume beating.

Record and plot your results on the data sheet on page 267 (Data Sheet 5). Calculate the Q_{10} for each 10-deg range of temperature used.

2. *Ciliary Movement*

Lay flat in a dissecting pan, ventral side up, the pithed frog used previously. Open the body cavity and slit the esophagus ventrally, as far posteriorly as the stomach. Pin down the edges of the cut esophagus to expose the inner ciliated lining as a flat surface. Using a medicine dropper, moisten this lining with Ringer solution.

Now place a small piece of cork (1 mm^3) on the surface of the palate, between the eyes. Time the rate of movement of the cork in centimeters per minute. Repeat once or twice and record the average on Data Sheet 5.

Prepare a test tube with Ringer solution warmed to about 30°C. Pour a little of this fluid over the esophageal lining, repeat several times, and then run the cork test as above. Make two or three determinations and record the average.

Similarly prepare Ringer solution chilled to about 10°C, cool the esophageal lining, and again time the movement of the cork. Record.

From the data, conclude how temperature influences ciliary activity. Calculate the approximate Q_{10} for each 10-deg range of temperature studied.

IV analysis

1. From your data in expt. A2, what generalizations can you make about the relation between diffusion rate and concentration? What relation would you expect to exist between diffusion rate and temperature? How could this be tested experimentally?

2. In expt. A2, what do the results in tube 3 demonstrate? In tube 4?

3. Explain the results you obtained in expt. B. Did it illustrate diffusion, osmosis, or both? Was the WATER concentration greater in the beaker or in the dialysis bag?

4. In the light of the experiments in sections A and B, define DIFFUSION and OSMOSIS. Distinguish carefully between the two processes. For each, show in which direction water migrates, in which direction dissolved transmissible particles migrate, and what happens to dissolved nontransmissible particles. Show also how (*a*) the water concentration, (*b*) the particle concentration, changes from the initial to the terminal state.

5. Would you expect the rate of osmosis to depend on the chemical nature of the dissolved particles, on molecular size, or on molecular weight? Explain.

6. If 1,000 NaCl molecules and 1,000 $C_6H_{12}O_6$ molecules were dissolved in equal volumes of water, would their osmotic pressures be the same or not? Explain.

7. Define COLLOID. What is the actual size range in which particles are colloidal? Name different classes of colloids, and give examples of each.

8. Which chemical compounds of cells are of colloidal size?

9. What is Brownian motion due to? Do only colloidal particles display this motion? Does Brownian motion conceivably serve any function in cells? Would you expect this motion to be influenced by temperature? If so, how?

10. How does a gel differ from a sol? In molecular terms, explain the effect of heat on a gel and of cold on a sol, as in expt. C2. Why did cold not have the same effect on the diluted as on the undiluted gelatin?

11. From the data of section D, show how tonicity affects hemolysis, hence penetration of particles through membranes. Explain the basis of this effect. Account for the result in tube 5 of expt. D1.

12. What prevents hemolysis from occurring under normal conditions within the body? What would you expect the hemolysis time to be if red corpuscles were suspended in (*a*) an isotonic solution of proteins, (*b*) a hypertonic solution of NaCl?

13. How does temperature affect hemolysis, hence penetration of particles through membranes? Explain the basis of this correlation.

14. What is the molecular basis of the effect of temperature on heartbeat and on living processes in general? Does YOUR heart rate change like that of the frog when the weather becomes warmer or colder?

15. How would you design an experiment to test the effect of pH on (*a*) ciliary movement, (*b*) heart rate, (*c*) permeability?

16. Why did the frog heart stop beating when the temperature became too high? Why exactly did the temperature become "too high"? Do living processes stop when the temperature becomes too low? Why?

17. What is the effect of temperature increase on most ordinary chemical reactions? Is this borne out by your results in expt. E2? What is a Q_{10}?

18. Was the pithed frog you experimented on alive? Was the heart you used in expt. E1 alive? Was it dead? Discuss.

19. Does a colloid freeze as readily as plain water? Explain. Does a gel freeze as readily as a sol? Explain. Does the water of a colloidal system evaporate as readily as plain water? Explain.

20. Show in what ways the physical properties of living matter can influence its chemical behavior. Then show in what ways the chemical properties of living matter can influence its physical behavior.

exercise 13 cells: microscopic structure

I materials

Each student

microscope
medicine dropper
dissecting instruments
2 blank slides, cover slips
hand lens
letter "e" or other microscope trial slide
frog epidermis, surface view, prepared slide
leaf epidermis, surface view, prepared slide
pig liver section, prepared slide
onion (*Allium*) root tip, longitudinal section, prepared slide

Class stock

acetocarmine stain, in dropping bottles (see Appendix)
0.9% NaCl solution
dissecting microscopes, for demonstration materials
methyl cellulose suspension (see Appendix)
glass rods
alcohol lamps
toothpicks
Amoeba proteus, living culture
Stentor coeruleus, living culture
Spirogyra, living culture and/or prepared slides
Elodea, living
onion roots, living, on bulbs kept in water-filled beakers for 3 or more days
assorted optional demonstration materials showing cells, living and/or prepared slides

II introduction

As an essential prerequisite to a study of cellular biology, the first section of this exercise will be devoted to the microscope and its use. In the remaining sections, you will examine the structure of CELLS, both as complete unicellular organisms and as basic components of multicellular organisms.

Note that each phase of the work calls for TWO operations on your part: OBSERVATION and on-the-spot STUDY. Thus it is not sufficient merely to observe. Observation by itself is useless if it does not lead to contemplative thought and searching inquiry into the significance of the observation.

Hence first observe, and observe PRECISELY. This means that you must use your BRAIN, not just your eyes. As you probably well know, one can often look for hours without actually "seeing" anything. This is what you should do to "see": as you look, PUT INTO WORDS what you observe. Phrase sentences in your mind, keep up a running, silent commentary, and LISTEN to this inner speech.

After having observed, THINK. In this exercise, guide your thinking along the following lines:

1. What structural features are COMMON to the different cells observed? What structural features are UNIQUE to each type of cell?

2. To what extent, therefore, is a given cell SPECIALIZED in structure, and how is this correlated with its specialization in function?

3. What ARE the various functions carried out by each cell? In what way are these functions particularly suited to aid in survival? And in what DIFFERENT ways are the functions performed by different cells?

Formulate answers to such questions WHILE you observe. This is the best way to exploit the exercise fully.

III directions

A. the microscope

1. Principles and Methods of Use

The procedure of learning to use the microscope will take the form of a class exercise, directed by the instructor. While he speaks on the topics below, you will have your microscope in front of you, and you should take notes and carry out manual operations as directed.

a. Basic principles of optics and physics of microscope; types of microscopes.

b. Parts of instrument and function of parts; care and cleaning of microscope.

c. Lighting, light control, and proper use of eyes.

d. Low-power focusing; exercises with trial slide.

e. High-power focusing; depth focusing; exercises with trial slide.

f. Magnification.

g. Manufacture and use of prepared slides; fixation and staining.

h. Wet mounts; trials with hair and air bubbles in saliva.

2. Estimation of Microscopic Sizes

Focus on the letter "e" or any other trial slide under high power. Take a small millimeter ruler and lay it on the stage of the microscope so that one end of the ruler points at you. Now look into the microscope with one eye and AT THE SAME TIME look at the ruler with the other eye. With a little practice you should be able to see simultaneous superimposed images of the millimeter scale and the object you are looking at under the microscope. Now read off the size of the microscopic image as so many millimeters; designate this number as *a*. It represents the MAGNIFIED size of the object. To obtain the ACTUAL size, divide *a* by the total magnification of your microscope. The latter is determined by multiplying the magnifications of ocular and objective (stamped into the metal jackets of these lens systems). If the high-power objective magnifies 43× and the ocular 10×, then the total magnifying power of the microscope will be 430. Divide the total magnification into *a*, and the result will be the actual size of the microscopic object, in millimeters (mm). Convert this into MICRONS, the biological unit of length [1 mm equals 1,000 μ (microns)]. How large is the microscopic object in inches?

B. cells as organisms

1. Spirogyra

Under low and high power, study prepared slides and/or a wet mount of a piece of *Spirogyra* filament. Note the PATTERN of cell arrangement. In an individual cell identify CELL WALL, CYTOPLASM, NUCLEUS (in prepared slide), and the large green CHLOROPLAST. Describe its shape. What can you see of the internal structure of the chloroplast?

Is an "individual" of *Spirogyra* a single cell or a whole filament? Are all cells of a filament alike? What are the adaptive advantages of the organization of *Spirogyra* into filamentous aggregations of cells? What group of organisms does *Spirogyra* represent?

2. Amoeba

Prepare a wet mount of a living amoeba and

cover. Study under high power. Note the CYCLOTIC STREAMING of the cytoplasm and its contents, and the extrusion of the fingerlike PSEUDOPODS. Observe the pseudopodial LOCOMOTION of the organism for several minutes and keep track of its path. Is this path regular in some fashion or is it random?

What are the characteristics of the CELL SURFACE? Describe the appearance of the CYTOPLASM. How many different types of CYTOPLASMIC INCLUSIONS can you identify? Is the NUCLEUS visible?

Where do amoebae live in nature? What group of organisms does an amoeba represent?

3. *Stentor*

Put a ring of methyl cellulose on a blank slide, and place a drop of water with one or more stentors into the ring. Cover, and after the organisms have slowed down sufficiently, examine under low and high power and, if possible, also under a dissecting microscope. Identify the MEMBRANELLES, large anterior cilia forming a ring around the GULLET; the CONTRACTILE VACUOLE, located anteriorly to the side of the gullet; the nodular chain of the MACRONUCLEUS: the HOLDFAST at the posterior end; and the PIGMENTED STRIPES on the body surface, alternating with longitudinal ROWS OF BODY CICILA. The organism possesses several dozen micronuclei, but these are too small to be seen in your preparation. (Read pertinent sections of your text to familiarize yourself with the roles of macronuclei and micronuclei in this group of organisms.)

Keep the slide undisturbed for some minutes and note how the organism extends to full length. Note also the cyclotic streaming of the cytoplasm and the behavior of the contractile vacuole. While continuing to observe, pound the table with your fist: the organism should contract suddenly. This movement is brought about by CONTRACTILE FIBRILS under the body surface of *Stentor* (but not visible in the living organism).

In what respects is the cellular structure of *Stentor* specialized?

C. cells as tissue components

1. *Elodea Leaf*

Put a leaf of the common water plant *Elodea* into a drop of water on a slide and cover with a cover slip. In low and high power, note the PATTERN of cell arrangement and the cell shapes. Focus up and down with the fine adjustment and identify the two cell layers that compose the leaf. Reduce the light admitted through the microscope (by narrowing the aperture of the diaphragm or by tilting the mirror somewhat), and then concentrate on an individual cell (preferably near the edge of the leaf). Identify the CELL WALL on the outside; the VACUOLE, a very large, water-filled organelle occupying most of the cell interior; the CYTOPLASM, confined to a thin layer between cell wall and vacuole; and the green, chlorophyll-containing CHLOROPLASTS. How many of these are there and what are their shapes? Move the slide if necessary until you find cells in which active CYCLOSIS is taking place, readily evident by the movement of the chloroplasts. Watch the cyclotic motion for some minutes, and determine if the streaming occurs continuously at unchanging speeds and in the same direction. Nuclei and other organelles cannot usually be seen in such preparations, but if the cytoplasm bulges into the vacuole in one region of the cell, the nucleus is generally located in this bulge.

Estimate the size of a leaf cell. In what ways are such cells specialized and adapted to their environment?

2. *Onion Root Tip, Fresh Preparation*

Onions have been kept for 3 to 4 days on top of beakers with the lower parts of the bulbs submerged in water. Roots have sprouted and the tips of these are to be used now for the study of cells. Obtain one of the roots and, with a razor blade, cut off ½ to 1 mm of the tip (the shorter the piece the better). Transfer this tip to a slide and add a drop of acetocarmine stain. Heat the slide for a few seconds (for example, over an alcohol lamp or a light bulb) WITHOUT letting the stain come to boiling. Add another drop of stain and repeat the heating. Then place a cover slip over the root tip and press down GENTLY with the eraser part of a pencil to crush and spread the tissue. Examine this preparation under low and high power. Study the cells and identify their parts. Which organelles are stained? Are all cells alike in shape? Compare the cells with those of *Elodea* and interpret any differences in the light of the different functions of the cells. Compare them also with the cells to be studied next.

3. Onion (Allium) Root Tip, Prepared Longitudinal Section

In low power, identify the ROOT TIP, the single layer of surface cells forming the ROOT EPIDERMIS, and the interior tissues. What is the shape of the epidermal cells? In interior tissues, how does cell SHAPE change with increasing distance from the root tip?. Describe the PATTERN of cell arrangement and individual cell SHAPE. Estimate the average cell SIZE. Distinguish between NONDIVIDING and DIVIDING cells, that is, cells in which a distinct spherical NUCLEUS can be seen and cells in which, instead of such a nucleus, several darkly stained filaments are visible. The latter are CHROMOSOMES. Note at which regions dividing and nondividing cells are most abundant.

In high power, focus on nondividing cells. Identify the cellulose CELL WALL, the interior CYTOPLASM, the NUCLEAR MEMBRANE, and within the latter, the CHROMATIN GRANULES and the larger NUCLEOLUS. In many of these nondividing cells a nucleus cannot be seen; explain, considering the mechanics of cutting thin tissue slices. Focus on a dividing cell and examine the CHROMOSOMES.

4. Frog Epidermis, Surface View

Examine the prepared slide of a surface view of frog skin. In low power, note the close packing of the flat cells. An animal tissue so constructed is classified as a SQUAMOUS EPITHELIUM. What is the shape of the cells? What are the dark patches of tissue?

In high power, examine an individual cell and identify CELL MEMBRANE, CYTOPLASM, NUCLEUS, CHROMATIN GRANULES (within the nucleus). What are these granules? Should chromosomes be visible? Can cytoplasmic inclusions be seen?

From the directions in section A2 estimate the SIZE of an epidermal cell. How is the structure of this tissue geared to function? Compare the organization of these cells with that of the cells of *Elodea.*

5. Mouth Epithelium, Man

Lightly scrape the inside of your cheek with the broad end of a toothpick and place the scrapings into a drop of physiological saline solution (0.9% NaCl) on a slide. Add a drop of acetocarmine stain and cover with a cover slip. Examine under low and high power. Describe the shape of the cells and compare shapes and sizes with those of the other cell types studied above. In individual cells identify the CELL MEMBRANE, the CYTOPLASM, the NUCLEUS, and within the latter, the vacuolelike NUCLEOLUS. In what respects are such cells specialized? Can they be considered to form a squamous epithelium?

6. Liver Section

Examine the prepared slide of liver tissue and study liver cells under high power. Describe the PATTERN of cell arrangement and individual cell SHAPE. Estimate the average cell SIZE. Channel-like spaces will be found between rows of cells. These spaces are called SINUSOIDS. Blood flows through them past liver cells.

D. additional materials

Other living or preserved materials pertinent to a microscopic study of cells may have been set out. If so, study these as directed by the instructor.

IV analysis

1. List structures common to all cell types you have seen. What are the functions of these structures?
2. List structures unique to particular cell types you have seen. What are the functions of these structures?
3. Based on your observations, what structural characteristics appear to distinguish plant and animal cells generally?
4. Describe the different structural modifications of the cell surfaces you have observed in unicellular organisms. What other surface modifications are known to occur in such organisms? What are the functions of such surface structures?
5. Describe structural modifications of the cell surfaces in multicellular organisms. Are such modifications more or less elaborate than in unicellular organisms?
6. Based on your observations of cell structure, can unicellular organisms be regarded as "simpler" than cells of multicellular organisms? Discuss fully and carefully.

7. Would you consider an amoeba to be less highly or more highly specialized than (*a*) *Stentor,* (*b*) a liver cell?

8. Based on your observations, what is the average size of cells generally? How do the sizes of plant cells and animal cells compare?

9. Is *Spirogyra* better regarded as a filamentous colony or as a truly multicellular organism? What is the conceptual difference between these designations?

10. Describe the different shapes of the cells you have studied. Can any one shape be said to be typical or predominant for cells generally? Does each shape have an adaptive or functional significance? What factors determine cell shape?

exercise 14 cells, tissues, organs: plants

I materials

Each Student

microscope
dissecting instruments
blank slides, cover slips
razor blade

Each 2 or more students

IKI reagent, in dropping bottle
phloroglucinol reagent, in dropping bottle (see Appendix)
prepared slides of:

leaf epidermis, surface view
Ranunculus, stem cross section
Ranunculus, root cross section
Cucurbita, stem cross section
Nymphaea, leaf cross section
Pinus, 1-yr-old stem, cross, radial, and tangential sections
macerated wood

Class stock

fresh supplies of:

onions
pears
celery stalks
potato tubers
germinating radish seeds, with rootlets and root hairs

II introduction

The objectives of this and the following exercise are first, to study various cells and cell types of selected multicellular organisms; secondly, to examine how such cells are combined into tissues of various kinds; and thirdly, to determine how tissues of different types may cooperate to form organs.

In pursuing these objectives, mere mechanical observation will be insufficient. What is required is extensive correlation of observed structures with the functions known to be performed by the structures. How does the shape of a cell or the nature of its cytoplasmic inclusions equip that cell for given specialized activities? What are the contributions of each cell toward the functioning of a tissue? How does each different tissue contribute toward the total functioning of an organ? Is the architectural ARRANGEMENT of the cells in a tissue, or of the tissues in an organ, of significance in the functioning of that tissue or organ? Questions like these should be asked and answered as part of the STUDY accompanying each observation. Only in this way will the components of a multicellular organism be appreciated as more than just heaps of cells, namely, as functionally meaningful, ORGANIZED wholes.

III directions

A. epidermis

1. Study the prepared slide of a surface view of leaf epidermis (see also Fig. 14.1).

Low power: describe the PATTERN of cell arrangement and individual cell SHAPE. Note the pairs of small sausage-shaped GUARD CELLS, arranged like two lips. What is their function? The space bounded by a pair of guard cells is the STOMA, leading into the interior of the leaf.

High power: focus on a large epidermal cell and identify the structural components. Do likewise with a guard cell. In it, identify the CHLOROPLASTS. What is their function? Determine epidermal cell SIZE.

2. An onion bulb consists of a shortened, disklike stem to which concentric layers of fleshy white leaves are attached. Each leaf is bounded by a shiny, one-cell thick epidermis that can be studied readily. Obtain a piece of a leaf of an onion bulb and, with the aid of a scalpel, peel off a portion of the inner or outer epidermal layer and quickly place it into water. Cut off a tiny piece of this epidermis and transfer it into a drop of water on a slide. Add a drop of IKI solution as a stain, cover with a cover slip, and examine under low and high power. Study cell shapes and cell arrangements and the structure of individual cells. Note the NUCLEOLI (two per nucleus). Do the cells contain chloroplasts? Are guard cells and stomata present in this tissue?

3. Examine the prepared slide of a buttercup (*Ranunculus*) stem cross section and make a high-power study of the outermost cell layer. Note the EPIDERMAL CELLS, the CUTICLES on the outer surfaces of these cells, and, in places, the STOMATA, which appear as interruptions in the epidermal layer. Note the GUARD CELL on each side of a stoma. Label Fig. 14.2.

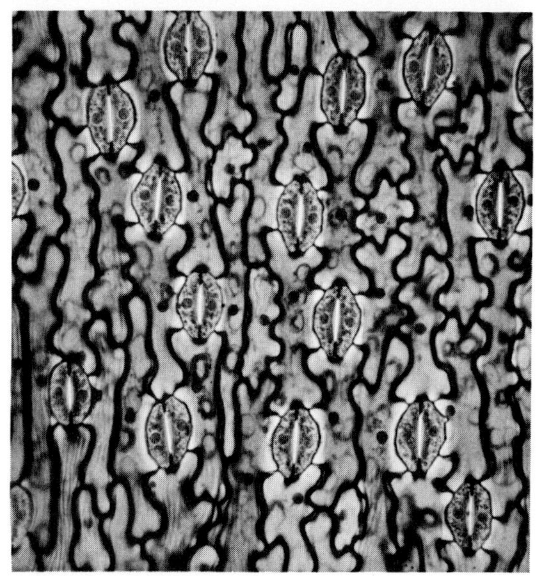

Fig. 14.1 Surface view of the epidermis of a lily leaf. (Courtesy of Ward's Natural Science Establishment, Inc.)

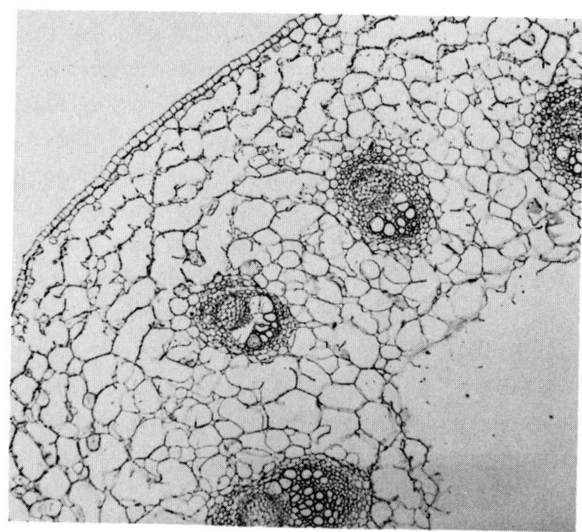

Fig. 14.2 Portion of a cross section through the stem of a buttercup. Label in detail. (Courtesy of General Biological Supply House, Inc.)

4. Now examine the epidermal layer of a root cross section of the buttercup. Do the epidermal cells here possess cuticles? Are guard cells and stomata present? Label Fig. 14.3.

5. With forceps pick out a germinating radish or

turnip seed carrying a rootlet, cut off and discard the seed portion, and mount the rootlet on a blank slide in a drop of water. Cover, and examine under low and high power. Can you make out the ROOT CAP, at the growing tip of the rootlet? By depth-focusing on several levels, identify the ROOT HAIRS, and note their distribution along the rootlet: can you make out a ROOT-HAIR ZONE? Concentrate on one of the smaller root hairs under high power: what is its structural relation with the root epidermis?

B. parenchyma, collenchyma

1. With a very sharp, wetted razor blade cut an ultrathin slice from a liberally wetted cut surface of a potato tuber. Transfer the thinnest portion of the slice to water on a slide and add a cover slip. If properly done, the potato slice will be so thin that water will form a continuous cushion between slide and cover slip and the latter will not rock on the slide. Examine this preparation under low and high power and note the PARENCHYMA composing the tuber. In the thinnest portions of the slice study individual cells of the tissue. Place a drop or two of IKI solution on one edge of the cover slip, and with a piece of paper toweling draw some water out from the preparation at the opposite edge. The objective is to run the IKI into the tissue. After some seconds observe the parenchyma cells and note the STARCH GRAINS, stained blue-black by IKI. The grains are within food-storing plastids called LEUCOPLASTS (that is, nongreen plastids) or AMYLOPLASTS (that is, starch-storing plastids). Careful up-and-down focusing with the fine adjustment may show that a starch grain consists of several concentric oval layers of starch. Estimate the number of grains in a cell.

2. In the prepared slide of a cross section through a buttercup root, study the many PARENCHYMA cells forming extensive layers between the epidermal cells and the central (circularly arranged) tissues. What is the shape of these parenchyma cells? Are their walls thick or thin? Note the STARCH GRAINS stored in many of the cells (see also Fig. 14.3). What other structures can be identified within the cells?

3. In the stem cross section of the buttercup, similarly study the parenchyma cells situated just to the inside of the epidermal layer. How do these cells differ in size and shape from the parenchyma cells you observed in the root? What structures can be identified within the cells?

4. The stringy parts of a stalk of celery contain large numbers of COLLENCHYMA cells, packed together into soft but strong strands of tissue. Obtain a short piece of celery stalk and with a razor blade prepare an ultrathin cross-sectional slice. Put this slice on a slide with water, add a drop of IKI (which will stain the cell walls yellow), and cover with a cover slip. Under low and high power, examine particularly the collenchyma in the ridges of the stalk. Try to identify the thickened corners of the collenchyma cells.

5. In the prepared slide of the cross section through a pumpkin (*Cucurbita*) stem, identify groups of collenchyma cells at the rounded corners of the section. From the location of this tissue here and in celery, what would you consider to be the specific function of collenchyma? Check your answer against information in your text.

C. sclerenchyma

1. In a low-power view of the buttercup stem section, note the conspicuous, circularly arranged VASCULAR BUNDLES. Focus on a large one of these bundles and concentrate on the group of heavy-walled cells facing in the direction of the epidermal layer. These are SCLERENCHYMA cells, of a variety known as FIBERS. Note the MIDDLE LAMELLA between adjacent fibers. What are the walls of these cells made of? Where are the nuclei of the cells? What is the function of fibers? What is the shape of fibers in longitudinal view?

2. In the slide of a section through the leaf of the water lily *Nymphaea*, find the conspicuous star-shaped, heavy-walled SCLEREIDS, another variety of sclerenchyma cells. What is the function of sclereids? Are these living cells?

3. Put a drop of phloroglucinol solution on a slide and add to it a very small piece of the meat of a pear. Crush the tissue of the fruit in the reagent and, after a minute or two, add a cover slip and examine microscopically. Phloroglucinol produces a red color in LIGNIN, a complex organic material present in wood and also in sclerenchyma. Search for stained sclereids and describe the appearance of these supporting components.

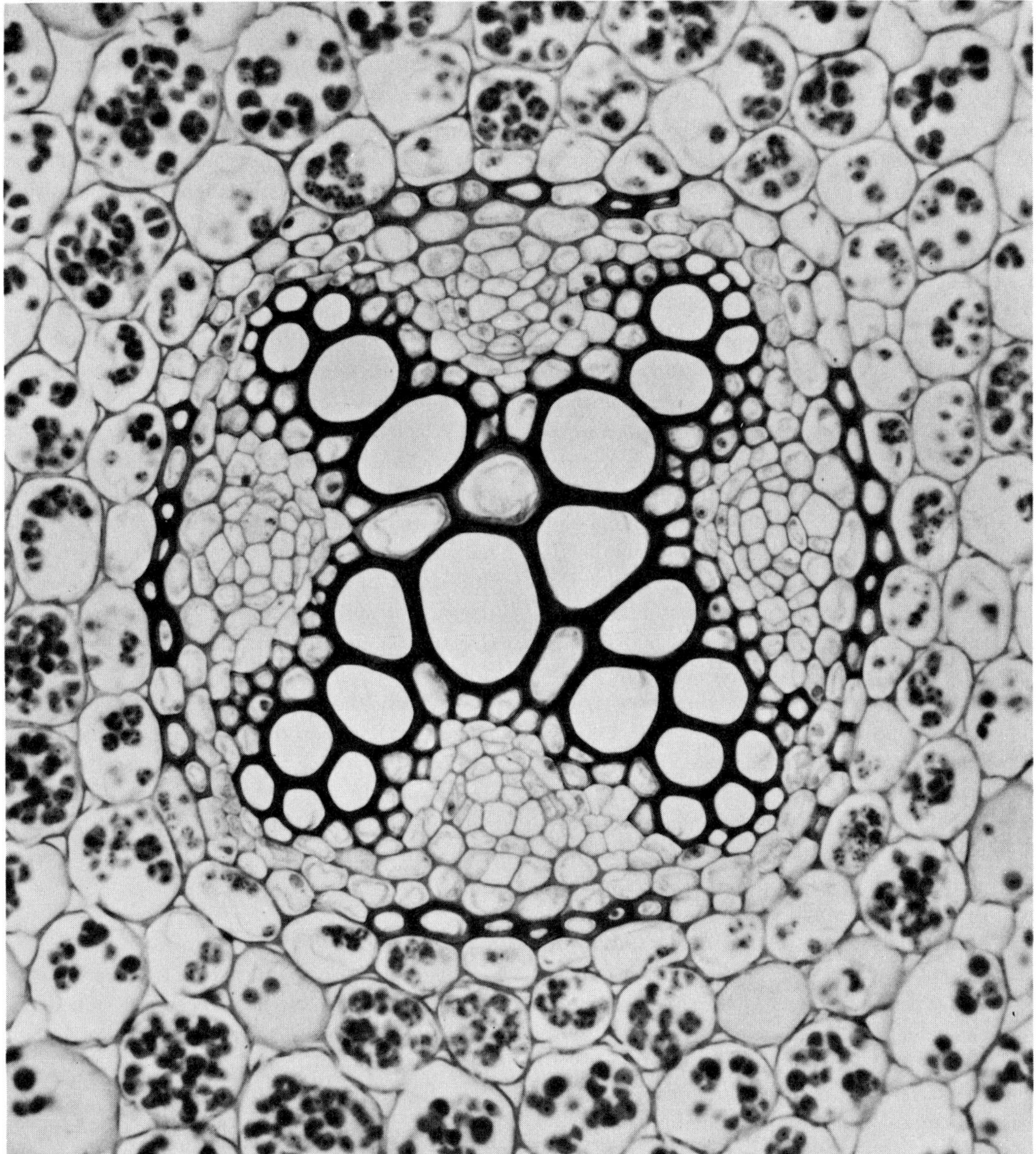

Fig. 14.3 The central portions of a cross section through the root of a buttercup. Label in detail. (Courtesy of General Biological Supply House, Inc.)

D. vascular elements

1. In the stem cross section of the buttercup, focus once more on a large vascular bundle and study the group of cells located just to the inside of the collection of fibers. Some of these cells are SIEVE-TUBE ELEMENTS, others are COMPANION CELLS, and still others are parenchyma. It may be difficult to tell which are which—what structural criteria would you look for to identify a given one of these cells precisely? What is the function of sieve-tube elements and companion cells?

Located to the inside of the cell group just studied is a group of conspicuous, fairly heavy-walled XYLEM VESSELS. The middle lamellae between adjacent vessels are quite noticeable. What is the function of such vessels?

2. In the root cross section of the buttercup, locate the large xylem vessels in the very center of the cross section, where they form an aggregate shaped like a star with several "arms." In the spaces between these arms, find the semicircular groups of thin-walled cells. These contain sieve-tube elements and companion cells (see also Fig. 14.3).

3. Study the slide or slides of cross, radial, and tangential sections of young pine stems (see also Chap. 10, "The Science of Biology"). The most conspicuous and most abundant cellular components here are TRACHEIDS. In the cross section, note that the tracheids are quite similar in appearance to the vessels studied above. The radial and tangential sections show the tracheids in longitudinal view. Note the oblique end walls of the tracheids and the numerous BORDERED PITS (seen in frontal view in the radial section and in side view in the tangential section). What is the structure of a pit? What is its function? What is the function of a tracheid?

4. Examine the slides of macerated wood. They give longitudinal views of tracheids and/or vessels. In what patterns are the secondary cell walls deposited here? Study the pits and describe their appearance. Visualize how packed groups of such wood components would appear in cross, radial, and tangential section, and correlate with the actual sections of this type just studied above.

5. Soak a small piece of filter paper in water, put a fragment of it on a slide, and tease it apart with needle and forceps. Add a drop of phloroglucinol, cover, and examine microscopically. Inasmuch as paper is a wood product, xylem components will be visible in the preparation. Compare the structure of these components with those seen in section 4, above.

E. tissues and organs

1. In the root cross section of the buttercup, identify the following tissues (proceeding from the outside toward the center, and identifying the cell types present in each of the tissues): EPIDERMIS, a single outermost layer of cells; CORTEX, composed of parenchyma; ENDODERMIS, a single layer of circularly arranged cells enclosing the central tissues (some endodermal cells are heavy-walled; others, called PASSAGE CELLS, are thin-walled); PERICYCLE, one or more layers of parenchyma just to the inside of the endodermis; XYLEM, the star-shaped group of vessels in the center; PHLOEM, the aggregations containing sieve-tube elements and companion cells, located between the arms of the xylem.

Study the positional relations of these tissues to one another in the light of the several functions performed by the tissues. Show how cooperative functioning makes the tissues collectively an organ, namely, a root.

2. Which of the above tissues can you identify in the stem cross section of the buttercup? Determine the tissue types present in the root but not in the stem and those present in the stem but not in the root. Analyze these structural differences in terms of functional differences between root and stem. Show again how cooperative functioning of its tissues makes the stem an organ.

3. Identify the tissues in the cross section of a pine stem. Focus on the very center of the section and note the PITH, a tissue containing parenchyma predominantly. Contrast the structure of this stem type with that of the buttercup root and the buttercup stem.

F. additional materials

Slides of various other cell types and tissue types in plants may have been set out. If so, study these as directed by the instructor.

IV analysis

1. Review the structural components common to all plant cells. On the basis of your observations, list structural features unique to specific plant cell types.

2. Which of the plant cell types you have studied would you regard as least specialized? Most specialized? Give reasons for your answers.

3. Cell shape is determined by various INTERNAL and EXTERNAL factors. Describe the nature of these factors, drawing in part on your actual observations of cell shapes. Show by spe-

cific example how cell shape may be important in cell function.

4. In the prepared slides you have seen, different parts within a cell were stained with different dyes. What is the chemical principle which makes it possible to stain cell structures DIFFERENTIALLY and SELECTIVELY? Can this principle be used to study cell FUNCTION?

5. Show how at least five of the different plant tissues you have examined are adapted structurally to carry out their specific functions.

6. List the tissues of a (*a*) plant stem, (*b*) plant root, from the outside inward. What cell types are present in each of these tissues?

7. Describe the (*a*) structure, (*b*) function, of each of the basic cell types of plants.

8. Describe the (*a*) structure, (*b*) function, of each of the basic stem and root tissues of plants. Show how each cell type present in a given tissue contributes to the overall function of the tissue.

9. Which organs of plants have you studied in this exercise? Show how each of its tissues contributes to the overall function of a given organ.

10. Describe the (*a*) structure, (*b*) function, of pits. What is a middle lamella? Distinguish between primary and secondary cell walls.

11. Based in part on your observations, name cell and tissue types in which each of the following may be found: (*a*) lignin, (*b*) cellulose, (*c*) chloroplasts, (*d*) leucoplasts.

12. Distinguish structurally and functionally between (*a*) fibers and sclereids, (*b*) parenchyma and collenchyma, (*c*) tracheids and vessels.

13. Name the cell types and simple tissues composing (*a*) xylem, (*b*) phloem. With the aid of your text review the development of these composite vascular tissues.

14. Name the regions within a stem and within a root in which the following may be found: (*a*) parenchyma, (*b*) sclerenchyma, (*c*) endodermis, (*d*) sieve tubes. Which mature cellular components of plants are nonliving?

15. Do both root and stem contain (*a*) endodermis, (*b*) pericycle, (*c*) pith? What plant tissues form a stele? A vascular bundle?

exercise 15 cells, tissues, organs: animals

I materials

Each student

microscope
dissecting instruments
2 blank slides, cover slips
wax pencil

Each 2 or more students

prepared slides of:

frog epidermis, surface view
liver section, pig
frog intestine, cross section
fibroelastic connective tissue
cartilage
bone, cross section of shaft
muscle, skeletal, cross and longitudinal sections
muscle, smooth, teased
muscle, cardiac (optional)
neurons
tendons
ligaments
adipose tissue
kidney tubules
human skin and/or mammalian esophagus

Class stock

blood lancets
disinfectant alcohol
pithing equipment
frogs, living adult

II introduction

Reread the introduction to the preceding exercise; the objectives outlined there for plant material apply identically to this exercise on animal material.

III directions

A. connective tissues

1. *Loose Fibroelastic Tissue*

Study the prepared slide of this tissue under low and high power. This type of connective tissue is found widely under the skin, between epithelia, and generally wherever one tissue is "connected" to another. Identify the CELLS, dispersed within the extensive INTERCELLULAR MA-

Fig. 15.1 Elastic connective tissue from the wall of an artery. (Courtesy of Carolina Biological Supply Co.)

TERIAL. How many different cell types can you identify on the basis of shape, size, and staining properties? FIBERS of various kinds are the most conspicuous components of the intercellular material. Note the thin ELASTIC FIBERS, and the tough, relatively thicker COLLAGEN FIBERS. Estimate the relative proportions of these fiber types.

How is fibroelastic tissue adapted architecturally to its function?

2. Tendons and Ligaments

Examine prepared slides of each of these two connective tissues (see also Fig. 15.1). Identify the CELLS and the INTERCELLULAR FIBERS. From their appearance, can you determine whether the fibers are elastic, collagenous, or of both types? Which type is predominant in each tissue? How are the fibers arranged, and how is this arrangement of functional significance?

3. Adipose Tissue

Examine the prepared slide of this tissue under low and high power. How much intercellular material does this tissue contain relative to cellular material? In an individual cell, identify the NUCLEUS and the FAT VACUOLE. What is the function of adipose tissue? How does the structure of the tissue adapt it for the performance of this function?

4. Cartilage

Study the slide of this connective tissue under low and high power (see also Fig. 15.2). Note the CELL ISLANDS (in spaces called LACUNAE) dispersed through the solid intercellular material (here often called MATRIX).

How does such a tissue grow? What is the general composition of the matrix? What is the adaptive advantage of the location of cartilage

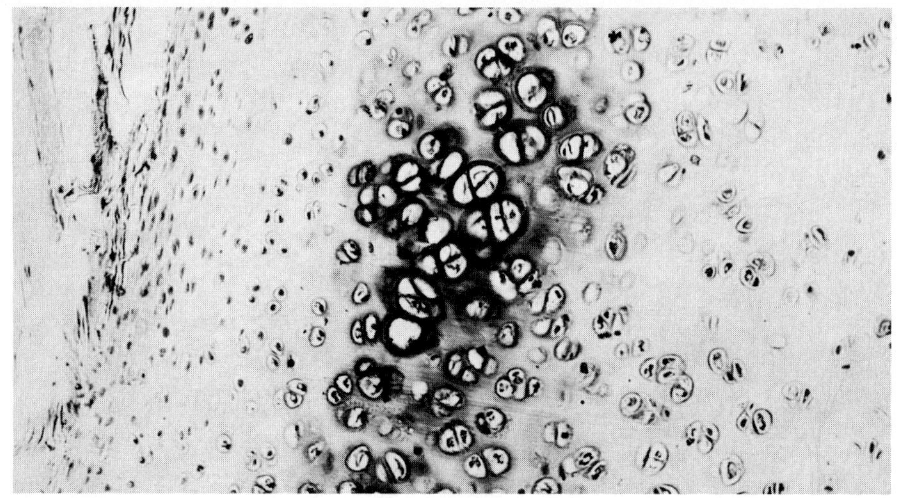

Fig. 15.2 Section through cartilage. (Courtesy of General Biological Supply House, Inc.)

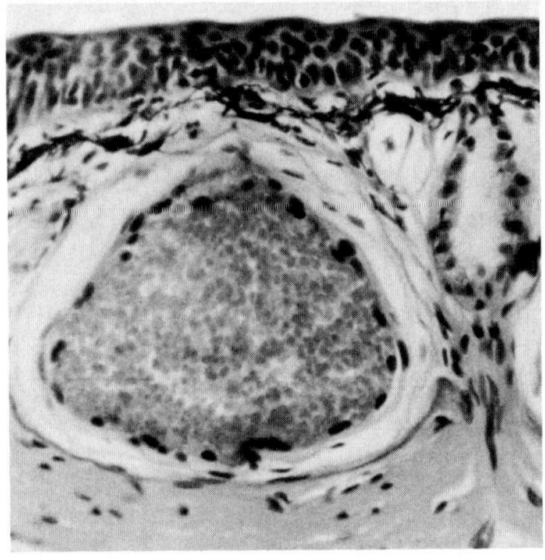

Fig. 15.3 Cross section through frog epidermis. The large body just under the skin is a gland. Note the dark dermal pigment cells under the epidermis. (Courtesy of Dr. Mac E. Hadley, Brown University.)

cells WITHIN the matrix, rather than on the outside, as a cover over the solid substance?

5. *Bone*

Study a cross section through the shaft of a long bone under low and high power. Identify a HAVERSIAN SYSTEM, that is, a unit of bone tissue consisting of concentrically arranged layers of intercellular bone substance and cell islands. In the center of such a system is a HAVERSIAN CANAL, filled with bone cells, blood, and nerve fibers. Numerous Haversian systems together form the bulk of a bone shaft.

Examine the architectural arrangement of bone tissue near the inner and outer surfaces of the shaft. How does it differ from the concentrically layered arrangement within the substance of the shaft? Identify the PERIOSTEUM, covering the outer surface and the ENDOSTEUM, covering the inner surface of the shaft. These tissues produce the bone substance near the shaft surfaces.

What is the general composition of bone substance? What is the adaptive advantage of the presence of bone cells WITHIN bone substance as well as along the surfaces? How is the internal architecture of bone geared to the function and development of this tissue?

B. epithelia

1. *Squamous Epithelium*

Study again the prepared slide of a surface view of frog epidermis, already encountered in exercise 13. Follow the pertinent directions given there. Then examine the prepared slide of a cross section through frog epidermis (see also Fig. 15.3). Note the ARRANGEMENT of the epidermal cells and the SHAPE of each cell, and identify the BASEMENT MEMBRANE on which the epidermal cells lie.

2. *Cuboidal Epithelium*

Examine the prepared slide containing sections through kidney tubules. Move the slide until you locate a section through a duct. Note the cuboidal shape of the cells forming this duct, and the BASEMENT MEMBRANE on which the cells lie.

3. *Columnar Epithelium*

In the prepared slide of a cross section through the frog intestine, focus on the innermost layer; this is the MUCOSA, a columnar epithelium (see also Fig. 15.4). The cells here form a single-layered sheet, and the cells themselves are tall and narrow.

Search within the mucosa until you find a GOBLET CELL, interspersed among other mucosal cells. These cells are so called because of their goblet-shaped clear regions which normally contain a mucous secretion. This secretion is discharged into the gut cavity.

In high power, focus on an individual mucosa cell. Identify the boundary of CELL MEMBRANE, the CYTOPLASM, and cytoplasmic GRANULES, NUCLEUS, CHROMATIN GRANULES, and NUCLEOLUS. Note the ciliated surface BRUSH BORDER on the side where the cell faces the cavity of the gut. Note the BASEMENT MEMBRANE on the side where the cell faces the underlying tissues of the gut wall.

What is the function of the mucosa, and how is the tissue adapted structurally to carry out this function?

4. *Stratified Epithelium*

Examine prepared slides of sections through human epidermis (the outer layers of skin) and/or a mammalian esophagus (see also Fig. 15.5). Note the multilayered, stratified epithelium (darkly stained) and the BASEMENT MEMBRANE on which this epithelium lies. How does cell shape vary with increasing distance from the basement membrane? Where are the oldest and the youngest cells in such an epithelium?

C. blood, muscle, and nerve cells

1. *Frog and Human Blood, Living*

The instructor will have pithed a frog, and the liver will have been dissected out and detached.

With a wax pencil mark off left and right halves on a CLEAN blank slide. Label one half F (for frog), the other M (for man). Take the liver of the freshly killed frog and draw it lightly across the F side of the slide. A faintly red film of fluid will stick to the glass. Cover this part with a cover slip. Now puncture the skin at the tip of your little finger with a sterile blood lancet, and press out a small drop of blood. Transfer this drop to the edge of the M side of the slide, and with the sharp edge of another clean blank slide draw the blood into a very thin smear. Cover this with a cover slip.

In making this preparation, only VERY LITTLE blood should be used. Any smear having more than a very faint reddish tinge can be assumed to be useless. Work RAPIDLY, so that you can make your observations before the bloods dry out.

High power: make a comparative study of RED BLOOD CORPUSCLES of frog and man. Use only

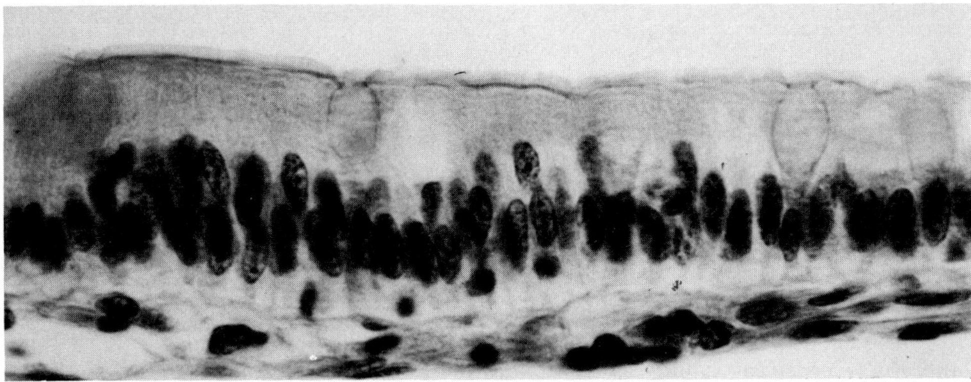

Fig. 15.4 Section through the mucosa of the frog intestine. (Courtesy of General Biological Supply House, Inc.)

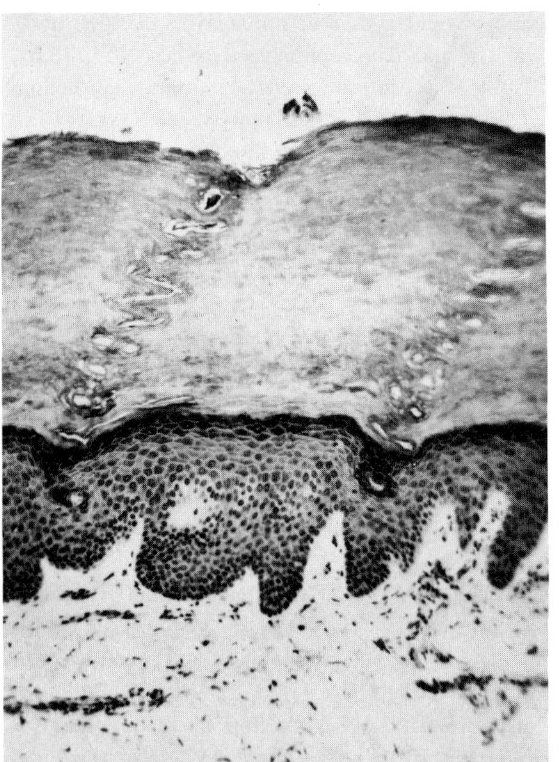

A

those parts of the slide where the smears are thinnest, that is, where individual corpuscles can be seen singly. Describe their SHAPE, and estimate their SIZE. Is a nucleus present? Can you find WHITE BLOOD CELLS, somewhat larger than red corpuscles, and BLOOD PLATELETS, small, irregularly shaped bodies? How do each of these differ structurally from the red corpuscles?

2. Muscle

Study cross and tangential sections of SKELETAL MUSCLE, under low and high power (see also Fig. 15.6). Identify an individual MUSCLE FIBER, a MULTINUCLEATE strand of protoplasm without internal cell boundaries. Within the fiber, try to make out the alternating dark and light CROSS-STRIATIONS, characteristic of skeletal muscle. If possible, note also the internal longitudinal FIBRILS running the length of a muscle fiber. Study the arrangement of several muscle fibers as a MUSCLE BUNDLE, and of several bundles as a MUSCLE. Note that the bundles are separated from one another by layers of loose connective tissue.

Study prepared slides of SMOOTH MUSCLE. Note here the distinct, spindle-shaped MUSCLE CELLS,

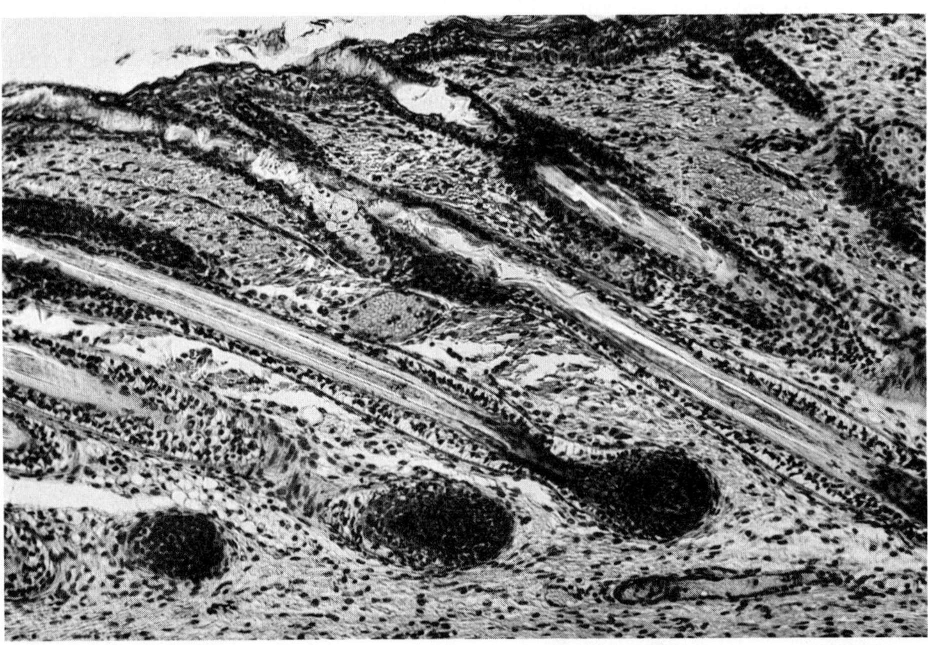

B

Fig. 15.5 Two sectional views of human skin, showing thick cornified layers and ducts of sweat glands in (A) *and portions of (scalp) hair in* (B). (A, *courtesy of Dr. W. Montagna, Oregon Regional Primate Research Center;* B, *courtesy of Carolina Biological Supply Co.*)

each with a single nucleus. Note also the absence of cross-striations but, as in skeletal muscle, the presence of internal longitudinal FIBRILS.

If available, study the prepared slide of CARDIAC MUSCLE (see Fig. 15.6). Describe the gross and fine architecture of this tissue, and contrast with that of smooth and skeletal muscle.

In terms of the shape and architecture of its components, how is muscle tissue adapted to the function of contraction? What is the advantage of the SYNCYTIAL, multinucleate organization of skeletal muscle fibers?

3. *Nerve Cells*

Study the prepared slide of nerve cells, or NEURONS. In an individual neuron, distinguish the nucleus-containing CELL BODY and the filamentous processes growing out from the cell body. These processes are called DENDRITES if they carry nerve impulses toward the cell body, AXONS if they carry impulses away from the cell body.

What is the general shape of a cell body? How is the architecture of neurons suited to their functioning?

D. organs and organ systems

1. *Human Skin*

In the skin slide already used earlier, focus again on the epidermis. Identify the outermost STRATUM CORNEUM, a sublayer of highly cornified, dead cells. Underneath it lies the prominent, darkly stained STRATUM GERMINATIVUM, the principal (stratified epithelial) tissue of the epidermis. In skin of certain body regions (for example, the palm of the hand), the stratum corneum is exceedingly thick, and between it and the stratum germinativum may be recognized two additional, thin sublayers (STRATUM LUCIDUM, STRATUM GRANULOSUM).

Underneath the whole epidermis note the thick connective tissue DERMIS, itself underlain by layers of adipose tissue and muscle. What types of connective tissues can you recognize in the dermis? Are nerves and blood vessels visible? Move the slide if necessary until you find portions of a HAIR SHAFT and/or a HAIR FOLLICLE. Note the many cell layers in the hair and the epidermis-lined canal in which the hair lies. Study the structure of a follicle; identify the DERMAL

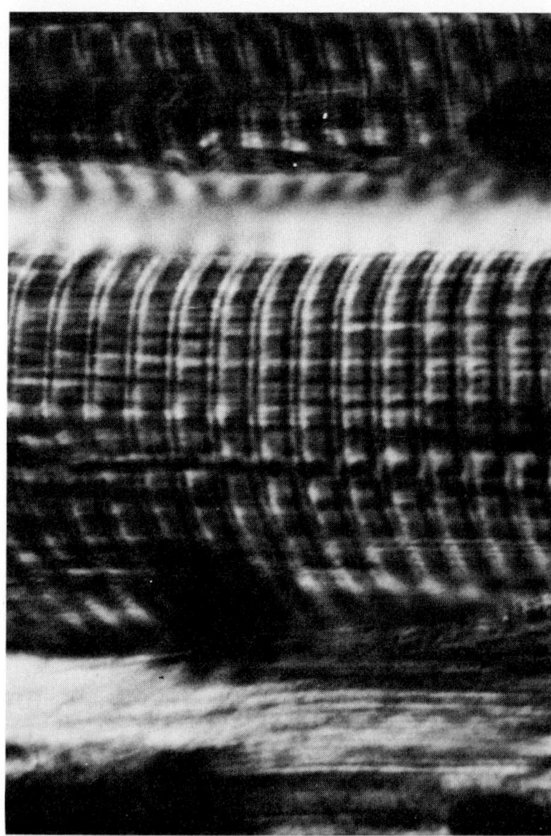

A

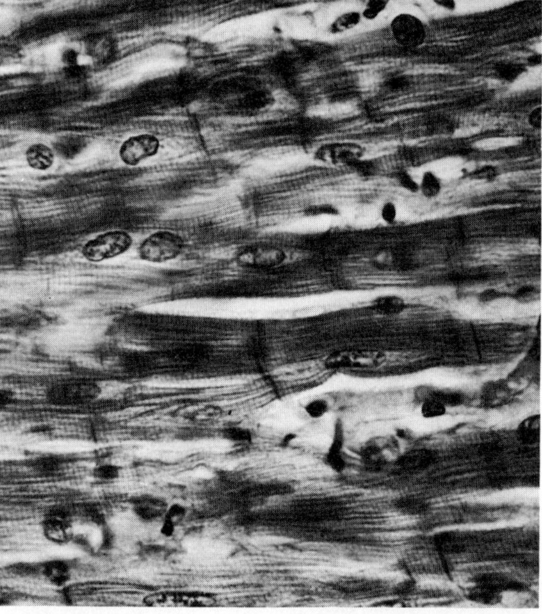

B

Fig. 15.6 A, *a high-power view of striated muscle fibers. Identify the parts.* B, *fibers of cardiac muscle. (Courtesy of General Biological Supply House, Inc.)*

PAPILLA projecting into the epidermal portion of the follicle. It is possible that the section on your slide also contains portions of SWEAT GLANDS, each composed of a coiled ball of tubules deep within the dermis and a meandering duct leading from there to the surface of the epidermis. Search your slide for such glands. Similarly look for portions of SEBACEOUS GLANDS. These are present in the dermal region along hair shafts and they open into the hair canals. What is the function of sweat and sebaceous glands?

2. Frog Intestine

In the intestine slide used above (section B3), focus on a section of gut wall. Using low and high power, study the tissue layers composing the wall, working from the inside out:

a. Mucosa. Note the many folds in this layer, already studied in detail above. Does this folded arrangement have any functional significance? Identify again the basement membrane, appearing as a thin line under the mucosal cells and separating this layer from the submucosa, that is, the tissue underneath.

b. Submucosa. This appears as a broad band and is composed of loose connective tissue. Identify the cellular and intercellular components. Describe the structural differences between cells of the submucosa and the mucosa. Locate the BLOOD VESSELS ramifying through the submucosa. What is their specific function, and what is their connection with the body circulation as a whole?

c. Muscularis. This is a layer of SMOOTH MUSCLE. Note that there are two sublayers, one with cells aligned longitudinally, the other with cells aligned circularly. Which of the two is outside the other? Concentrate on individual cells. What is their shape and size? Identify their nuclei. What is the function of the muscularis?

d. Serosa. This is the very thin outermost layer,

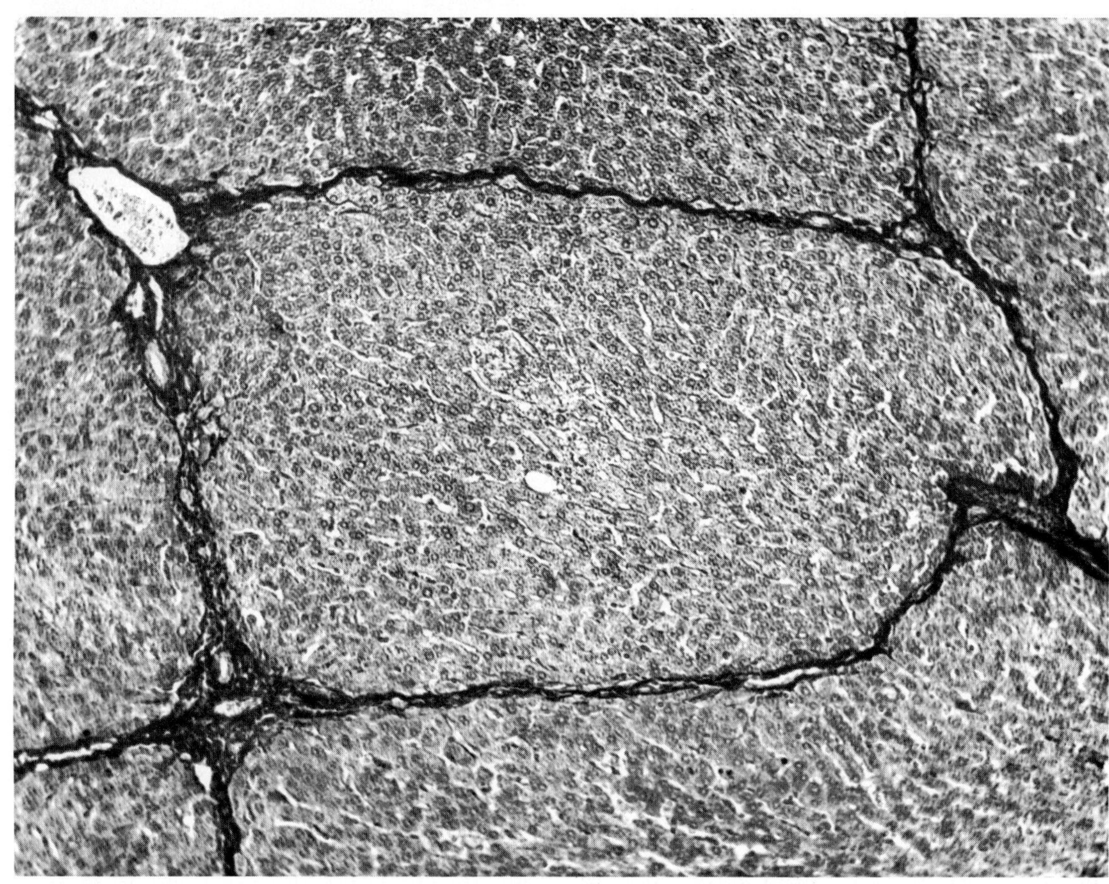

Fig. 15.7 Section through pig liver. Label in detail. (Courtesy of Carolina Biological Supply Co.)

continuous with the mesentery supporting the gut. The serosa is a squamous epithelium, seen here in cross section. Describe the shape and arrangement of the cells.

What contribution does each of these tissues make toward the overall function of the intestine?

3. *Pig Liver*

Study again the liver slide already examined in exercise I.1, this time concentrating on ALL the different tissues which compose the liver. Observe each tissue both under low and high power (see also Fig. 15.7).

The structural unit of the liver is a LOBULE, each forming a roughly pentagonal area in the slide. Each lobule is characterized by radially arranged double rows of cells, the rows converging toward a relatively large central space. In such a lobule, identify the following tissues:

a. Parenchyma. These are the liver cells proper, already examined in exercise I.1. As noted, they form radial double rows, a blood-containing sinusoid separating one double row from another. Bile capillaries are present among the cells of a double row; special techniques must be used to visualize these capillaries, and they cannot be seen in your slide. Note, however, that blood flows past a liver cell on one side and that bile is secreted on the other side.

b. Branch of hepatic vein. This is the central space in the lobule. Blood cells may be present in it. The hepatic vein carries blood AWAY from the liver, into the general circulation of the body.

c. Loose connective tissue. Such tissue will be found between adjacent lobules. These partitions are part of the STROMA, a continuous, connective tissue layer surrounding entire groups of lobules and also the liver as a whole. In the stroma are carried nerves, blood vessels, and bile channels.

d. Branch of hepatic portal vein. This vessel may be found in the connective tissue stroma between lobules, usually near one of the corners of a lobule. Two other vessels are present there. The hepatic portal branch is the largest of the three. Blood cells may be in it. The hepatic portal vein carries blood TO the liver from the intestine. Blood thus flows from this vein, through the sinusoids in the parenchyma, toward the centrally located branch of the hepatic vein.

e. Branch of hepatic artery. This vessel is in the vicinity of the branch of the hepatic portal vein. It is the smallest of the three types of ducts found in the stroma. Note that the artery has comparatively much thicker walls than the portal vein. As its name indicates, the hepatic artery supplies the liver with arterial blood from the general body circulation. This blood mixes with the venous flow from the hepatic portal vein, and the mixture eventually reaches the branch of the hepatic vein located in the center of a lobule.

f. Branch of bile duct. This is the third type of vessel found in the stroma, and its size is intermediate between that of the artery and that of the portal vein. This bile channel collects the bile secreted within a lobule and leads into larger channels, which eventually emerge from the liver as a whole as a single large bile duct.

Make sure you understand the flow patterns of bile and blood through a liver lobule and the contribution of each tissue toward the functioning of the organ as a whole.

E. additional materials

A variety of slides showing other animal tissues and organs may have been set out. If so, examine these as directed by the instructor.

IV analysis

1. On the basis of your observations, list structures common to (*a*) animal cells, (*b*) all cells. In what structural respects do most animal cells appear to differ from most plant cells? State some of the adaptive and functional consequences of such differences.

2. Which of the animal cell types you have studied would you regard as least specialized? Most specialized? Give reasons for your answers.

3. Describe the (*a*) structure, (*b*) function, of each of the following tissues: tendon, ligament, adipose tissue, stratified epithelium.

4. What is the function of each of the components of fibroelastic connective tissue? Where are such tissues found?

5. Review the fine structure of bone. What kinds of cellular components are found in it? In the light of this, should a bone be regarded as a tissue or an organ? Is it justifiable to regard cartilage as a tissue?

6. How are connective tissues distinguished from epithelia? On what basis are (*a*) epithelia, (*b*) connective tissues, classified? How are blood, muscle, and nerve cells classified as tissues? How would you classify the tissues composing a branch of the bile duct in a liver lobule?

7. Where are red blood corpuscles produced, and how do they mature? Do mature red blood cells of (*a*) the frog, (*b*) man, divide? What adaptive advantage might be served by the absence of nuclei from mature human (and which other?) red corpuscles?

8. What is the composite, overall function of the intestinal mucosa? Show how each of the mucosal cells contributes an individual bit toward this total function. What structural specializations of each mucosal cell allow the cell to carry out its specific individual function? Do these considerations agree with the definition of TISSUE?

9. What is the composite, overall function of the gut wall? Show how each of the tissue layers contributes an individual bit toward the total function. What structural specializations of each tissue allow it to carry out its specific individual function? Do these considerations agree with the definition of ORGAN?

10. Review the structure of skin and the cell-replacement processes taking place in the epidermis. Classify each of the following as a tissue or an organ: a hair, a sweat gland, a fingernail. Justify the designation of skin as an organ system.

11. Review the internal architectural organization of the liver. What are the sources of blood flowing into the organ, what is the course of blood within the organ, and how does blood leave the liver? Describe the path of bile flow.

12. State the function of each tissue found in the liver. Then show why each of these tissues is necessary, and how they cooperate in structural organization toward the overall function of the liver as a whole.

13. In what respects is the contraction of smooth muscle different from that of skeletal muscle? Relate this difference to the structural distinction between these two types of muscle tissues. Justify the designation of a whole muscle as an organ.

14. How does the multinucleate condition of a skeletal muscle fiber arise? Do muscle cells divide? Do neurons or liver cells divide? Relate the occurrence of cell divisions with cell SPECIALIZATION.

15. For each of the organs you studied in this exercise, name the organ system of which it is a part, and name some other organs composing that organ system. Name the organ systems and some of the component organs not encountered in this exercise.

exercise 16 ecology: organism and environment

I materials

Each student

microscope
millimeter ruler
medicine dropper
2 blank slides, cover slips

Each group of 4 students

funnels, ca. 50 ml capacity, as many as different soils
beakers, 250 ml, as many as funnels
50 to 100 ml 1% $CaCl_2$ solution
20 ml 1% Na_2CO_3 solution
20 ml 10% NaCl solution
1 doz test tubes
test-tube rack or holding beaker
wax pencil
universal pH testing papers

Class stock

as available locally (3 or more):
water from pond surface, fresh stock sample with organisms
water and bottom deposits from pond, fresh stock sample with organisms
water and bottom deposits from river shore, fresh stock sample with organisms
water from tide pool, fresh stock sample with organisms
water and bottom deposits from sandy ocean beach, fresh stock sample with organisms

as available locally (3 or more):

fresh stock samples of different soils, with organisms
well-dried stock samples of above soils
methyl cellulose suspension (see Appendix)
absorbent cotton
finger bowls
graduated cylinders, assorted
color chart for pH testing papers

II introduction

The aim of this exercise is to gain insight into the characteristics of certain types of ECOSYSTEMS. An ecosystem may be defined as the totality of the living and nonliving constituents of a particular geographic region, that is, the community of organisms present in the region plus the physical medium of the region itself. The "environment" of any one organism thus always includes BIOTIC, or living, components—all other organisms of the ecosystem—as well as ABIOTIC, or nonliving, components—the inanimate and dead materials of which air, water, or land are composed.

In this laboratory study of ecosystems, you will (*a*) examine samples of certain water and land environments, (*b*) examine the living organisms found in these environments, and (*c*) assess the relationship between the environments and the organisms—more specifically, try to determine how a given environment makes possible and influences the existence of certain organisms there, and how the organisms in turn influence the environment. In the course of the exercise you will observe organisms whose names you do not know and which will be unfamiliar in other respects as well. The instructor may identify some of these organisms for you. But understand that for the purposes of the exercise it is immaterial whether the name and taxonomic position of a given organism is known or not. Your primary goal should be to try to understand HOW organism x is able to live in the particular environment in which you find it. "Living" means that certain vital processes must be carried out; living in a particular environment means that this environment will impose certain limitations and conditions which may affect the method, or the ease, with which given vital processes can be carried out. Your procedure therefore should be as follows:

1. Study the nature of a given external environment; and fix in your mind the physical, chemical, and biological factors which distinguish this environment from others.
2. Fix in your mind the vital processes ANY organism must perform if it is to remain "living."
3. Correlate (1) with (2); that is, determine what problems a given environment is likely to create for an organism in the exercise of specific vital functions.
4. Then examine the appearance, internal structure, behavior, color, etc., of a given organism, and judge how many of such features you believe to be solutions to the particular problems created by the environment.

What you will in fact study is the ADAPTATION of an organism to its environment. It should be clear from the above that thinking and weighing evidence will be as important a part of this exercise as mere looking. An excellent device to guide your thinking along appropriate channels is to put yourself in the place of the organism you are observing: "If *I* were this creature, and if *I* had to live as it does, which of my human characteristics would necessarily have to become different, and why, and what changes would my new environment impose on my daily routine?"

Thus, you should begin to appreciate that life, even your own, does not take place in a vacuum but in a limiting environment with very definite and unescapable properties; and that such environments shape and have shaped living structure, function, and evolutionary histories.

III directions

A. the aquatic ecosystem

1. As available locally, fresh samples of three or more different aquatic environments are provided as class stock, for example,

a. Water from the surface layers of a richly populated freshwater pond

b. Water and bottom deposits from the shore of the pond

c. Water and bottom deposits from the shore of a flowing stream

d. Water from a marine tide pool

e. Water and bottom deposits from a sandy ocean beach

Make covered wet mounts of drops of these samples, one at a time, and study each thoroughly and without hurry, as outlined below. Select your drops from the bottom layers of the samples, where the concentration of living organisms is likely to be greatest. Also, to make your preparation as representative as possible, you may put several drops from a given sample on the same blank slide, taking the drops from different regions of the stock sample. Put cover slips over all drops. Use the low power of your microscope for general surveys of your preparations, and follow this with high-power studies of detail.

2. Conduct your microscopic examination of each sample from the following points of view. Make sketches and take notes as necessary, and record all quantitative observations in the table on page 268 (Data Sheet 6).

a. Presence of objects. What is the relative abundance of discrete objects of all kinds? Count the number of objects in three different high-power fields and record the average. How "clear" is the water in the container from which you took your drop, when viewed in bulk?

b. Types of objects. Roughly what fraction of all discrete objects seems to be living, and what fraction seems to be nonliving? What criteria do you use to make this distinction? Make counts of living and nonliving objects in three different high-power fields and record the average.

c. Nonliving material. Considering the properties and the nature of the environment of which this preparation is a sample, and from what can be seen through the microscope, what are the nonliving objects likely to be? What are they made of? Are they likely to influence the living organisms in any way? If so, how?

d. Motility of organisms. Of the living organisms, what proportion is motile and what proportion is nonmotile? Make counts of each in three different high-power fields and record the average. Do the moving organisms have different speeds? Do they move in regular or irregular paths?

If fast-moving organisms are present, prepare a clean blank slide and paint a shallow ring of methyl cellulose on it, about ¼ to ½ in. in diameter. Put a fresh drop of the sample you are studying into this ring and cover. After a few minutes, some of the methyl cellulose will have diffused centrally into the waterdrop, which will slow down or stop any fast-moving organisms.

e. Types of motility. Among motile forms, how many different patterns of movement can be distinguished? Does close observation reveal by what kinds of structures the movements are produced?

f. Shapes of organisms. How many different shapes are distinguishable among the organisms (motile as well as nonmotile)? Sketch the various shapes. Is there any correlation between shape, motility, and speed of locomotion?

g. Size of organisms. Into how many different size classes can you group the living organisms? Estimate the range of size between the extremes. Are any extremely tiny particles visible, almost at the limits of visibility? If so, what might these be?

h. Color of organisms. How many different colors are displayed by the living organisms? Is there any predominant color? Can you correlate color with motility or nonmotility?

i. Translucence of organisms. What is the relative proportion of translucent and opaque organisms? How is translucence correlated with coloration?

j. Internal structure. In the translucent forms, what details of internal structure can be made out? Make quick sketches of what can be seen. Where possible, relate behavior and structure, and identify mouth parts, alimentary tract, muscles, chloroplasts, cilia, etc., if such are present.

k. Number of species. On the basis of all the above, estimate the number of different species present, and decide tentatively how many of these are plant or plantlike species and how many are animal or animallike species.

l. Other characteristics. Describe any other noteworthy features of the visible organisms and of the preparation as a whole. Also, measure the pH of a test-tube-lot of the sample by using the universal pH testing paper provided and checking the result against the color chart supplied with the paper.

3. After examining each of the stock samples independently, as above, make an item-by-item comparison. The data table will already have been completed; use it as your source of information. Interpret the data along the lines suggested in the introduction; that is, relate every visible feature of a given organism (points a to l, above) to (*a*) a particular vital process that must be performed; (*b*) the limitations imposed by the specific environment on the performance of that process; (*c*) corresponding features in other organisms, living in other environments. Determine in this way if the similarities and differences of the features can be associated significantly with the similarities and differences of the environments. Check your understanding of this part of the exercise by trying to answer the pertinent questions in the Analysis section.

B. the terrestrial ecosystem

Three or more samples of soil, as available locally, will be provided as class stock. These soils will differ in coarseness; that is, they may contain varying proportions of gravel, loam, and fine sand; and in composition; that is, they may contain varying proportions of inorganic colloidal materials, CLAY, and organic colloidal materials, HUMUS. Of each type of soil two lots will be available—one thoroughly dry, the other, smaller one (recently collected) fresh and moist.

The first objective will be to examine the kind of physical environment that is provided by each of the soils. Soil organisms and their adaptations will be studied subsequently. Sections 1, 5, and 6 below are to be done individually by each student; in 2, 3, and 4, four students will work together as a team.

1. Microscopic Characteristics

Put a drop of water on a clean blank slide and add to the drop a pinch of DRY soil from a given sample. Leave uncovered and study microscopically under low and high power. Do this for each of the soils available; two or three can be handled on the same slide. Examine each soil from the following points of view and record your observations in the table on page 269 (Data Sheet 7).

a. Types of particles. What proportion of the particles seems to be of mineral nature, and what proportion appears to be organic detritus?

b. Shapes of particles. What proportion of particles displays jagged, irregular shapes, and what proportion has smoother surfaces and more rounded outlines? Which type is predominant?

c. Sizes of particles. What is the size range of the particles; what is the predominant and average size?

d. Other characteristics. Are the particles colored, translucent, opaque? What proportion of each? Are the particles clumped together, and if so, what is the average size of the clumps? How many particles float on the surface of the drop, and how many sink? Record any other noteworthy features.

2. Air-holding Capacity

Clean test tubes of equal size, one for each of the soils available plus an additional one. Put identical, measured volumes of water (about 5 to 6 ml) into each tube, mark the water level with a wax pencil, then add another identical volume of water to each tube and mark the new level also. Pour out the water from one of the tubes completely and drain and wipe thoroughly; this tube should be as dry as possible. From all other tubes pour out water till the level comes exactly to the halfway mark. Into the empty dry tube put dry soil of a given type, up to the halfway mark. Shake the soil down so that the allotted space is filled evenly. Pour all this soil into one of the water-containing test tubes. Shake and let settle. Mark the water level, measure distances between marks, and from these data calculate the percentage volume of air held in this particular soil. Repeat the procedure for each soil type available. Record your observations in the table.

3. Water-holding Capacity

Place funnels into beakers, as many as there are available soils. Put a small plug of water-soaked cotton into the bottom of each funnel. Measure out identical volumes of the various dry soils (about 30 to 50 ml each), and pour each of these measured samples into a different funnel. Measure out identical volumes of water (about 50 ml each) and pour over the soils in the funnels, taking care to wet each sample uniformly. Clock the time elapsed from the moment of adding the water until no more fluid drips into the beakers. Then measure the volume of fluid in each beaker. From this, calculate and record the percentage volumes of water retained by each soil. From the time data, rank the soils according to porosity and leaching speed. Save the funnel assemblies for the next section.

4. Mineral-holding Capacity

Pour a test-tube-full of 1% calcium chloride ($CaCl_2$) solution over each of the soil samples in the funnels, and discard the runoffs. Clean three or four times as many test tubes as there are funnels, and put 3 ml of 1% sodium carbonate (Na_2CO_3) solution into each. Now wash each soil by pouring one test-tube-full of water over it. Let the first portion of each runoff flow into the beakers, but catch 5 drops of the last portion in one of the tubes containing Na_2CO_3. Shake and set aside (mark the tubes so that they can be correlated with corresponding funnels). Wash the soils once more with one test-tube-full of water each, and again catch 5 drops of the last runoffs in a new set of tubes containing Na_2CO_3. For each soil sample, continue with successive washings, as above, until 5 drops of the runoff in a tube of Na_2CO_3 no longer produce a precipitate.

Record and compare the number of washings that have been necessary to reach this end-point in the different soils. On the basis of this, rank the soils according to their salt-holding capacity.

Now prepare another test tube containing 3 ml of the Na_2CO_3 solution. Pour one test-tube-full of 10% NaCl solution over the soil in one of the funnels, and catch the FIRST 5 drops of the runoff in the tube with the Na_2CO_3 solution. Shake and compare with the last wash test made on this soil. What does this test demonstrate? Explain all procedural steps in this section.

Discard the soils and clean all glassware thoroughly.

5. *Soil Organisms*

Examine each of the fresh, newly collected lots of soil for their content of living organisms. Put small samples of each soil into finger bowls, add some water, and stir to loosen and spread the contents. Watch for a few minutes to see if signs of life are noticeable with the unaided eye.

Then put a few drops of a given soil-water mixture on a blank slide, and examine uncovered under low and high power. Repeat for all other soil samples. If living organisms are found, study them from the same points of view as outlined in points a to l, section A2. Record all observations.

In both the class stocks of the fresh soils and your diluted samples in the finger bowls, measure the pH of each by again making use of the testing papers supplied. Record.

6. *Data*

When the data table is completely filled in, interpret these results on terrestrial environments in a comparative manner, just as you did in section A3 for aquatic environments. In other words, show how organisms living on or within soil solve problems of survival created by their specific terrestrial environments. Test your understanding of this part of the exercise by trying to answer the pertinent questions in the Analysis section below.

IV analysis

1. Discuss your data on organisms living in different aquatic environments. Account for the recorded differences point for point, in terms of adaptations to specific environmental conditions.

2. Discuss how each of the following features of aquatic organisms might be adaptively significant in the performance of given vital functions: size, shape, coloration, translucence, motility, nonmotility.

3. What physical and chemical conditions distinguish the oceanic and the freshwater environments? What biological processes are likely to be particularly affected by these conditions?

4. What physical and chemical conditions distinguish the following freshwater environments: open pond water, pond bottom and shore, open river water, river bottom and shore, large lake?

5. What physical and chemical conditions distinguish the following oceanic environments: open surface waters, deep waters, sea bottom, coastal waters, tidal zone?

6. How do the conditions described in items 4 and 5 vary with geographic latitude and longitude? Are any of these conditions likely to affect specific biological processes? If so, which processes and how?

7. Make a point-by-point comparison of the soils you studied. From your knowledge of conditions necessary for the performance of vital functions, which of the soils would you consider best suited for living organisms? Do you think your recorded observations on soil organisms bear this out?

8. Discuss your data on organisms living in the soils you studied. Account for the observed differences in terms of adaptations to specific environmental conditions.

9. What physical and chemical conditions uniquely characterize the environment of any organism living within soil? How are such conditions likely to affect specific vital functions, and how does this vary with soil type?

10. Discuss how each of the following features of organisms living (*a*) within soil, (*b*) on the land surface, might be adaptively significant in the performance of given vital functions: size, shape, coloration, translucence, motility, nonmotility.

11. What structural, functional, or developmental characteristics of your own body can be regarded as specific adaptations to your particular environment? What characteristics cannot be so regarded?

12. What physical and chemical conditions distinguish the following terrestrial environments: deserts, plains, woodlands, level land, sloped land, irregular hilly land?

13. Are any of the conditions you named in item 12 likely to affect specific biological processes? If so, which processes and in what ways? How do such conditions vary with geographic altitude and latitude?

14. Based in part on the data from this exercise and in part on information from lectures and reading, how would you expect (*a*) the amount, (*b*) the diversity, of living matter in an ecosystem to vary with differences in (1) environmental pH, (2) environmental temperature, (3) mineral content, (4) altitude above sea level, (5) depth below sea level, and (6) latitude?

15. Based solely on the data of this exercise, state whether water or soil environments appear to support the greater (*a*) total amount, (*b*) diversity, of living matter. Does this conclusion coincide with what is actually known for the aquatic and terrestrial components of the biosphere generally? If not, suggest possible reasons for the discrepancies.

part 3 the world of life: nonanimal organisms

exercise 17 monera and photosynthetic protista

I materials

Each student or each group of students or each class

microscopes
hand lenses
blank slides, cover slips
methyl cellulose suspension (see Appendix)
dissecting instruments
bacteria, prepared slides of bacilli, cocci, spirilla
Bacillus megatherium, living culture (see Appendix)
sterile covered petri plates with nutrient agar, 4 per student or group (see Appendix, "Agar")
IKI reagent
methylene blue stain (see Appendix)
penicillin (and/or other antibiotic) disks
Gloeocapsa, prepared slides
Nostoc, prepared slides and/or living culture
Oscillatoria, prepared slides and/or living culture
Chlamydomonas, living culture
Pandorina, prepared slides and/or living culture
Volvox, prepared slides and living culture
Chlorella, living culture
Bryopsis, prepared slides
Acetabularia, prepared slides
Protococcus, prepared slides and/or living culture
Spirogyra, prepared slides and living culture
desmids, prepared slides
Ulothrix, prepared slides and/or living culture
Ulva, prepared slides and preserved specimens
Chara, prepared slides (whole mount) and preserved specimens
Euglena, prepared slides and living culture
Vaucheria, prepared slides
diatoms, prepared slides
dinoflagellates, various, prepared slides
Ectocarpus, prepared slides
Fucus, section of tip; whole specimens
Laminaria, section of blade; whole specimens
red algae, assorted whole specimens; slides of vegetative body

II introduction

In this exercise you will examine representatives of the Monera and of most of the algal (hence predominantly photosynthetic) phyla of the Protista. The specimens will be partly living, partly preserved, partly on slides. The instructor will inform you of the working procedure to be followed. For example, the whole class may work on a single complete set of specimens, different students or groups of students studying different organisms at any given time. Alternatively, each student or specified group of students may work on a complete set of all organisms.

Study the detailed cellular structure of every organism and the supracellular organization of every multicellular organism available. If given living specimens are motile (for example, *Chlamydomonas, Euglena*), put a ring of methyl cellulose on a slide and put a drop containing the specimens into the ring; examine the organisms after they are slowed down sufficiently.

In addition to such investigations of organismic structure, study each organism also from the following standpoints (consult your text freely, for example, Chaps. 8 and 9 of "The Science of Biology"):

What is the specific way of life of the organism, how does it perform its various metabolic and self-perpetuative functions, and what are the environmental adaptations of the organism?

What taxonomic group does the organism belong to, what are the identifying characteristics of this group, and what other organisms are members of this group? Moreover, what is known or suspected about the evolutionary relation of this group to other groups?

III directions

A. monera

1. *Schizophyta: Bacteria*

a. Study a prepared slide or slides of stained bacteria under the highest power of the microscope. Identify round COCCI, rod-shaped BACILLI, and coiled SPIRILLA (see also Chap. 8, "The Science of Biology"). Identify the CELL WALL. What is the composition of such walls? Determine if any distinct organelles are visible within a bacterial cell. What organelles would you expect to be present in a bacterium?

b. A living culture of *Bacillus megatherium* is available as class stock. This organism is a very large bacterium; it is about 4 μ long and about 1 μ wide. Put a drop of water on a blank slide, and with a clean glass rod (pass it through a flame before use and cool), transfer a drop of the bacterial culture to your slide. Add a cover slip and examine microscopically. After studying the bacteria, stain them as follows. Carefully remove the cover slip and gently heat the slide (face up) over an alcohol lamp or the bulb of your desk lamp. This process will kill and fix the bacteria to the slide. Do not overheat. Then put a few drops of methylene blue stain on the slide and after about 1 min wash the dye off with water. Replace the cover slip and examine.

c. With a clean toothpick scrape material off the base of your teeth, spread these scrapings on a clean blank slide, add a drop or two of IKI reagent, cover, and examine microscopically for the presence of bacteria. The scrapings will probably contain whole cells and other debris that should not be mistaken for bacteria. What appears to be the predominant bacterial shape?

Repeat this test with scrapings from under your fingernails.

d. Perform the following classical tests. Obtain four sterile covered petri dishes containing nutrient agar, number them, and then:

1: leave the plate uncovered for ½ hr, exposed to air, then re-cover and set aside.

2: leave exposed as in (1), but before re-covering the plate put a penicillin disk (or other antibiotic-impregnated disk) on the agar.

3: spread tooth scrapings over one-half of the agar, fingernail scrapings over the other; then re-cover, identify the halves, and set aside.

4: gently press the tips of two or three of your fingers into the agar of one-half of the plate, and cover the plate; then thoroughly scrub these fingers with soap and hot water, rinse them well, and thereafter press them into the agar in the other half of the plate; re-cover, identify the halves, and set aside.

Leave all plates at room temperature for 2 or 3 days and then in the refrigerator until the next laboratory period. The instructor may specify that plates of some students be put into the refrigerator right away and that those of others be kept at 37°C for 2 or 3 days. The effect of temperature on microbial growth may be studied in this manner. The instructor may also keep a covered, untreated plate as a class control. All plates will be examined in the following laboratory period (see exercise 18).

2. Cyanophyta: Blue-green Algae

Study living specimens and/or prepared slides of *Gloeocapsa, Nostoc,* and *Oscillatoria,* as available. Identify the GELATINOUS SECRETIONS and the CELLS imbedded in them. What are the growth patterns in each case? What cellular organelles can you identify? In which genus can you find enlarged HETEROCYSTS? What are HORMOGONES?

B. chlorophyta: green algae

1. Flagellate Line: Chlamydomonas, Pandorina, Volvox

Study living specimens and/or prepared slides, as available. In *Chlamydomonas,* what cellular structures can you identify? In *Pandorina* and *Volvox,* what are the patterns of cell arrangement? How is movement produced? In *Volvox,* what are the smaller spheres inside many of the organisms?

2. Coccine Line: Chlorella, Bryopsis, Acetabularia

Study living specimens and/or prepared slides, as available. In *Chlorella,* what cell structures can you identify? Describe the structures of *Bryopsis* and *Acetabularia.* How do these organisms grow in size? How many (*a*) nuclei, (*b*) cells, are present? What defines a coccine state of existence?

3. Sporine Line: Protococcus, Spirogyra, Desmids, Ulothrix, Ulva

Study living specimens and/or prepared slides, as available. Examine the (*a*) cell structure, (*b*) growth pattern, of each organism. Where does each of these organisms live? What identifies a sporine state of existence?

C. charophyta: stoneworts

Examine the preserved specimens and/or the prepared whole mount of *Chara.* Describe the anatomical organization of this organism. Where does it live, and how is it adapted to this environment? What characteristics make *Chara* a member of (*a*) the green-line algae, (*b*) a quite unique protistan phylum?

D. euglenophyta: euglenoid algae

Examine living specimens and/or prepared slides of *Euglena.* In living organisms, describe the motion and the changes of body shape during motion. How is locomotion produced? What cell structures can you identify? How do the organisms procure nutrients? What characteristics distinguish this algal phylum?

E. chrysophyta: golden-brown algae

1. Xanthophyceae: Vaucheria

Examine the prepared slide and study the structure of *Vaucheria.* What is the growth pattern? How many (*a*) nuclei, (*b*) cells, are present? Is the organism flagellate, coccoid, or tetrasporine? Where does *Vaucheria* live? What are its pigments?

2. Bacillariophyceae: Diatoms

Study prepared slides and/or living specimens under low and high power. Describe the shape and structure of the cell walls. What are the cell walls made of? Where are diatoms found? What state of existence do these organisms represent?

F. pyrrophyta: fire algae

Examine the prepared slides of dinoflagellates. One of the genera is likely to be *Ceratium,* an armored type with "spines" projecting from the body. How many cells is a dinoflagellate composed of? Can you make out the flagella? If so, how many are there on each organism? Are chloroplasts present? What state of existence do dinoflagellates represent? What other kinds of algae are included among the pyrrophytes?

G. phaeophyta: brown algae

Examine the preserved or fresh specimens and the prepared slides of *Ectocarpus, Fucus,* and *Laminaria,* as available. Describe the (1) gross anatomical organization, (2) microscopic cellular organization, of each. In *Fucus,* note the AIR BLADDERS, the RECEPTACLES, and the DICHOTOMOUS growth pattern. What and where are the CONCEPTACLES? In *Laminaria,* identify HOLDFAST, STIPE, BLADE. Where does each organism live? What are the group characteristics of brown algae?

H. rhodophyta: red algae

Examine the preserved or fresh specimens and the prepared slides of various red algae, as available. Describe the (1) gross anatomical organization, (2) microscopic cellular organization, of the group. Where do these organisms live? What are the group characteristics of the phylum?

IV analysis

1. In what structural respects are bacteria and blue-green algae different from other organisms you have studied? Review the various general methods by which bacteria obtain nourishment.

2. What are the (*a*) shapes of individual cells, (*b*) colonial growth patterns, of bacteria and blue-green algae? What are the taxonomic subgroups of bacteria and cyanophytes, and what are the characteristics of these subgroups? In what different ways do various moneran groups move?

3. How does a virus differ from a bacterium? Is a virus an organism? A cell? Living?

4. What characteristics identify the Protista? How are Protista distinguished from other categories of organisms? What pigments are found in each of the algal phyla? What are the (*a*) food-storage compounds, (*b*) cell-wall compounds, of each of these phyla?

5. Show (*a*) where each of the organisms you have studied lives in nature, (*b*) in what ways each organism is specialized and adapted to its way of life in a particular environment.

6. Describe the various kinds of cell surfaces you have observed. Summarize the functions of cell surfaces. What is the difference between a cell membrane and a cell wall? Does each organism you saw have cell membranes? Cell walls?

7. Show how each of the organisms you have studied carries out the following functions: (*a*) gas exchange, (*b*) excretion and maintenance of internal water balance, (*c*) internal transport of materials, (*d*) protective activities and steady-state activities in general.

8. Review the methods of (*a*) nutrition, (*b*) locomotion, encountered among the algal groups you have seen. What other methods occur in the living world?

9. Characterize the flagellate, amoeboid, coccine, and sporine states of Protista. Which of these states occur in each of the algal phyla? Name one specific representative genus for each state in each phylum.

10. What different flagellation patterns characterize each of the algal phyla? Review the presumed evolutionary interrelations of all algal groups (consult your text if necessary).

11. List the group characteristics of the (*a*) green-line, (*b*) brown-line, (*c*) red-line, algae. Which phyla are included in each group?

12. Describe the (*a*) cellular structure, (*b*) body structure, of at least one representative genus for each algal phylum. Show how this genus is adapted to its specific environment.

13. On the basis of your observations, show how brown algae are adapted to live in shallower water, nearer to shore, than red algae. Do either brown or red algae occur in fresh water?

14. Which of the algae you have studied are (*a*) major components of plankton, (*b*) benthonic? Which of the groups include (*a*) unicellular types only, (*b*) multicellular types only, (*c*) both unicellular and multicellular types?

15. Which of the algal types you have studied are related to forms that are nearly identical except that photosynthetic capacity is lacking? Which types exhibit more than one form of nutrition simultaneously?

exercise 18 monera and nonphotosynthetic protista

I materials

Each student or each group of students or each class

microscopes
hand lenses
blank slides, cover slips
methyl cellulose suspension
dissecting instruments
IKI reagent
methylene blue stain
Physarum, living culture
Stemonitis, prepared slides (whole mount)
slime molds, assorted other material
Saprolegnia, prepared slides (whole mount)
Rhizopus, prepared slides and living
Penicillium, prepared slides (whole mount)
yeast, prepared slides and living
Peziza, prepared slides of fruiting body
Tuber, prepared slides of fruiting body
Coprinus, section through whole fruiting body
mushrooms, assorted specimens
lichens, prepared slides and living specimens
fungi, assorted other material
Trichomonas, prepared slides
Trypanosoma, prepared slides
zooflagellates, prepared slides of various types
Pelomyxa, living culture
Arcella, living culture
Difflugia, living culture
Actinosphaerium, living culture
Foraminifera, prepared slides
Radiolaria, prepared slides
Paramecium, prepared slides and living culture
Blepharisma, living culture
Stentor coeruleus, prepared slides and living culture
Vorticella, prepared slides and living culture
Euplotes, prepared slides and living culture

II introduction

Apart from the agar plates prepared in the preceding exercise, the materials to be studied now are representatives of the fungi, the slime molds, and the protozoa, that is, the heterotrophic, nonphotosynthetic Protista. Reread the introduction to the preceding exercise; the guidelines set forth there for the study of algae apply here equally for the examination of the other Protista. Consult your text again as desired (for example, Chap. 9, "The Science of Biology").

III directions

A. monera

Obtain your petri plates from the previous week and examine the growths on the agar with the unaided eye and a hand lens. How have different temperatures affected the amount of growth? Distinguish and record SIZES, SHAPES, and COLORS of colonies. Study scrapings of each type of colony under the microscope (use IKI and/or methylene blue staining if desired), and ascertain which growths are bacterial, which fungal. Can colonies of bacteria and of molds be distinguished with the unaided eye? In the bacterial colonies, which cellular shapes appear to predominate?

Save the plates until after you have completed section C below, on fungi. Then try to identify some of the fungal growths on the agar.

B. phylum myxophyta: slime molds

1. *Physarum*

Examine a living culture of this myxomycete. What stage of the life cycle is represented? What is the microscopic organization of a PLASMODIUM? How does the organism (*a*) obtain nutrients, (*b*) move, (*c*) grow? What are the group characteristics of (*a*) myxomycetes, (*b*) slime molds as a whole? What state of existence do slime molds exemplify?

2. *Stemonitis, Other Slime Molds*

Examine the specimens and/or prepared slides of fruiting bodies of *Stemonitis* and other slime molds, as available. At what point in the life cycle, and how, are fruiting bodies formed? What is the (*a*) general structure, (*b*) specific function, of a fruiting body? How does the structure of fruiting bodies vary in different slime molds?

C. phylum mycophyta: fungi

1. *Phycomycetes: Saprolegnia (Water Mold), Rhizopus (Bread Mold)*

Study living specimens and prepared slides of these fungi, as available. What is a HYPHA and what is its structural organization? How many (*a*) nuclei, (*b*) cells, are present in a vegetative hypha? What is a MYCELIUM? How does it grow? Where do *Saprolegnia* and *Rhizopus* live? How do they obtain nutrients? Do the organisms form fruiting bodies? Describe their structural organization.

2. *Ascomycetes: Saccharomyces (Yeast), Penicillium (Blue Mold), Peziza (Cup Fungus), Tuber (Truffle), Other Representatives*

Study living specimens and prepared slides of these organisms, as available. What structural parts can you identify in yeast? Describe the structural organization of *Penicillium*. In this genus note the CONIDIA, chains of spores formed at the ends of many of the hyphae. Are transverse cell walls present in the hyphae? In the slides of sections through the fruiting bodies of cup fungi and truffles, study the hyphal organization of the fruiting bodies, and note the conspicuous layers of elongated spore sacs, or ASCI. Each of the latter contains a row of eight ASCOSPORES, though in each case all eight may not be apparent in the section. What general types of fruiting bodies are known in Ascomycetes? Where do the Ascomycetes you examined live and how do they obtain nutrients?

3. *Basidiomycetes: Coprinus, Agaricus, Other Representatives*

Study the prepared slide of a section through the fruiting body of *Coprinus*. Describe the anatomical organization. Identify the BASIDIA and the BASIDIOSPORES. In preserved or fresh mushrooms, identify the stalk and cap of the fruiting body and note the gills on the underside of the cap. Tease a small piece of a gill apart in a drop of water on a slide, cover, and examine microscopically. What is a gill composed of? Can you see any basidiospores? What other groups of fungi belong to the Basidiomycetes? How do their fruiting bodies differ in architecture? Where does each of these groups live?

4. *Lichens*

Study the living specimens and/or prepared

slides of various lichens. If fresh material is available, tease a small piece of a lichen in a drop of water on a slide, cover, and examine the preparation. How are these organisms constructed? What taxonomic groups do the algal and fungal members of lichens usually belong to? How does each of the two members of a lichen benefit from the symbiotic association?

D. phylum protozoa

1. *Subphylum Mastigophora: Trichomonas, Trypanosoma, Other Zooflagellates*

Study the prepared slides of these organisms. What cell structures can you identify? Where do these zooflagellates live and how do they obtain nutrients? What are the group characteristics of zooflagellates? What justifies their inclusion in the category Protista?

2. *Subphylum Sarcodina*

CLASS ACTINOPODEA—stiff supporting spikes (AXONEMES) present within the pseudopodia: *Actinosphaerium*, Radiolaria

Study living specimens of *Actinosphaerium* under the microscope. Note the halo of AXOPODIA, that is, pseudopodia with axonemes. Can you make out the body of the cells? How and on what does this organism feed? Examine the prepared slide of Radiolaria. What is the architecture and composition of the shells of these organisms? How do these protozoa (1) move, (2) feed? Where do they live?

CLASS RHIZOPODEA—pseudopodia are unsupported: *Pelomyxa, Arcella, Difflugia,* Foraminifera; also *Amoeba* (see exercise 13)

Study living specimens of each of these organisms on slides without cover slips. How are the shells of *Arcella* and *Difflugia* constructed? Observe the pseudopodial locomotion. Observe the locomotion of *Pelomyxa* for several minutes. Compare the behavior and internal structure of *Pelomyxa* and *Amoeba* (recall your observations and notes on the latter from exercise 13 or reexamine the organism if specimens are available). Is *Pelomyxa* simply a larger edition of *Amoeba*? How many nuclei are present in *Pelomyxa*?

Paramecia are the favorite food of *Pelomyxa*. If paramecia are present in your preparation, do not disturb the slide for some minutes and observe. You may be able to see how *Pelomyxa* feeds. If so, describe this process.

Using a pair of needles from your dissecting kit and a hand lens or a dissecting microscope, try to spear a pelomyxa with one needle and cut the animal in half with the other. Then examine under low power and observe how each half behaves.

Examine the prepared slide of Foraminifera. What is the architecture and chemical composition of the shells? How do these organisms (1) move, (2) feed? Where do they live?

3. *Subphylum Ciliophora: Paramecium, Blepharisma, Euplotes, Vorticella; Also Stentor (See Exercise 13)*

Study living specimens and prepared slides of these ciliates as available. Use methyl cellulose where necessary to slow the organisms down. Recall your observations and notes on *Stentor* from exercise 13 or reexamine this organism if specimens are available. In *Paramecium* and *Blepharisma*, identify BODY CILIA, GULLET REGION, CONTRACTILE VACUOLES, and, if possible, MACRONUCLEI. In a prepared slide of stained paramecia, identify the MACRONUCLEUS and, if possible, the MICRONUCLEUS, a small, darkly stained body quite close to the macronucleus. How does *Euplotes* move? Describe the structure and the behavior of *Vorticella*. What characteristics distinguish ciliates as a whole from other protozoa?

IV analysis

1. Describe the general life cycle of slime molds. What are the taxonomic subgroups of slime molds? Describe the structural organization and the specific life cycle of one representative genus for each of these subgroups.

2. What are the identifying characteristics of (*a*) fungi, (*b*) each taxonomic subgroup of fungi? Describe the general body organization of a fungus. What are the microscopic characteristics of a hypha? Do fungi possess true cells? What protistan state of existence do fungi exemplify?

3. What groups of fungi belong to the Phycomycetes? Describe the specific body organization of such fungi. Name representative genera of (*a*) free-living, (*b*) parasitic, Phycomycetes.

4. What groups of fungi belong to the Ascomycetes? Describe the specific body organization of such fungi. Name representative genera of (*a*) free-living, (*b*) parasitic, Ascomycetes.

5. What types of fruiting bodies are formed by Ascomycetes? Do your actual observations of yeasts give evidence of the fungal nature of these organisms? What are conidia?

6. What groups of fungi belong to the Basidiomycetes? Describe the specific body organization of such fungi. Name representative genera of free-living and parasitic Basidiomycetes. What is the structure of a mushroom? What is the genus name of the typical mushroom of commerce?

7. What are the group characteristics of the protozoan phylum as a whole and what characteristics identify each subphylum?

8. If not otherwise specified, which protistan phyla could an amoeba belong to? A flagellate unicell? Has man evolved from amoebae?

9. Describe the cell structure of (*a*) *Paramecium*, (*b*) *Difflugia*, (*c*) *Vorticella*. Show why it would be completely erroneous to regard any of the unicellular organisms you have studied as representing a "simple" cell.

10. In what respects is the cellular structure of ciliates quite unique? What are likely adaptive advantages of these unique characteristics?

11. What protistan states of existence do the various protozoan groups exemplify? Review the likely evolutionary interrelations of (*a*) protozoan groups to one another, (*b*) protozoa as a whole to other nonphotosynthetic protists, (*c*) all nonphotosynthetic protists as a whole to the algae.

12. Review the chemical nature of (*a*) the cell surfaces, (*b*) the food storage compounds, (*c*) the flagellation patterns, (*d*) the forms of species dispersal or locomotion, in nonphotosynthetic protists.

13. What forms of nutrition are encountered among nonphotosynthetic protists? Which forms occur in which groups? Do two or more forms occur simultaneously in given types?

14. Ascertain the species number of each protistan phylum. Compare the relative adaptive success of the whole protistan category with that of the other main categories of organisms. Which protistan groups or types are of particular importance in the ecology of (*a*) nature generally, (*b*) man specifically? In what ways?

15. Review the data on what is believed to have been (*a*) the evolutionary source of Protista, (*b*) the process by which protistan ancestors might have given rise to the Metaphyta and Metazoa.

exercise 19 metaphyta: bryophytes

I materials

Each student

microscope
hand lens
dissecting instruments

Each 1 or 2 students

prepared slides of:

moss protonema, whole mount
moss stem, cross section
moss leaf, cross section
moss sporophyte, cross section of stalk
moss sporophyte, longitudinal section of capsule
Sphagnum, prepared mount of leaf
Marchantia, cross section of thallus
Marchantia, longitudinal section of sporophyte
Anthoceros, cross section of thallus
Anthoceros, cross section of capsule

Class stock

moss gametophytes, living (potted) or preserved
moss sporophytes, attached to gametophytes
Sphagnum gametophytes, preserved
Marchantia thalli, living (potted) or preserved
Marchantia thalli with mature sex organs, living or preserved
Porella or other foliose liverworts, preserved
Riccia, aquatic species, preserved
Anthoceros, living or preserved

II introduction

This study of representative bryophytes will concentrate primarily on the VEGETATIVE structure of the gametophyte and sporophyte stages; reproductive features will be examined separately in a later exercise. Nevertheless, familiarize yourself with the GENERAL pattern of the bryophyte life cycle, in sufficient detail to allow you to understand the significance of the gametophyte and sporophyte generations and the dominance of the gametophytes in bryophyte life histories (consult your text as warranted; for example, Chap. 10, "The Science of Biology").

III directions

A. class bryopsida: mosses

1. The Protonema

Study the prepared slide of a whole mount of a moss protonema. Identify the PROTONEMAL FILAMENT, the RHIZOIDS, the BUDS, and the young SHOOTS. Which of the cells are photosynthetic? What is the shape of the cells in the rhizoids? What life-cycle stage does a protonema represent? What structure gives rise to a protonema?

2. The Gametophyte

a. Obtain a mature shoot of a living moss from the potted specimens and examine this shoot with hand lens and dissecting instruments. Identify the STEM and the LEAVES. Do the leaves have midribs? In what pattern are the leaves attached to the stem? Examine the upper tip of the shoot: are SEX ORGANS present? How does such a shoot develop? What subsequent life-cycle stage will it give rise to?

b. Study the prepared slide of a cross section through the stem of a moss shoot. Identify the EPIDERMIS, the thick-walled sclerenchymalike cells forming the CORTEX, and the thin-walled parenchymalike cells in the CORE. What structural details can you recognize in the cells of each of these tissues? What are the functional roles of these tissues? Are stomata present in the epidermis?

c. Study the prepared slide of a section through a leaf of a moss. Along the upper surface, identify the upright COLUMNS OF CELLS and the AIR SPACES between the columns. What is the function of this tissue? Describe the organization of the other tissues present.

3. The Sporophyte

a. Examine a whole shoot with an attached sporophyte or a separate sporophyte. Using a hand lens, identify the CAPSULE and the STALK. Where is the FOOT? Dissect the capsule with needles and see if you can identify the outer hoodlike cap, or CALYPTRA, and the SPORANGIUM, partly hidden under the calyptra. How does the calyptra form?

b. Study the prepared slide of a cross section through a sporophyte stalk. Identify the EPIDERMIS and the PARENCHYMATOUS CELLS in the interior. Are STOMATA present? Are chloroplasts present? Study the prepared slide of a longitudinal section through a capsule. Identify the SPORANGIAL WALL, the COLUMELLA (which forms a parenchymatous central axis), and the SPORE-PRODUCING TISSUE between the outer wall and the columella. How are mature spores of mosses dispersed?

4. Sphagnum, Other Mosses

Examine preserved whole specimens or portions of the gametophyte of the peat moss *Sphagnum.* Note the broad protonema and the branched upright shoots. In a prepared slide of a leaf, identify the chloroplast-containing cells and the rows of water-filled cell hulls. In what ways are these features adaptive?

If other material on mosses is available, examine it as directed by the instructor.

B. class hepaticopsida: liverworts

1. The Gametophyte

a. Examine a living or preserved thallus of *Marchantia* with a hand lens. Which is the upper and which the lower side? Identify the RHIZOIDS. Does the thallus possess a midrib? On the upper surface, identify the fine DIAMOND-SHAPED MARKINGS and make a mental note of them for reference below. Note the DICHOTOMOUS growth pattern of the thallus, and locate the position of a GROWING POINT, in the notch between two branch lobes. How do new branch lobes form?

b. Study the prepared slide of a section through a *Marchantia* thallus. Locate the upper and lower surfaces, and identify, from the upper surface downward, the UPPER EPIDERMIS, and the AIR PORES in it (can you correlate the diamond-shaped markings seen above with the structural organization of the epidermis?); the PHOTOSYNTHETIC ZONE, with AIR SPACES communicating with the air pores; the large parenchymatous cells forming a STORAGE AND CONDUCTING ZONE; and the LOWER EPIDERMIS, from which project RHIZOIDS and thicker SCALES. What is the function of each of these tissues?

2. The Sporophyte

a. Examine living or preserved specimens of *Marchantia* bearing stalked receptacles with sex organs. Locate the position of the female sex organs, on the underside of receptacles shaped like radial groups of fingers.

b. Study the prepared slide of a longitudinal section through a sporophyte of *Marchantia.* Identify the FOOT, the STALK, and the CAPSULE. In the capsule, identify the SPORANGIAL WALL, the SPOROGENOUS TISSUE and the SPORES, and the ELATERS interspersed among the spores. What is the function of elaters? Are chloroplasts present in any tissue of the sporophyte? Contrast the structure of the sporophytes of mosses and liverworts.

3. *Other Liverworts*

Study preserved specimens of *Porella* or other available FOLIOSE liverworts and contrast their structure with that of thallose types like *Marchantia.* Study specimens or slides of gametophytes of aquatic liverworts such as *Riccia natans* or *R. fluitans,* and again compare with *Marchantia.* Are the aquatic species foliose or thallose?

Examine any other liverwort material available as directed by the instructor.

C. class anthoceropsida: hornworts

1. *The Gametophyte*

Examine living or preserved specimens of *Anthoceros.* What are the structural characteristics of the thallus? Study a prepared slide of a section through a thallus. What tissues can you identify? How does the internal structural complexity compare with that of liverwort thalli? How many chloroplasts per cell are present?

2. *The Sporophyte*

Examine a whole mount of an *Anthoceros* sporophyte. Identify FOOT and CAPSULE. How does the organization of the capsule differ from that in mosses and liverworts?

Study the prepared slide of a cross section through the capsule. Identify EPIDERMIS, with external CUTICLE and GUARD CELLS enclosing STOMATA; parenchymatous CORTEX, with AIR SPACES; SPOROGENOUS TISSUE, SPORES, and ELATERS; and the central COLUMELLA. Which of these tissues are photosynthetic? How does the structural complexity of the sporophyte compare with that of the (*a*) gametophyte, (*b*) moss and liverwort sporophyte?

IV analysis

1. Describe the general life-cycle pattern of bryophytes. Define GAMETOPHYTE, SPOROPHYTE. In what sense is the gametophyte stage of bryophytes dominant?

2. Describe the external and internal structure of the moss (*a*) gametophyte, (*b*) sporophyte. How does each stage obtain nutrients? What is a thallus?

3. Describe the external and internal structure of the *Marchantia* gametophyte. What are the functions of each of the body parts? Distinguish between THALLOSE and FOLIOSE thalli. Give an example of each.

4. Describe the structure of the *Marchantia* sporophyte. Compare this sporophyte with that of mosses.

5. Describe the external and internal structure of the *Anthoceros* (*a*) gametophyte, (*b*) sporophyte. Compare each stage with the corresponding stages of liverworts. What aspect of hornwort cell structure is unique for bryophytes?

6. Compare the gametophytes of mosses, liverworts, and hornworts. Which is structurally most complex? Least complex? Make similar comparisons of the sporophytes.

7. How are spores discharged in each of the bryophyte classes? What are elaters?

8. Define *dichotomous growth, growing point.* What growth patterns other than that of dichotomy are encountered among plants?

9. List the diagnostic taxonomic characteristics of (*a*) the three bryophyte classes, (*b*) bryophytes as a whole. What characteristics make bryophytes members of the Metaphyta? How are Metaphyta distinguished from Protista?

10. In what environments do bryophytes live? What are their adaptations to these environments? What is the general importance of bryophytes in the economy of terrestrial life?

exercise 20 metaphyta: tracheophytes

I materials

Each student

microscope
hand lens
dissecting instruments

Each 1 or 2 students

prepared slides of:

Psilotum, cross section of stem
Lycopodium, cross section of stem
Selaginella, cross section of stem
Selaginella, longitudinal section of strobilus
Equisetum, cross section of stem
fern leaf with sorus, section
Osmunda, cross section of root
Dicksonia, cross section of rhizome
Polypodium, cross section of rhizome

Class stock

living or preserved specimens of:

Psilotum
Lycopodium
Selaginella
Equisetum
ferns

II introduction

Inasmuch as the dominant life-cycle stage of all tracheophytes is the sporophyte, that stage will be emphasized in this exercise; all plants and plant parts to be examined will be sporophytic. Nevertheless, with the aid of your text (for example, Chap. 10, "The Science of Biology"), familiarize yourself with the general pattern of the basic tracheophyte life cycle, which, as in bryophytes, includes sporophytic as well as gametophytic stages. The latter, as also the reproductive processes of tracheophytes, will be studied in detail later.

You will find that the cellular composition of most of the basic tissues of stems, roots, and leaves are quite similar in all tracheophytes. This cellular composition has already been studied in exercise 14 and may profitably be reviewed at this juncture. You will also find, however, that the patterns in which the basic tissues are arranged differ importantly in different body parts and in different tracheophyte groups. Such variations of vegetative structure, internal as well as external, should receive your primary attention in the course of this study.

III directions

A. subphylum psilopsida: psilopsids

1. Examine preserved specimens of *Psilotum*. Note the horizontal underground RHIZOME, the upright AERIAL STEMS with dichotomous branch patterns, and the bulbous SPORANGIA. Are leaves present? Where do psilopsids live and how are the plants adapted to this environment? How do psilopsids absorb nutrients from the soil?

2. Study the prepared slide of a cross section through an aerial stem of *Psilotum* (see also Chap. 10, "The Science of Biology"). Identify, from the outside inward, EPIDERMIS, with CUTICLE and STOMATA; extensive CORTEX, largely parenchymatous but containing a layer of sclerenchyma; the STELE in the core, consisting of outer PHLOEM and central XYLEM. This is a PROTOSTELE, that is, a stele without pith. Note that the cross-sectional arrangement of the stelar tissues is star-shaped. Steles of this type are called ACTINOSTELES, and *Psilotum* thus possesses an ACTINOSTELIC PROTOSTELE.

B. subphylum lycopsida: club mosses, ground pines

1. Lycopodium, the Club Moss

a. If available, examine fresh or preserved specimens of the club moss *Lycopodium*. Identify the horizontal underground RHIZOME, the ROOTS and the AERIAL STEMS growing out from the rhizome, and the LEAVES on the aerial stems. What kinds of leaves are these? Are sporangium-bearing cones, or STROBILI, present? If so, what is their location? What is the branch pattern of the aerial stems? Where do club mosses live?

b. Study the prepared slide of a cross section through a stem of *Lycopodium* (see also Chap. 10, "The Science of Biology"). Identify EPIDERMIS, CORTEX, STELE, and the PERICYCLE, PHLOEM, and XYLEM within the stele. Is an ENDODERMIS present? What cell types characterize each of these stem tissues? Is this stem protostelic? What is the geometric arrangement of the vascular tissues? A banded appearance of these tissues identifies a so-called PLECTOSTELE, a variant form of a protostele. The stem you observe may have an irregular combination of plectostelic and actinostelic features. Note that the internal structure of the roots is essentially similar to that of the stem.

2. Selaginella, the Ground Pine

a. Examine living or preserved material of *Selaginella*. What type of branching exists in this plant? Note the arrangement of the leaves on the aerial stems. Identify the RHIZOPHORES, aerial roots arising from the stems. Are STROBILI present? If so, identify and describe these spore-containing structures. Are they all alike?

b. Study the prepared slide of a cross section through the stem of *Selaginella* (see also Chap. 10, "The Science of Biology"). Note the waxy cuticles on the outer cells and the absence of stomata. How many stelar regions are present in the stem cross section you are examining? The stele type of *Selaginella* is a DICTYOSTELE, that is, xylem and phloem are formed into more or less circularly arranged VASCULAR BUNDLES. Several variants of dictyosteles are known. The one usually encountered in *Selaginella* is a MERISTELIC dictyostele; that is, in any vascular bundle the xylem forms a central core and the phloem forms a sleeve around it. Inasmuch as several meristelic dictyosteles may be present within one stem of *Selaginella*, this plant may be said to be POLYSTELIC.

Examine the ENDODERMIS, present as radiating strips of tissue which interconnect the steles and the cortex and which traverse a conspicuous AIR SPACE. Note the bands of CUTIN on the endodermal cells.

c. In a longitudinal section through a strobilus, examine the most basal leaf. Note the disposition of VASCULAR TISSUE. Examine the LIGULE on the upper leaf surface. What kinds of tissue compose this appendage, and what is known about its significance? Compare the leaves of *Selaginella* and *Lycopodium*, and note the size and number of chloroplasts in the cells.

C. subphylum sphenopsida: horsetails

1. If available, examine fresh or preserved specimens of *Equisetum*. Note the horizontal underground RHIZOME; the ROOTS, LATERAL BRANCHES, and AERIAL STEMS growing out from nodal regions on the rhizome; the whorls of LEAVES attached to nodes on the stems; and the longitudinal RIBBING of the stem surface. Are stems with STROBILI present? Where do sphenopsids live?

2. Study the prepared slide of a cross section through the stem of *Equisetum* (see also Chap. 10, "The Science of Biology"). Identify, from the outside inward, the heavily cutinized EPIDERMIS, with RIDGES forming the longitudinal ribs seen externally; pairs of STOMATA between the epidermal ridges, the pairs forming two vertical columns in external view; the CORTEX, with a massive sclerenchymatous outer layer and a parenchymatous photosynthetic inner layer; the CORTICAL AIR CANALS, large spaces passing longitudinally through the cortex; the central parenchymatous PITH, with a very large CENTRAL CANAL through it; and the VASCULAR BUNDLES, arranged circularly between cortex and pith. In one such bundle, identify the surrounding ENDODERMIS, the PHLOEM facing outward, and the XYLEM facing inward.

Note that the stele of *Equisetum* is a dictyostele; that is, the xylem and phloem are formed into circularly arranged vascular bundles. Note also that the roots of *Equisetum* are predominantly actinostelic protosteles.

D. subphylum pteropsida: large-leafed tracheophytes

Class Filicineae: Ferns

1. Examine a potted, living fern plant. Note the horizontal underground RHIZOME and the ROOTS and large leaves, or FRONDS, branching away from the rhizome. In a leaf, note the principal (stem-like) midrib and the leaf blade, which is dissected into a regular array of LEAFLETS. In each leaflet, note the VEINS which originate ultimately from the principal midrib of the whole leaf. On the underside of some of the leaflets, note the rows of sporangium-containing structures, or SORI. The externally visible covering tissue of each sorus is the INDUSIUM. What is the shape of young, immature leaves, if present? What is meant by CIRCINATE VERNATION?

2. Study the prepared slide of a section through a fern leaf bearing a sorus on the underside. In the leaf portion, identify, from the upper surface downward, UPPER EPIDERMIS; PALISADE MESOPHYLL, composed of densely placed parenchymatous cells; SPONGY MESOPHYLL, with AIR SPACES; LOWER EPIDERMIS. On which surface are STOMATA present? Which cells or tissues contain chloroplasts?

In the sorus on the underside, note the central STALK bearing the terminal INDUSIUM, placed parallel to the lower leaf surface. Attached to the stalk and covered by the indusium, note the lateral stalked SPORANGIA, with SPORES in the interior.

3. Study the prepared slide of a cross section through the root of the fern *Osmunda*. Identify EPIDERMIS, parenchymatous CORTEX, ENDODERMIS, PHLOEM, and XYLEM. The stelar pattern here, as in the majority of tracheophytes, is that of an actinostelic protostele.

4. Study the prepared slide of a cross section through the rhizome of the fern *Dicksonia* (see also Chap. 10, "The Science of Biology"). Identify, in sequence from the outside inward, EPIDERMIS, CORTEX, PHLOEM, XYLEM, PHLOEM, PITH (with parenchymatous outer layers and sclerenchymatous core). A stele like this, where pith is present and where the vascular tissues surround the pith completely like a sleeve, is known as a SIPHONOSTELE. Several variant types of siphonosteles are known.

5. Study the prepared slide of a cross section through the rhizome of the fern *Polypodium*. Identify EPIDERMIS, CORTEX, central PITH, and the circularly arranged VASCULAR BUNDLES. The stele here is a dictyostele, essentially as in sphenopsids studied earlier. Note that most major types of steles occur among fern stems, that is, protosteles (without pith), siphonosteles (with pith and complete sleeves of vascular tissue), and dictyosteles (with vascular tissues formed into circularly arranged vascular bundles).

IV analysis

1. Describe the external and internal structure of *Psilotum*. How does this plant absorb nutrients from the soil? Are leaves present? What are the taxonomic group characteristics of the Psilopsida?

2. Describe the external and internal structure of *Lycopodium*. What is the internal structure of the roots? What are the taxonomic group characteristics of the Lycopsida? What plants other

than *Lycopodium* are included in this group?

3. Describe the external and internal structure of *Equisetum*. In what kinds of environments does *Equisetum* live and how is the aerial stem adapted to such environments? What is the internal structure of the roots? What are the taxonomic group characteristics of the Sphenopsida? What plants other than *Equisetum* are included in this group?

4. Describe the external structure of ferns. Describe the internal structure of fern (*a*) leaves, (*b*) roots, (*c*) stems. What are the group characteristics of (*a*) Pteropsida generally, (*b*) ferns specifically? In what environments do ferns live?

5. Define MICROPHYLL, MEGAPHYLL. In which tracheophytes does each of these leaf types occur? What are the structural differences between these leaf types?

6. Define STELE. Distinguish between PROTOSTELE, SIPHONOSTELE, and DICTYOSTELE. In which tracheophytes do each of these three stelar types occur? What variant forms of protosteles are known, and where does each variant occur? What is the characteristic stelar type in tracheophyte roots?

7. What is a rhizome? What is its adaptive value? Define BULB, CORM, TUBER. Give an example of each. What are PERENNIAL, BIENNIAL, and ANNUAL plants? Characterize the plants you have examined in these terms.

8. Are any of the plants you have examined woody? Does the xylem of the plants you have examined contain tracheids or vessels? Which of the plant types you have examined attain considerable sizes and heights, and what internal structures permit them to attain such sizes?

9. List the diagnostic taxonomic characteristics of tracheophytes. Which subphylum is today most abundant? Describe the general life-cycle pattern of tracheophytes and contrast it with that of bryophytes.

10. Apart from ferns, what other groups does the subphylum Pteropsida contain? What are their characteristic differences from ferns?

exercise 21 metaphyta: seed plant stems

I materials

Each student

microscope
hand lens
dissecting instruments

Each 1 or 2 students

prepared slides of:

Capsella, longitudinal section of embryo in seed
Coleus, longitudinal section of stem tip
Zea, cross section of stem
Ranunculus, cross section of stem
Helianthus, cross section of stem
Pinus, cross section of 1-yr stem
Tilia, cross section of 3-yr stem
Pinus, cross, radial, and tangential sections of wood
Magnolia, cross, radial, and tangential sections of wood

Class stock

germinating bean seeds, living
bean seedlings, living
wood blocks with transversely, radially, and tangentially cut surfaces
wood slices with intact bark
woody twigs in winter condition
Sambucus, prepared slides of lenticel sections

II introduction

In this exercise you will study the structure of the stems of the pteropsid classes Gymnospermae and Angiospermae. These coniferous and flowering plants collectively constitute the seed plants. A first objective will be to examine processes of PRIMARY GROWTH, that is, the ways in which sporophyte embryos give rise to specific types of green HERBACEOUS stems. A second objective will be to examine processes of SECONDARY GROWTH, that is, the ways in which herbaceous stems in the early primary condition transform into WOODY stems. At the end of the exercise, therefore, you should understand not only the detailed three-dimensional stem structure of a green herb or a woody tree, but also how such a structure has developed. It may be profitable in the context of this exercise to read or reread the pertinent chapters in your textbook.

III directions

A. the embryonic stem

1. *The Embryo*

Study the prepared slide of a longitudinal section through the embryo-containing seed of *Capsella*, the shepherd's purse. Identify the SUSPENSOR, which attaches the embryo to the wall of the seed, and the remains of the ENDOSPERM, the nutritive tissue surrounding the embryo. In the embryo, identify the two COTYLEDONS, or seed leaves, present in bent position; the APICAL SHOOT MERISTEM, in the angle where the cotyledons join the embryonic stem; the APICAL ROOT MERISTEM at the opposite end, where the suspensor is attached; and the embryonic STEM-ROOT SYSTEM. In the latter identify the early PRIMARY MERISTEMS, namely, the PROTODERM on the outside, the PROCAMBIUM in the center, and the GROUND MERISTEM between the protoderm and the procambium. What adult tissues will each of these primary meristems give rise to? Label Fig. 21.1.

2. *The Seed and Seedling*

Using hand lens and dissecting instruments, examine a germinating bean seed. Identify the brown SEED COAT, the pair of COTYLEDONS making up the bulk of the seed, and the small, white EMBRYO.

On a young bean seedling, identify ROOTS, STEM, shriveled COTYLEDONS, and early MATURE LEAVES. Locate the GROWING TIP of the stem and thus the position of the APICAL SHOOT MERISTEM.

3. *The Stem Apex*

Study the prepared slide of a longitudinal section through the stem tip of *Coleus* (see also Fig. 13.13, "The Science of Biology"). Identify APICAL SHOOT MERISTEM, PROTODERM of stem, GROUND MERISTEM of stem, and PROCAMBIUM of stem. In the lower part of the stem, some distance behind the apical tip, can you find evidence of the differentiation of the primary meristems into adult tissues? Near the apical tip, note the LEAF BUDS and, in the axils of older leaves lower down, the BRANCH BUDS.

B. primary growth

1. *Atactosteles*

Study the prepared slide of a cross section through a corn stem (*Zea*). Identify EPIDERMIS, parenchymatous CORTEX and PITH, and the scattered VASCULAR BUNDLES. In one of the bundles note the XYLEM and the PHLOEM. A stem possessing scattered vascular bundles represents an ATACTOSTELE. Note that steles of this type are characteristic of the stems of MONOCOTS, that is, the subclass Monocotyledonae in the class of angiosperms. How does a mature atactostele de-

Fig. 21.1 Section through an embryo of Capsella. *Label in detail. (Courtesy of General Biological Supply House, Inc.)*

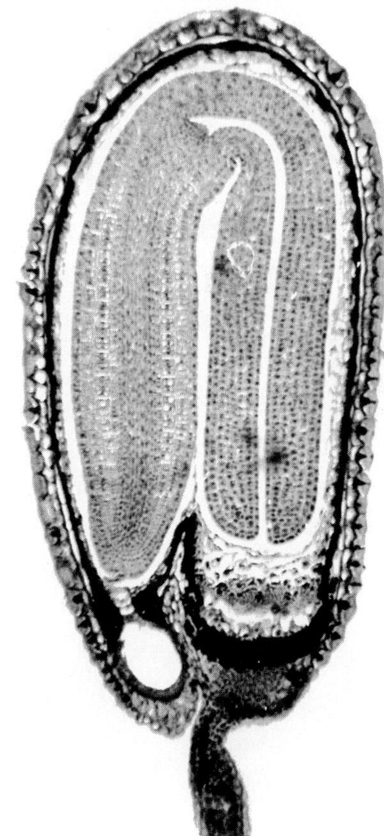

velop from the embryonic condition studied in section A? What other stele type is an atactostele most closely related to? Label Fig. 21.2.

2. Dictyosteles

Study the prepared slide of a cross section through a buttercup stem (*Ranunculus*). Identify EPIDERMIS, CORTEX, PITH with a large CENTRAL CANAL, and the circularly arranged VASCULAR BUNDLES. In one such bundle note the XYLEM, the PHLOEM, and the FIBER TISSUE (see also exercise 14, section C1). A stem of this type will be recognized as representing a DICTYOSTELE, already encountered in the preceding exercise. Note that, among seed plants, dictyosteles are the characteristic results of primary stem growth in all GYMNOSPERMS and also in the DICOTS, that is, the subclass Dicotyledonae in the class of angiosperms. How does a mature dictyostele develop from the embryonic condition studied in section A? Label Fig. 21.3.

3. The Semiherbaceous Stem

Study the prepared slide of a cross section through a sunflower stem (*Helianthus*). Identify EPIDERMIS, CORTEX, PITH, and the circularly arranged VASCULAR BUNDLES. In one of the bundles, identify, from the outside inward, FIBER TISSUE, PHLOEM, CAMBIUM (one-cell-layer-thick and not greatly different in appearance from the innermost layers of phloem), and XYLEM.

The stem pattern here is that of a typical dictyostele, except that a functional cambium is present. This SECONDARY meristem tissue will proliferate in older portions of sunflower stems, with the result that a completely continuous sleeve of cambium is formed. Such a sleeve of cambium then separates xylem and pith on the inside from phloem

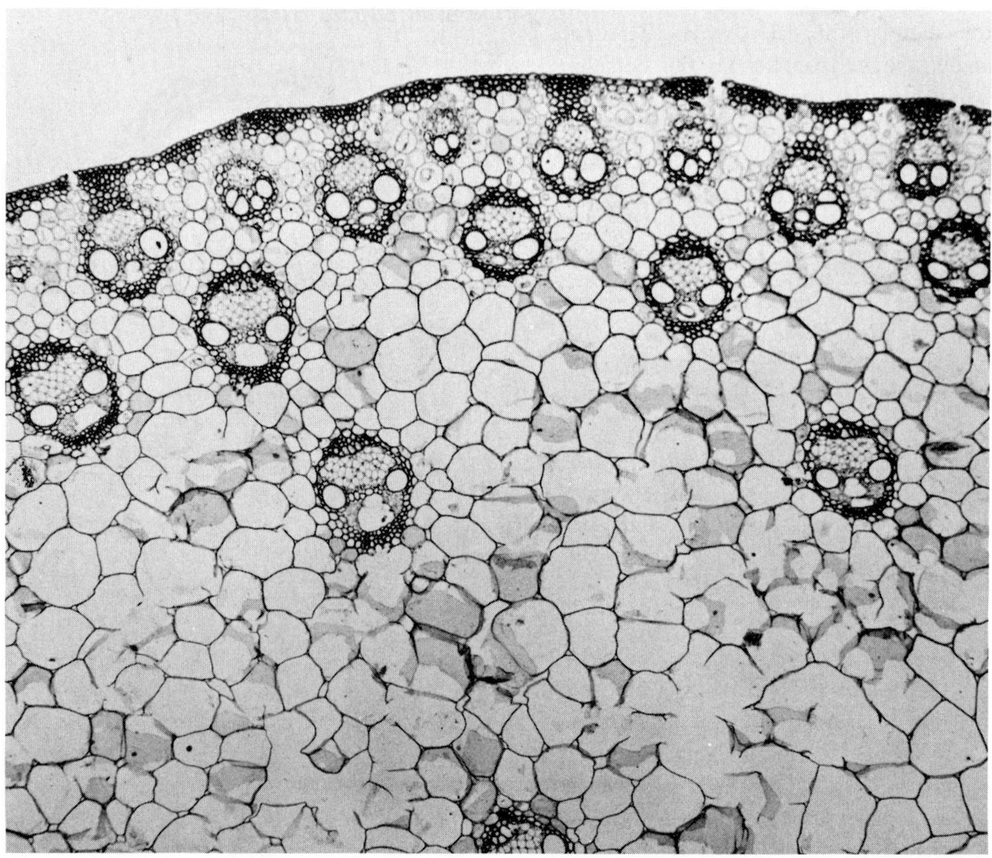

Fig. 21.2 Section through a portion of a corn stem. Label in detail. (Courtesy of General Biological Supply House, Inc.)

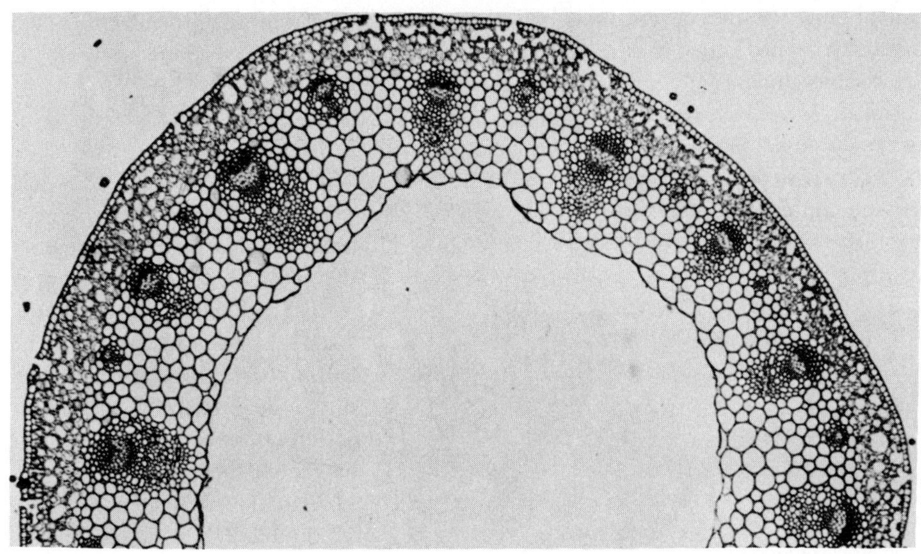

Fig. 21.3 Section through a portion of a buttercup stem. Label in detail. (Courtesy of General Biological Supply House, Inc.)

and cortex on the outside. Similar events occur also in the (dictyostelic) stems of plants which become woody. Older corn stems actually are often woody at the base, and this SEMIHERBACEOUS condition thus foreshadows the fully woody condition produced by secondary growth. Label Fig. 21.4.

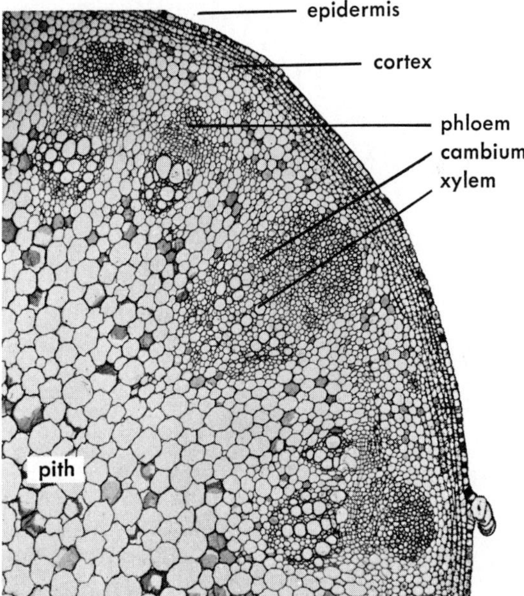

Fig. 21.4 Section through a portion of a sunflower stem. Label in detail. (Courtesy of General Biological Supply House, Inc.)

C. secondary growth

1. *The Early Woody Stem*

Study the prepared slide of a cross section through a 1-yr-old pine stem (*Pinus*). Identify, from the center outward, PITH, XYLEM (WOOD), CAMBIUM (one-cell-layer-thick and forming a complete ring around the xylem), PHLOEM, CORTEX with conspicuous RESIN CANALS, and the developing outermost PERIDERM. In the latter, CORK CELLS may be identified on the outside. What tissues collectively form BARK? How does such a stem increase in thickness? In length? How does such a stem develop from the primary dictyostelic condition studied earlier?

2. *The Later Woody Stem*

Study the prepared slide of a cross section through a 3-yr-old basswood stem (*Tilia*). From the inside outward, identify PITH; the three annual depositions of xylem forming ANNUAL RINGS; the wider vessels in SPRING XYLEM and the narrower vessels in SUMMER XYLEM, evident in each annual ring; CAMBIUM; PHLOEM; and the outer PERIDERM. The latter consists of three tissues identifiable under high power; from the inside outward: several layers of thick-walled PHELLODERM, a single layer of thin-walled PHELLOGEN (CORK CAMBIUM), and several layers of heavily suberin-impregnated PHELLEM (CORK CELLS).

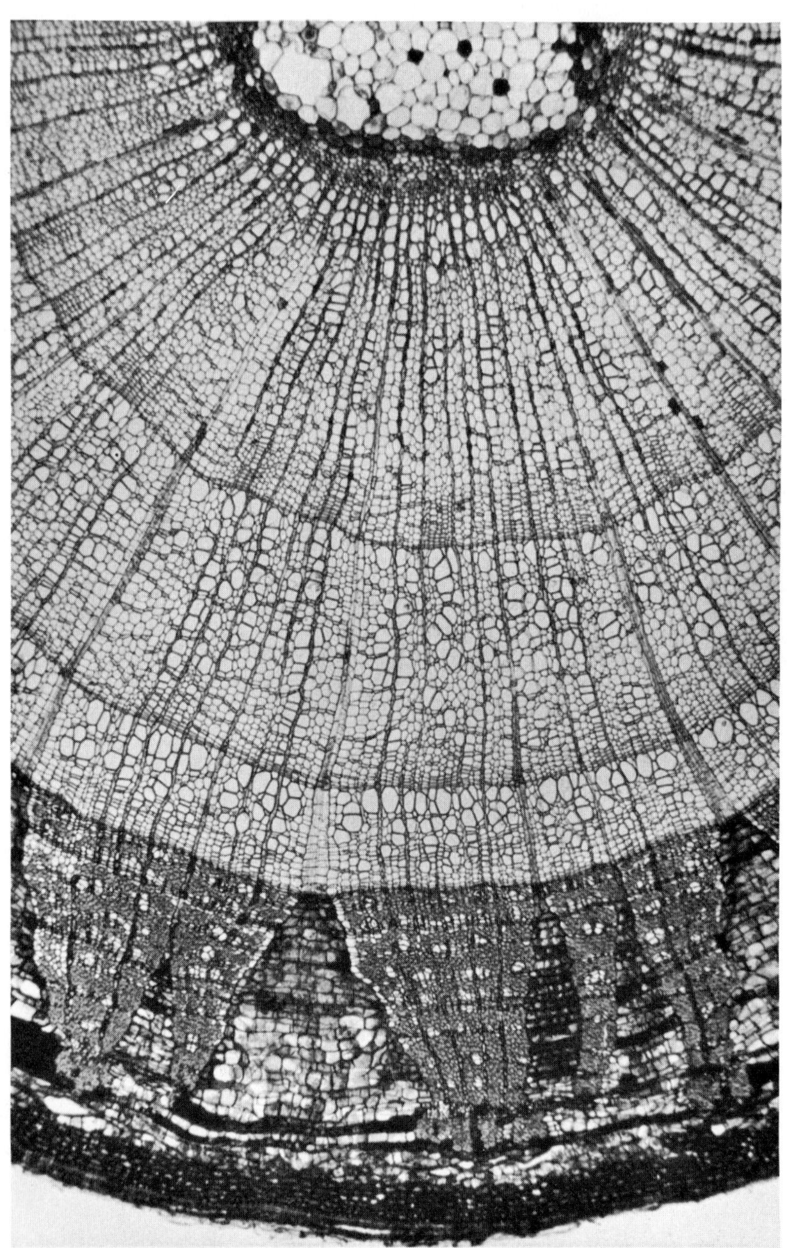

Fig. 21.5 Section through a portion of basswood stem. Label in detail. (Courtesy of General Biological Supply House, Inc.)

Which tissues constitute BARK? WOOD? How does the periderm develop and grow? Label Fig. 21.5.

3. *Wood Structure*

a. Examine a block of wood cut from a tree trunk in such a way that the surfaces represent transverse, radial, and tangential sections. Orient the block as it would be positioned in a tree and note the direction of the grain and the general texture of the cross, radial, and tangential cuts. Using these gross views as frames of reference, study the prepared slides of PINE wood and of MAGNOLIA wood, each with cross, radial, and tangential sections.

b. In the cross section of pine wood, note the longitudinally cut XYLEM RAYS, passing in places between the crosscut layers of TRACHEIDS. In the radial section, note the shape and arrangement of the tracheids, and the PITS (seen in frontal view) in the tracheid walls. In the tangential section, again note the tracheids, the pits (here seen in side view), and the xylem rays, which in this view are crosscut and appear as islands among the columns of tracheids.

c. In the cross section of magnolia wood, note the crosscut XYLEM VESSELS and again the longitudinally cut XYLEM RAYS. In both the radial and tangential sections, identify the ladderlike (SCALARIFORM) SECONDARY THICKENINGS in the walls of the xylem vessels. In the tangential section, again note the xylem rays, crosscut in this view.

Make sure you can visualize and sketch the three-dimensional structure of wood. Recall also your observations on macerated wood (exercise 14).

4. *The Woody Condition*

a. Examine a slice of wood with intact bark cut from cedar, oak, or some other tree trunk or large branch. Identify BARK, SAPWOOD, HEARTWOOD. Where is the vascular cambium? The pith? Note the ANNUAL RINGS and determine the age of the stem. Are the dark or the light rings produced by summer xylem? Does the width of the rings differ one from the other? In the light of this, draw conclusions about the weather during the years this tree has lived. What are the "knots" often found in cut wood?

b. Examine a woody twig in winter condition. Locate NODES and INTERNODES. Identify LEAF SCARS and BUD SCALE SCARS. What are these and how are they formed? Identify the BUDS, both LATERAL and TERMINAL. What does a bud contain? How is it formed? On the surface of the twig, note the LENTICELS. Study a prepared slide of a section through lenticels in the stem of the elderberry (*Sambucus*). Identify the parts of the periderm and describe the structure of a lenticel. What is its function?

IV analysis

1. Define APICAL MERISTEM, PRIMARY MERISTEM, SECONDARY MERISTEM. What are the three primary meristems? How and where do they arise and what is their later fate? Describe in detail.

2. What is the structure of (*a*) a dictyostele, (*b*) an atactostele? Suppose a longitudinal cut were made through a stem from the apical tip down; describe in detail the structural pattern at successive levels, and in this way show how primary growth can produce a mature (*a*) dictyostele, (*b*) atactostele.

3. What is a vascular cambium? What kinds of cells does it contain? Where in the stem, and how, does it develop? What is its function?

4. Show how a stem exhibiting a primary condition transforms into one exhibiting a secondary condition. Distinguish between primary and secondary xylem and between primary and secondary phloem. What is wood?

5. What are (*a*) xylem rays, (*b*) phloem rays? Where do they occur and how do they form? What is their function?

6. What is cork cambium? How does it develop? What tissues does it give rise to? What is the periderm? What is a lenticel?

7. What is bark? How does new bark form in an older tree trunk? List the tissues present in bark. List tissues of a woody stem that are (*a*) living, (*b*) nonliving.

8. Describe the three-dimensional structure of wood. In which tracheophyte groups does wood contain tracheids and in which does it contain vessels? Describe the structure and distribution of pits. What kind of secondary thickenings occur in the walls of tracheids and vessels? What is the adaptive value of such thickenings?

9. In which tracheophyte groups does secondary growth occur? What primary stele type is the usual starting condition on which secondary growth is superimposed?

10. How are annual rings formed in a stem? What is the difference between heartwood and sapwood? Which is older? Are both required equally for maintenance of stem functions?

11. Define NODE, INTERNODE. Where are leaf buds and branch buds formed? What are leaf scars and bud scale scars?

12. List and discuss the ways in which the woody plant is particularly adapted to continuous, year-round growth. If a tree is forced to grow intermittently, as in the Temperate Zone, will its stem structure reveal this?

13. If a woody stem is 10 ft high and grows 1 ft every year, how many annual rings would you find in the uppermost foot? In the lowest foot? Explain. If two knife marks are cut into a large tree, one 1 ft above the ground and the other 3 ft above the ground, what distance apart will these marks be after 1 yr of tree growth?

14. Does a corn stem enlarge in diameter through cambial activity? In the light of the answer to this question, explain the observation that corn stems are thicker at the base than at the tip.

15. What taxonomic characteristics identify the (*a*) gymnosperms, (*b*) angiosperms? What main groups of plants are included in each of these classes? List taxonomic characteristics distinguishing dicots from monocots.

exercise 22 metaphyta: seed plant roots and leaves

I materials

Each student

microscope
hand lens
dissecting instruments

Each 1 or 2 students

prepared slides of:

Capsella, longitudinal section of embryo in seed
Phaseolus, longitudinal section of root tip
Allium, longitudinal section of root tip
Ranunculus, cross section of root
pine or other woody plant, cross section of root
Salix, cross section of root with branch root
Coleus, longitudinal section of stem tip
Elodea, longitudinal section of stem tip
mesophytic leaf, cross section (for example, lilac, barberry)
Pinus, cross section of leaf
Yucca, cross section of leaf
Nymphaea or *Castalia*, cross section of leaf
Pyrus or *Sambucus*, cross sections of light- and shade-grown leaves

Class stock

root hairs on roots, prepared slides, longitudinal sections (optional)
fresh grasses or corn seedlings, with root systems
whole fresh carrots with root systems
whole fresh red beets with root systems
80% acetone
beakers
bunsen burners or electric heaters
fresh or preserved specimens of assorted leaf types (including coniferous, scaly, parallel-veined, and net-veined)
branch stems with leaves, to show assorted phyllotactic patterns

II introduction

Roots and leaves, like stems, are adapted to their environments. All roots and all leaves exhibit structural adaptations that permit them to carry out their fundamental functions, that is, nutrient absorption and mechanical support by roots, food manufacture by leaves. To this extent all types of roots have certain anatomical features in common, and so have all types of leaves. Beyond this, specific anatomical features may be modified in different ways in different plants, and in adaptation to particular climatic conditions additional unique features may be found in given plants.

In this respect leaves are likely to vary more than roots, since leaves are exposed directly to changing climates whereas roots are to some extent protected by soil. But even roots reflect in their structure the environmental conditions under which the aerial parts of a plant must live. In dry, hot climates, for example, roots might advantageously be adapted to store water; in temperate regions, they might be adapted to store food for the winter.

The aim of this exercise is (1) to study the basic structure of roots and leaves as well as the development of this structure, and (2) to examine how leaf structure is modified in response to different environments.

III directions

A. Roots

1. *The Primary Root Meristems*

a. Review the structure of the embryo of *Capsella*, studied in the previous exercise, section A1, and direct particular attention to the root portion. Then study the prepared slide of a longitudinal section through the root tip of a bean plant (*Phaseolus*). Identify the ROOT CAP, the APICAL ROOT MERISTEM, located just underneath the root cap, and the three PRIMARY MERISTEMS (PROTODERM, GROUND MERISTEM, PROCAMBIUM). How does the root grow in length?

b. Study the prepared slide of a longitudinal section through an onion (*Allium*) root tip. Again identify the APICAL ROOT MERISTEM, and proceeding backward from there in sequence, locate the ZONE OF DIVISION, where many cells are dividing mitotically; the ZONE OF ELONGATION, where cells are enlarging, primarily in the direction of the root axis; and the ZONE OF DIFFERENTIATION, where cells are developing and specializing into one of the primary meristems and subsequently into adult root tissues.

2. *Root Hairs*

Review your observations on living root hairs (exercise 14, section A5), or, if available, study a prepared slide of a longitudinal section through a root showing root hairs. What is the relation of the root-hair zone to the zones observed in section A1b above? What is the structural relation of a root hair to the root epidermis? What is the function of root hairs? Are such hairs permanent structures?

3. *The Mature Root*

a. Study the prepared slide of a cross section through the root of the buttercup (*Ranunculus*), a herbaceous dicot (and see again Ex. 14 , page 87). Identify EPIDERMIS, CORTEX, ENDODERMIS, PERICYCLE, XYLEM, PHLOEM. The stelar type seen here is the typical product of primary root growth in seed plants generally. What is the technical designation of this stelar type?

b. Study the prepared slide of a cross section through the young woody root of the pine or another woody plant. Identify PITH, XYLEM, CAMBIUM, PHLOEM, CORTEX (if present), and PERIDERM. How does root structure compare with stem structure? How does the woody condition develop from the primary root condition studied above? In the primary condition of a root that later undergoes secondary growth, where is the cambium located?

4. *Lateral Roots*

Study the prepared slide of a cross section through a willow root (*Salix*) bearing a branch root (see also Chap. 10, "The Science of Biology"). Identify the tissues of the main (or primary) root and note the stelar arrangement. Then identify the tissues of the branch (or secondary) root. Note particularly the primary meristems near the tip of the branch root and the differentiated tissues, if present, farther up. From which tissue of the primary root does the lateral root emanate?

5. *The Whole Root*

a. Examine the FIBROUS root systems of fresh grasses or corn seedlings. Contrast the arrangement of the roots here with that encountered in the FLESHY TAPROOT systems of whole fresh carrots and beets. What are PROP ROOTS, ADVENTITIOUS ROOTS, and AERIAL ROOTS, and in what kinds of plants would you find these?

b. Examine the external features of a whole raw carrot. Are there any nodes? With a scalpel, slice the carrot across near its upper end and examine the cut surface. Where is the most pigmented region? What microscopic tissue does this region correspond to? What is the pigment that gives the root its characteristic color? Locate the regions of endodermis, phloem, cambium, and xylem. Which tissue of the root takes up the greatest amount of space? Is this significant adaptively? Carefully cut the carrot lengthwise into two halves and again identify the various tissues. Where is the root-hair zone of the carrot?

Study a beet in exactly the same way as the carrot. Answer questions as above, substituting "beet" for "carrot."

c. Peel the epidermis off a piece of carrot and a piece of beet, wash the roots, and put each piece into a separate beaker of water. Boil for several minutes. What happens? Then boil two other, similar pieces of root in 80% acetone. What happens here? What do you conclude from these tests?

B. leaves

1. Leaf Buds

Review the prepared slide of a longitudinal section through the stem tip of *Coleus* (exercise 21, section A3, and see again Chap. 10, "The Science of Biology"). Study also a similar slide through the stem tip of *Elodea*. Identify the LEAF BUDS and the BRANCH BUDS. In a young developing leaf, note the differentiating EPIDERMIS, continuous with the protoderm of the stem; the early leaf MESOPHYLL, continuous with the ground meristem of the stem; and the immature VASCULAR TISSUE of the leaf, continuous with the procambium of the stem. Is a LEAF TRACE in evidence?

2. The Mature Leaf

a. Examine fresh or preserved specimens of needle-shaped, scaly, parallel-veined, net-veined, and other leaf types, as available. On a net-veined leaf, identify the PETIOLE, the STIPULES, and the leaf blade, or LAMINA. On stem branches bearing leaves, determine the pattern of PHYLLOTAXIS, that is, the geometric arrangement of the leaves on the stem. What are OPPOSITE, WHORLED, and SPIRAL phyllotactic patterns?

b. Study the prepared slide of a cross section through the leaf of a lilac, barberry, privet, or other mesophytic plant. Identify, from top to bottom, UPPER EPIDERMIS, the patterned, compact PALISADE MESOPHYLL, the loose SPONGY MESOPHYLL, the AIR SPACES in the spongy mesophyll, and the LOWER EPIDERMIS. Which leaf surface contains GUARD CELLS and STOMATA? Which cells or tissues contain chloroplasts? Move the slide if necessary until you find a cross section through a leaf VEIN. In it identify upper and lower FIBER TISSUE, XYLEM, and PHLOEM. Where is the xylem in relation to phloem? In some portions of the slide you will probably find tangential or oblique sections through leaf veins, identifiable by the horizontal columnar arrangement of the vascular

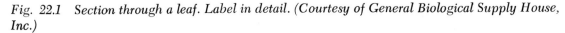

Fig. 22.1 Section through a leaf. Label in detail. (Courtesy of General Biological Supply House, Inc.)

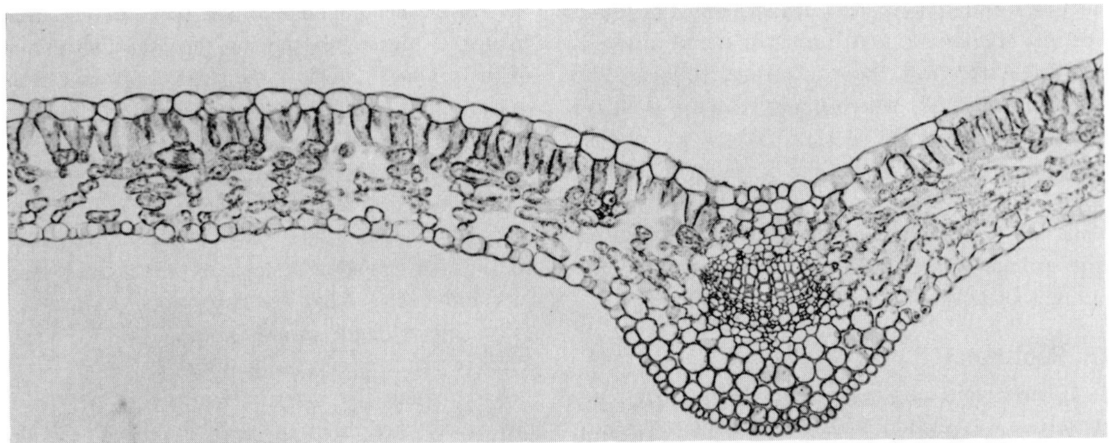

tissues. In such a section, identify the spiral SECONDARY THICKENINGS in the walls of the xylem vessels. Explain how oblique sections through veins come to be included in cross sections through leaves. Label Fig. 22.1.

3. *Leaf Adaptations*

a. Study the prepared slide of a cross section through a pine needle. Identify the heavily cutinized EPIDERMIS, with SUNKEN STOMATA; the CORTEX, with large LOBED PARENCHYMA cells; the ENDODERMIS; the bundles of PHLOEM and XYLEM; and surrounding the vascular tissues and in turn surrounded by the endodermis, the so-called TRANSFUSION TISSUE, composed of parenchymalike cells. As judged from this internal structure, what type of environment is the pine leaf particularly adapted to?

b. Study the prepared slide of a cross section through a *Yucca* leaf. What is the cross-sectional shape of the leaf? Note the large bundles of FIBER TISSUE at the edges of the leaf. Considering the upright positions of *Yucca* leaves, are these fiber bundles and the leaf shape of adaptive value? Identify the heavily cutinized EPIDERMIS, the SUNKEN STOMATA, the palisade and spongy MESOPHYLL, the AIR SPACES, and the VEINS. Compare the internal structure of this leaf with that of the leaf studied in section 2 above. On the basis of this, infer the nature of the environment in which the *Yucca* plant lives.

c. Study the prepared slide of a cross section through the leaf of a water lily such as *Nymphaea* or *Castalia*. Identify upper and lower EPIDERMIS, palisade and spongy MESOPHYLL, AIR SPACES, and VEINS. How is each of these tissues different from corresponding tissues in other leaves you have studied, both in relative abundance and in pattern of arrangement? Which surface contains stomata? On the basis of these considerations, show how the leaf of the water lily is specially adapted to its particular environment.

d. Study cross sections of light- and shade-grown leaves of plants such as *Pyrus* (apple) or *Sambucus* (elderberry). Carefully compare the correlated pairs tissue by tissue, and ascertain the effect of light on the development of leaf structure. Are both leaves of the same thickness? Compare the sizes of the epidermal cells and the cells of the mesophyll and palisade parenchyma in the two leaves. How does the thickness of the cuticles differ? What is the adaptive value of the modifications you observe?

IV analysis

1. Describe the growth processes through which an embryonic root transforms into a mature primary root. What is the characteristic primary structure of a mature root? How and where do lateral roots form?

2. Through what growth processes does a woody root develop? Describe in detail. If a cambium is present in a root, where is it located and how does it develop?

3. How are roots adapted for growth through abrasive layers of soil; for nutrient absorption; for food storage; for mechanical support of the whole plant; to particular climatic conditions affecting the aerial parts of a plant?

4. What tissue gives rise to root hairs? To root epidermis? Compare the structure of root epidermis and stem or leaf epidermis. Relate the differences to root function.

5. If a series of indelible equidistant marks is made along a root, between root tip and stem juncture, how will the marks be spaced after a period of root growth? Contrast the patterns of branching growth in root and stem.

6. Of the following, which are roots and what anatomical parts of a plant are the others: carrot, onion bulb, potato tuber, sugar beet, tulip bulb, turnip, lima bean, parsnip, tomato, radish, sweet potato?

7. Name the principal variant types of root systems and contrast their structural organization and adaptive roles.

8. Describe the characteristic internal structure of a leaf. How and where do leaves develop? What is a leaf trace? A leaf gap? Do leaves undergo secondary growth?

9. What tissues do roots, leaves, and stems have in common? What tissues occur uniquely in roots, in leaves, and in stems? Correlate the common and the different features with function.

10. Can a particular (*a*) root shape, (*b*) leaf shape, confer an adaptive advantage to a plant living in a given environment? Illustrate.

11. In flat leaf blades, what is the adaptive significance of the asymmetrical position of the

palisade mesophyll, near the top surface? Contrast with the symmetrical distribution of the palisade tissue in *Yucca*. Is the very existence of a palisade layer, with its densely packed cells, adaptively significant?

12. Show how leaf structure differs for mesophytic, xerophytic, and hydrophytic plants. Show how these differences are adaptive.

13. Which cells and tissues of a leaf are photosynthetic? What is the function of stomata? On which surface of a mesophytic leaf are stomata often more abundant? What is the adaptive value of such a distribution?

14. Construct an extensive table summarizing the structural differences between dicot and monocot stems, leaves, and roots.

15. Construct a table which correlates the following characteristics of plants: (*a*) dicot, monocot; (*b*) woody, herbaceous; (*c*) perennial, biennial, annual. Do plants exist for every possible combination of (*a*), (*b*), and (*c*) characteristics?

part 4 the world of life: animal organisms

exercise 23 metazoa: sponges and radiates

I materials

Each student

microscope
dissecting instruments
hand lens
blank slide, cover slip
razor blade

Each 1 or 2 students

Leucosolenia, prepared slide, cross section
Sycon or other syconoid, prepared slide, cross section
Obelia, prepared slide, colony of polyps
Obelia, prepared slide, medusa
Hydra, prepared slide, cross section
Hydra, prepared slides showing ovaries and testes
Aurelia, preserved or fresh
Metridium, prepared slide, cross section
Pleurobrachia, preserved

Class stock

Leucosolenia, fresh or preserved
sponge spicules, prepared slides
silicaceous and horny sponges, preserved
Hydra, living culture
assorted hydrozoan material
assorted scyphozoan material
Metridium, living and/or preserved
corals, assorted anthozoan material
assorted ctenophoran material

II introduction

In this and the following exercises, representatives of some of the main animal groups will be studied by gross examination and dissection. The objective is to obtain some familiarity with the structural organization, adaptations, and internal functions of the representative animal types. Accordingly, study each organism from these viewpoints. Do not be satisfied simply to identify the body parts, but also determine in each case what functions the parts have, where and how the animal lives, what its life cycle is, and how it is related to other animals in way of life, evolution, development, and taxonomy. Where applicable, make use also of the descriptions in exercise 7 and your notes and observations from that exercise. Furthermore, consult your text as warranted (for example, Chaps. 11, 12, and 13 of "The Science of Biology").

III directions

A. phylum porifera: sponges

1. Class Calcarea

a. Examine a branched colony of *Leucosolenia*, a common saltwater sponge exemplifying the ASCONOID pattern of sponge structure (see Chap. 11, "The Science of Biology"). Each terminal branch represents a single adult, and the short side branches are BUDS which will become adults. In a given adult note the OSCULUM, a large opening at the tip. What is the function of this opening?

Study a prepared slide of a cross section through an individual, or with a razor blade, make an EXTREMELY thin section of a whole individual and mount the section on a slide. Identify as many of the following features and cell types as you can. The body wall is lined on the outside with flat epithelial cells called PINACOCYTES and on the inside with COLLAR CELLS, or CHOANOCYTES. Between the pinacocytes and choanocytes is a gelatinous layer, the MESOGLOEA, in which are embedded calcareous SPICULES and irregularly shaped MESENCHYME CELLS. Also present are PORE CELLS, identifiable by their hollow centers. These form channels connecting the external environment with the large interior cavity of the sponge, the SPONGOCOEL.

What is the function of each of these structural components of a sponge?

b. Examine slides of sections through *Sycon* or some other sponge exhibiting the SYCONOID pattern of structure. Identify the central SPONGOCOEL and, radiating out from it, the pouched extensions, or RADIAL CANALS, lined with choanocytes. Are OSTIA visible in the epidermal layer? Where are spicules located? From your text ascertain the nature of the LEUCONOID pattern of sponge structure and contrast it with the asconoid and syconoid patterns.

2. Other Sponges

Study preserved specimens of silicaceous and horny sponges. What structural patterns do these exemplify? Determine the path of water through such sponges.

Examine a slide or slides of mounted calcareous, silicaceous, and horny spicules. Contrast the patterns of construction and of spicule development.

B. phylum cnidaria: coelenterates

1. Class Hydrozoa

a. Study a slide showing a POLYP COLONY of *Obelia*. Note the branched upright stems and, if present, also the horizontal stems, or STOLONS. In a stem identify the thin, transparent, chitinous exoskeleton, or PERISARC, and the tissues within, or COENOSARC. The colony grows by budding, fully grown buds usually remaining attached to the colony. Concentrate first on the short side branches of the colony, each terminating in a tentacled, bell-shaped HYDRANTH, or feeding individual (GASTROZOOID). In a hydranth note the mouth, or MANUBRIUM, the GASTROCOEL in the interior, and the ring of stinging-cell–bearing TENTACLES around the manubrium. Where does the perisarc terminate in relation to the hydranth? How many tissue layers does the coenosarc consist of?

Next examine the regions where hydranth-bearing polyps fork off the main stem. At some of these branch points will be found club-shaped reproductive polyps, or GONOZOOIDS. In their interior develop small bell-shaped MEDUSAE which, when mature, escape from the gonozooids and assume a free-swimming existence. Label Fig. 23.1.

b. Examine the slide showing a medusa of *Obelia*. Note the tentacled BELL, the central MANUBRIUM, the RADIAL CANALS, and the four globular SEX ORGANS along the radial canals. The sexes are separate. Fertilization takes place in open water and a ciliated PLANULA larva develops from the zygote. After it settles, the planula gives rise to a new polyp colony. Evidently, like most Hydrozoa, *Obelia* is polymorphic; the life cycle includes two distinct alternating phases, namely, the sessile, vegetatively reproducing polyp phase and the motile, gametically reproducing medusa phase. Label Fig. 23.1.

c. Transfer a living *Hydra* from the class culture to a slide and examine it with a hand lens and under the low power of your microscope. Note the shape of the animal and identify the MOUTH, surrounded by TENTACLES. Observe the

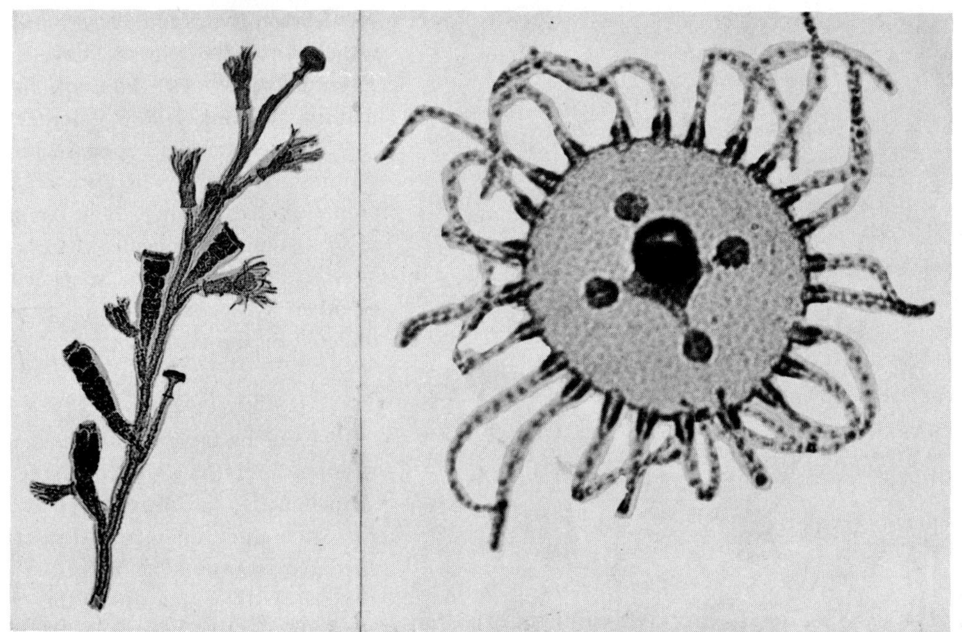

Fig. 23.1 Polyp colony (left) and medusa (right) of Obelia. *Label. (Courtesy of Carolina Biological Supply Co.)*

activities of the specimen for some minutes. If you or someone else in the class finds a hydra with an attached BUD, study this instance of vegetative reproduction. Return the living specimen to the class culture.

d. Study a prepared slide of a cross section through an adult *Hydra*. Note the EPIDERMAL (ectodermal) and the GASTRODERMAL (endodermal) cell layers. What kinds of cells are present in each? *Hydra* is an unusual coelenterate in that a middle (mesodermal) body layer is virtually lacking; in most other coelenterates such a middle layer forms a prominent gelatinous MESOGLOEA, particularly extensive in jellyfishes. Where is the nerve net of *Hydra* located? Label Fig. 23.2.

Study slides of hydras showing OVARIES and TESTES. These organs will be seen protruding from the side of the body (see also Fig. 23.3). Note the position and structure of the sex organs, and identify the gametes in the interior. There are many sperms in a testis, but typically only one or a few large eggs in an ovary. Some species are hermaphroditic; that is, sperms and eggs are both produced by the same individual. In other species the sexes are separate. Sperms are released through pores in the testes, and they swim through water to an egg, which has become partially extruded from the ovary but still remains attached to the parent for the time being. After

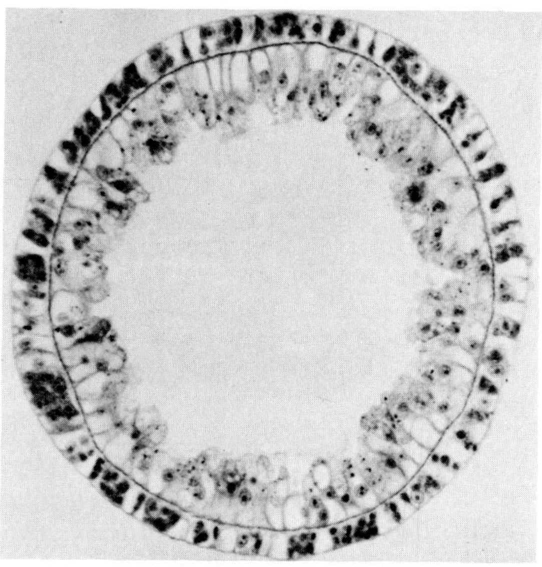

Fig. 23.2 Cross section through the body of Hydra. *Label. (Courtesy of Ward's Natural Science Establishment, Inc.)*

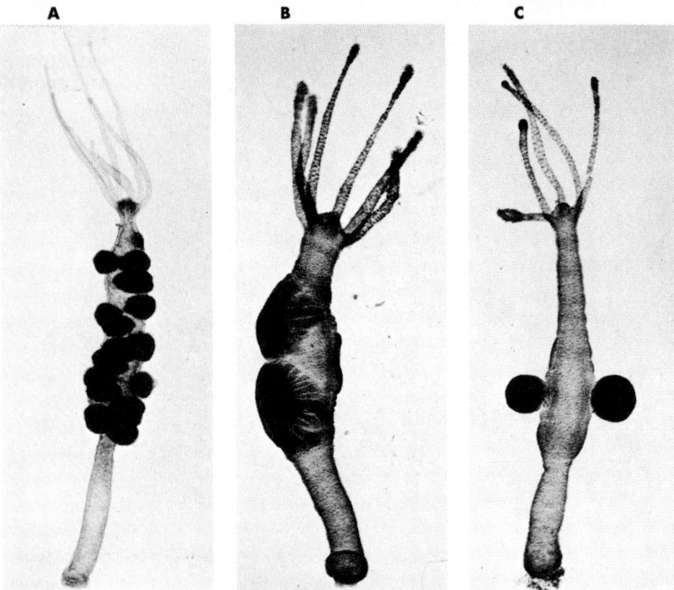

Fig. 23.3 Gametic reproduction in Hydra. A *and* B, *adults, showing position of testes and ovaries, respectively.* C, *embryos develop within cysts protruding from the body wall of the parent. Such cysts will eventually drop off and independent offspring hydras will emerge directly. (Courtesy of Ward's Natural Science Establishment, Inc.)*

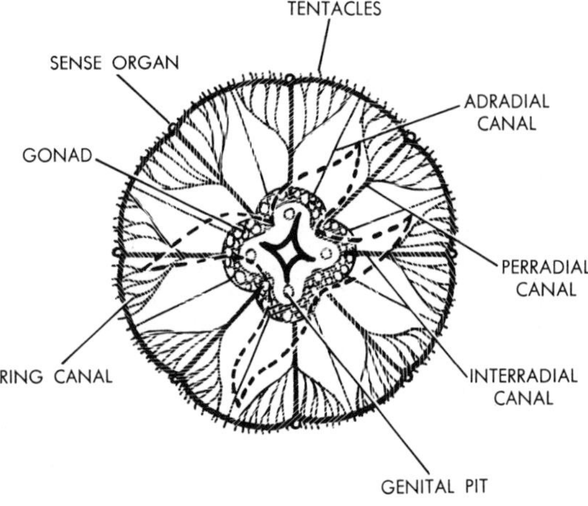

Fig. 23.4 Symmetry and the canal system in Aurelia. *Interradial and periradial canals are branched, adradials are unbranched. Dashed lines mark the positions of the tentacular arms of the manubrium. A ring canal, present in* Aurelia, *is not found in most other scyphomedusae.*

fertilization the zygote encysts and, still remaining attached to the parent, develops in the cyst. Eventually the cyst drops off the parent and a mature offspring *Hydra* emerges from the cyst. In this coelenterate a medusa phase is evidently suppressed entirely. In view of the existence of *Hydra* in fresh water, how could the life cycle of the animal be considered to be adaptive?

e. Examine preserved specimens and/or slides of other hydrozoan material as available and as directed by the instructor.

2. *Class Scyphozoa*

a. Examine fresh or preserved specimens of the common jellyfish *Aurelia.* Note the umbrella-shaped body, the LAPPETS (how many?) around the bell margin, the marginal TENTACLES, the four-cornered MANUBRIUM with the MOUTH in the center of the underside, the RADIAL CANALS, the prominent, horseshoe-shaped SEX ORGANS along the four radial canals, and the system of INTERRADIAL CANALS (see also Fig. 23.4). Does *Aurelia* possess a RING CANAL? What kinds of sense organs does the animal possess, and where are they located? Ascertain which body parts are ectodermal, mesodermal, and endodermal, respectively. How does the animal propel itself?

b. Study other scyphozoan material as available and as directed by the instructor.

3. *Class Anthozoa*

a. Examine living and/or preserved specimens of the sea anemone *Metridium* and the prepared dissection of this animal (see also Fig. 23.5). Identify the ORAL DISK, with TENTACLES and elongated MOUTH. Can you make out the position of the SIPHONOGLYPH? In the interior note the GASTRIC SEPTA, with the GASTRIC FILAMENTS along the thickened edges and the bundles of LONGITUDINAL MUSCLES along one side. Where is the exoskeleton of the animal? If living specimens are available, study their responses to mechanical stimuli.

b. If available, study a prepared slide of a cross section through *Metridium.* Identify the EPIDERMIS, the GASTRODERMIS, and the MESOGLOEA. What is the histological structure of the latter? In what regions of the body wall are muscles and nerve cells located? How many gastric septa are in evidence?

c. Examine coral specimens and other anthozoan skeletal materials as available. Ascertain the genus name for each type and make sure you understand the location of the living tissues in relation to the skeleton. How do Anthozoa multiply, and what is their life cycle?

C. phylum ctenophora: comb jellies

1. Study preserved specimens of the comb jelly *Pleurobrachia* with a hand lens and under the low power of your microscope. A MOUTH is located at the ORAL POLE and a SENSE ORGAN at the ABORAL (forward) POLE. Note the eight rows of COMB PLATES extending from one pole to the other. A pair of TENTACLES, usually retracted, is present near the aboral pole. The mouth leads into a narrow GASTROVASCULAR CAVITY, which branches in the interior of the animal.

In what respects is this ctenophore rather like a coelenterate medusa? What is the function of each of the body parts identified above?

2. Study other ctenophoran material as available and as directed by the instructor.

Fig. 23.5 Metridium, *a sea anemone. (Courtesy of Carolina Biological Supply Co.)*

IV analysis

1. Describe the cell and tissue structure of a sponge. How are the cells arranged, and what are their separate and collective functions? How many body layers are present? Are these homologous to the layers of other Metazoa? Discuss.

2. Distinguish between the three basic patterns of sponge structure. Name representatives of each type. Show how, during development, each type arises.

3. Review the taxonomic distinctions between the classes of sponges and the identifying features of the phylum as a whole. How do sponges (*a*) feed, (*b*) respond to stimuli, (*c*) reproduce?

4. Describe the life cycle of *Obelia,* and distinguish between polyps and medusae (*a*) structurally, (*b*) functionally, (*c*) reproductively. What basic body layers occur in coelenterates, and what cell types occur in each? What are cnidoblasts, and how do they function?

5. Describe the structure and life cycle of *Hydra* and show in what respects this animal is an atypical hydrozoan. Name some other representatives of the Hydrozoa.

6. Define hydranth, manubrium, coenosarc, stolon, gonozooid, dactylozooid, planula. Review the life cycle of Scyphozoa. Describe the structure of *Aurelia.* What are the larval forms of Scyphozoa?

7. Describe the anatomical and histological structure of a sea anemone, with special attention to differences as compared with Hydrozoa and Scyphozoa. Describe the life cycle of Anthozoa. Define siphonoglyph, gastric septum, gastric filament. What are the functions of these body parts?

8. Apart from sea anemones, what other kinds of animals belong to the Anthozoa? Review the structure of the latter. What are the identifying features of the coelenterate phylum as a whole and of each of the classes?

9. What are the phylum characteristics of ctenophores? In what respects are ctenophores (*a*) similar to, (*b*) different from, coelenterates? What are colloblasts?

10. From your text, compare the species numbers of sponges, coelenterates, and ctenophores. In what habitats is each of these animal groups found? Which groups have representatives in fresh water, and what are some of the adaptations to this environment?

exercise 24 metazoa: acoelomates, pseudo-coelomates, lophophorates

I materials

Each student

microscope
blank slide
dissecting instruments
dissecting pan, pins
hand lens
Dugesia, whole mount
Clonorchis sinensis, whole mount
Taenia, whole mounts of scolex, young proglottids, and ripe proglottids
Philodina or other rotifer, whole mount
Ascaris, preserved specimen
Lingula, preserved specimen

Each 2 or more students

Dugesia, prepared slides, cross sections through various body levels
eggs, rediae, and cercariae of flukes, prepared slides
Cerebratulus, preserved specimen
Ascaris, prepared slides of cross sections through pharynx and other body levels
acanthocephalan worm, whole mount
Bugula, whole mount
Plumatella, whole mount

Class stock

Dugesia, living culture
fresh shredded meat (for example, liver)
polyclads and other assorted turbellarian material
assorted fluke material
tapeworms, preserved, and other assorted cestode material
assorted nemertine material
rotifers, living culture
Trichinella, whole mounts, and other nematode material
gastrotrichs, living culture
assorted ectoproct material
Bugula, preserved
Plumatella, preserved

II introduction

In this exercise you will begin a study of the grade Bilateria, that is, animals exhibiting a primary bilateral symmetry. The groups to be examined will include representatives of the subgrades Acoelomata and Pseudocoelomata, and also the presumably primitive members of the subgrade Coelomata, namely, the lophophorates. Recall that in acoelomates a body cavity is lacking, mesoderm derivatives filling the space between the ectodermal body wall and the endodermal alimentary system. In pseudocoelomates a body cavity is present; it is a PSEUDOCOEL, that is, lined by ectodermal and endodermal tissues, and mesoderm derivatives are restricted to particular localized regions. Coelomates possess a "true" body cavity, namely, a mesoderm-lined COELOM. In the lophophorates such coeloms arise in a variety of unique ways, and these animals are identified also by a LOPHOPHORE, a tentacular feeding apparatus.

III directions

A. phylum platyhelminthes: flatworms

1. Class Turbellaria: Free-living Types

a. Put a living representative of the planarian genus *Dugesia* into a shallow dish and observe with a hand lens. Identify anterior, posterior, dorsal, and ventral regions. Is the designation "flatworms" justified? Is there a head? What are the means of locomotion of this animal? By putting your desk lamp into different positions, determine the responses of *Dugesia* to light. Locate the PHARYNX on the underside. Add a little shredded meat to the dish and observe ingestion. Return the animal to the class culture.

b. In a prepared whole mount of planaria, study the organization of the alimentary system. What is this organization? What other structures in head and body can you identify? Label Fig. 24.1.

Examine prepared slides of cross sections through various body regions of *Dugesia*. Identify the ventral NERVE CORDS, the EXCRETORY and REPRODUCTIVE ORGANS, the DIGESTIVE SYSTEM, and the BODY WALL. What tissues are present in the body wall? What fills the space between the body wall and the digestive system? Is there a coelom? Label Fig. 24.2.

c. Study mounts or demonstration specimens of polyclad turbellarians and any other material on free-living flatworms that may be available. The instructor will give appropriate directions.

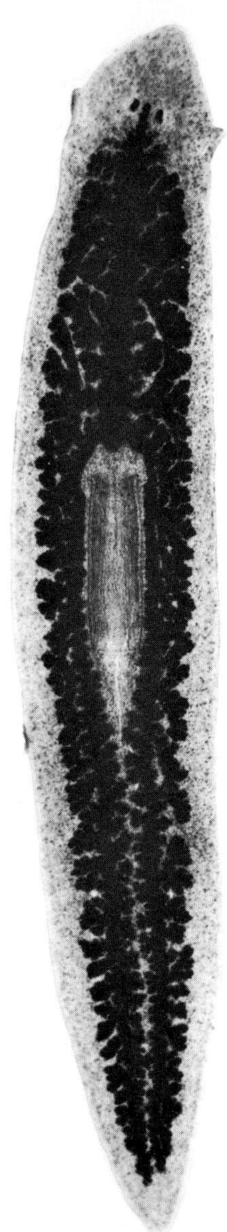

Fig. 24.1 Whole mount of a planarian. Label in detail. (Courtesy of General Biological Supply House, Inc.)

2. Class Trematoda: Flukes

a. Study a whole mount of *Clonorchis sinensis*, the Chinese liver fluke. Anteriorly note the ORAL SUCKER, in the center of which is the MOUTH. Behind it is the PHARYNX, thick and bilobed. The esophagus branches posteriorly into two blind INTESTINAL POUCHES, which pass to the posterior

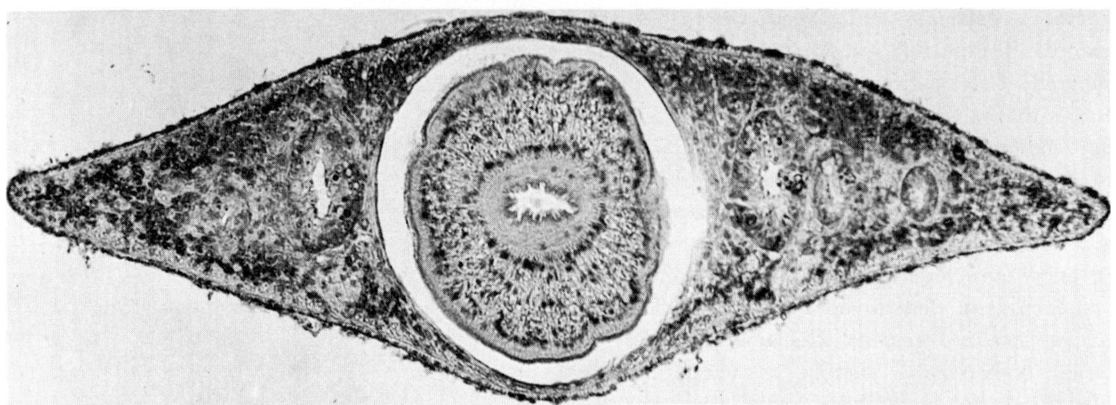

Fig. 24.2 Transverse section through a planarian. Identify the body level at which the section was cut and label in detail. (Courtesy of Carolina Biological Supply Co.)

end of the animal. Between the intestinal pouches, about one-third of the distance from the mouth, is the VENTRAL SUCKER. The central third of the body contains the coiled UTERUS and, posterior to it, the OVARY and the SEMINAL RECEPTACLE. Also present here, lateral to the intestinal pouches, are the YOLK GLANDS. A pair of irregularly branched TESTES occupies the posterior third of the body. A duct from each of the testes leads into the region of the uterus. There the two ducts join, and the common duct exists at a GENITAL PORE just in front of the ventral sucker.

Determine the function of each of these body components. Compare the organization of this fluke with that of planaria. Review the life cycle of the Chinese liver fluke. Label Fig. 24.3.

b. Examine slides showing some of the life-cycle stages of flukes, for example, EGGS, REDIA larvae, and CERCARIA larvae. In the larval types, compare the internal structure with that of the adults, and show how the larva is adapted to its particular functional role in the life cycle.

c. Study mounts or demonstration specimens of other flukes as available and as directed by the instructor.

3. Class Cestoidea: Tapeworms

a. Study mounts of the tapeworm ***Taenia*** showing the three kinds of body parts: the SCOLEX (head region), MATURE PROGLOTTIDS (mid-region), and RIPE PROGLOTTIDS (hind region).

Note the SUCKERS and HOOKS of the scolex. What is their specific function, and what is the function of the scolex as a whole? Note also the many proglottids developing behind the scolex. How does such a proglottid arise? Label Fig. 24.4.

In a mature proglottid, note the lateral GENITAL PORE. Into it leads an anterior coiled SPERM DUCT and a posterior straight VAGINA. The sperm duct connects with small TESTES scattered throughout the proglottid; the vagina connects with paired OVARIES located posteriorly in the proglottid. Also connected by ducts to the ovaries are a UTERUS, a straight, elongated structure running antero-posteriorly through the center of the proglottid, and a YOLK GLAND, located most posteriorly in the proglottid. In a ripe proglottid, again locate the uterus and its contents. Which structures identified in the mature proglottid can you again recognize in this ripe section? Where are the others? Note the NERVE CORDS and EXCRETORY CANALS running laterally through successive proglottids.

Summarize in your mind the pattern of development of a proglottid. What is its fate? Review the life cycle of a tapeworm.

b. Examine demonstration specimens of whole tapeworms and any other cestode material available. The instructor will give appropriate directions.

B. phylum nemertina: ribbon worms

Preserved specimens of *Cerebratulus* and slide mounts or sections of nemertine worms may be available. Study these with the aid of your text and as directed by the instructor.

C. phylum aschelminthes: sac worms

1. Class Rotifera: Rotifers

Put some living rotifers such as *Philodina* on a slide and observe these animals. How large are they in comparison with the protozoa that may be present? Describe the locomotion of the rotifers.

Select one of the animals for careful study, and/or examine a prepared whole mount (see also Chap. 11, "The Science of Biology"). Note the division of the body into HEAD, TRUNK, and posterior FOOT. A CUTICLE with transverse folds

Fig. 24.3 Whole mounts of Chinese liver fluke (A) *and* Fasciola hepatica, *another liver fluke* (B). *Label both in detail. (Courtesy of Carolina Biological Supply Co.)*

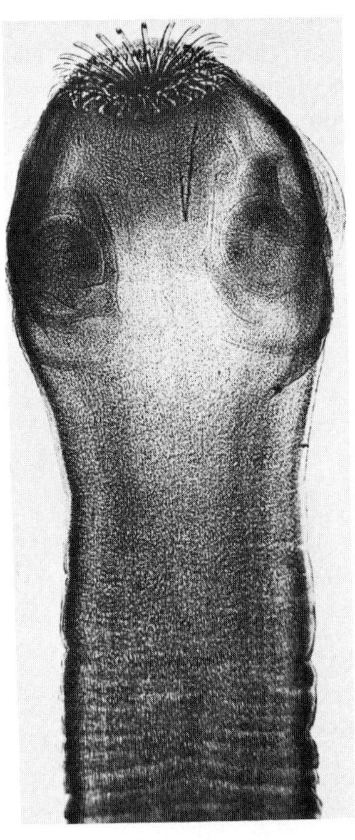

Fig. 24.4 The scolex of a tapeworm. Label. (Courtesy of General Biological Supply House, Inc.)

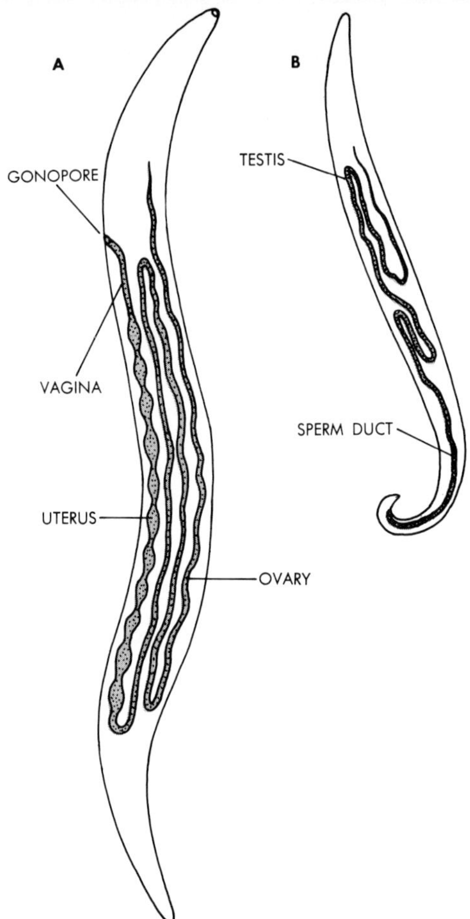

Fig. 24.5 The reproductive organs of nematodes, diagrammatic.

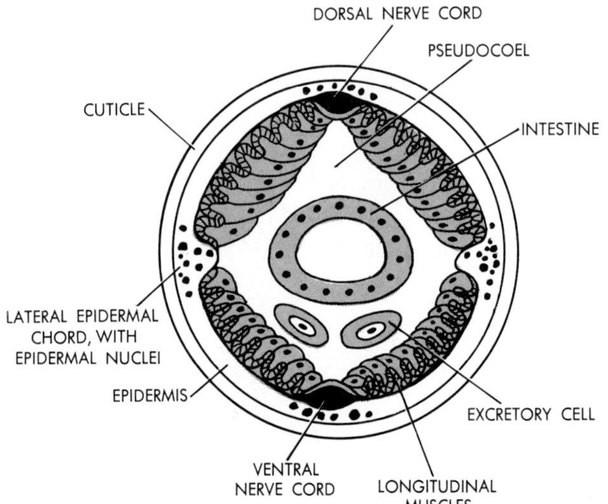

Fig. 24.6 Diagram of a cross section through the anterior region of a nematode.

covers the exterior. Anteriorly, identify the ciliated WHEEL ORGAN, which gives the class its name. What is the function of this organ? The MOUTH is along the ventral border of the wheel organ and leads into a muscular PHARYNX. The grinding organ present in the pharynx is the MASTAX. The pharynx continues into the STOMACH, and this organ communicates via a short INTESTINE with the CLOACA. The ANUS is dorsal, near the base of the foot. Leading into the cloaca by ducts are the OVARY and the EXCRETORY SYSTEM. In the head, note the dorsal BRAIN GANGLION, and in the foot, the CEMENT GLAND. What are the functions of these various body components? What is the space between the body wall and the alimentary system? How do rotifers breathe and transport materials within the body? Review the life cycle of rotifers.

2. Class Nematoda: Roundworms

a. Examine a preserved specimen of the parasitic roundworm *Ascaris*. Note the external CUTICLE and the two narrow white streaks and two broad brown streaks extending over the whole length of the body. The white streaks are dorsal and ventral, the brown ones lateral. On the ventral side locate the EXCRETORY PORE, just behind the MOUTH, and the slit of the ANUS, just before the posterior end of the animal. Male worms are smaller than female ones, and the posterior end has a slight ventral curvature.

b. Dissect the animal. Pin the worm anteriorly and posteriorly, dorsal side up, and make a long slit along the dorsal midline. Pin the flaps of body wall down. In the interior, identify the PHARYNX behind the mouth, and the INTESTINE, which is separated from the pharynx by a slight constriction. In a female worm, locate the GENITAL PORE, roughly one-quarter the distance from the anterior end; the short VAGINA, leading away from the genital pore; and the two UTERI, which in turn lead away from the vagina. The uteri are attached to the much-coiled OVIDUCTS, and these connect to the OVARIES (see Fig. 24.5).

c. Study a prepared slide of a cross section through the anterior region of *Ascaris*. Identify the BODY WALL, consisting of CUTICLE, EPIDERMIS, and a layer of longitudinal MUSCLES arranged in quadrants; the lateral EXCRETORY CANALS and the dorsal and ventral NERVE CORDS; and the conspicuous central PHARYNX, with its characteristically triradiate cavity and muscular walls (see Fig. 24.6).

In cross sections through more posterior regions, identify OVARY and UTERUS in female specimens and TESTES and SPERM DUCTS in male specimens. What is the nature of the body cavity in these worms? Label Fig. 24.7.

d. Examine slide mounts of *Trichinella* and of other parasitic nematodes as available and as directed. Study also living specimens of the class Gastrotricha as well as any other aschelminth material set out.

Fig. 24.7 Sections through the posterior body regions of a male (A) *and a female* (B) *nematode. Label in detail. (Courtesy of Carolina Biological Supply Co.)*

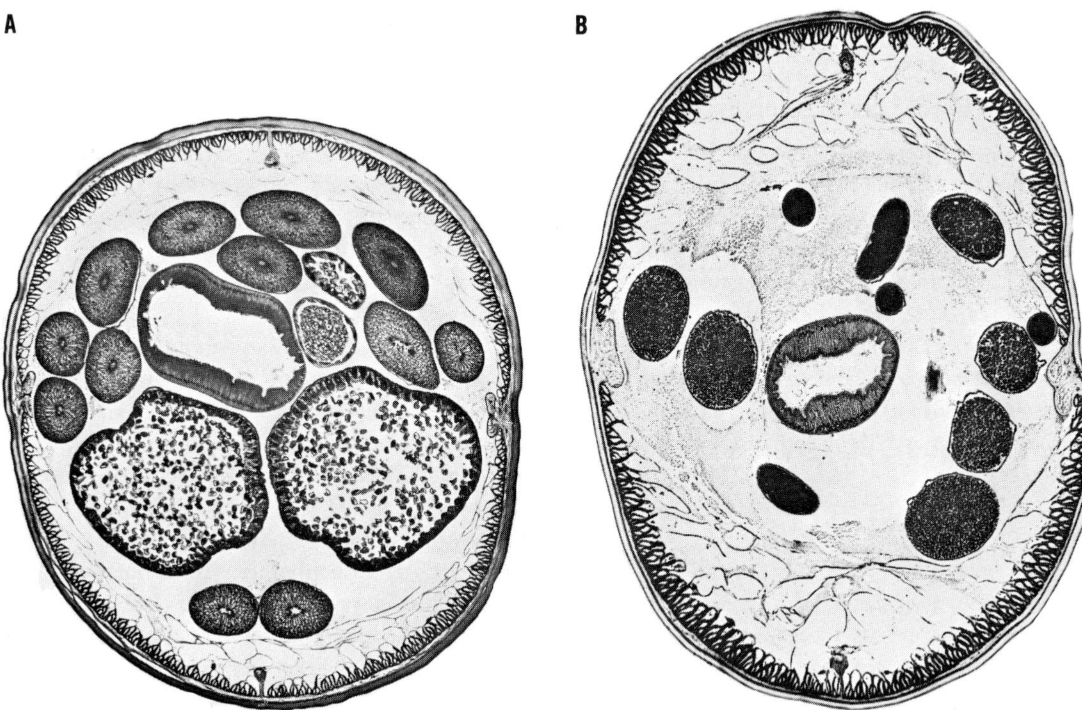

D. other pseudocoelomates

1. Study a slide mount of a spiny-headed worm, phylum Acanthocephala. Identify the spiny PROBOSCIS, the TRUNK, the BODY WALL, and, in the interior, the visible portions of the LEMNISCI, the LIGAMENT SACS, and the REPRODUCTIVE ORGANS. Review the ways of life and the unique structural features of these worms.

2. Examine colonies, specimens, or any other material of the phylum Entoprocta as available and as directed.

E. schizocoelomates: lophophorates

1. *Phylum Ectoprocta: Ectoprocts*

Study preserved colonies and specimens of marine ectoprocts such as *Bugula* and of freshwater ectoprocts such as *Plumatella*. In individual ZOOIDS note the EXOSKELETON, calcareous in the marine types, gelatinous in the freshwater types.

In slide mounts of these animals identify the tentacle-bearing LOPHOPHORE, the U-shaped ALIMENTARY SYSTEM, the ANUS (located outside the lophophore), the COELOM, and the BODY WALL, composed of PERITONEUM, EPIDERMIS, and EXOSKELETON. In freshwater specimens note also the dense, oval STATOBLASTS, located predominantly in the FUNICULUS, a tissue strand between stomach and body wall. What is the function of statoblasts?

2. *Phylum Brachiopoda: Lamp Shells*

Examine a preserved specimen of *Lingula*. Note the dorsal and ventral VALVE and the PEDUNCLE. Carefully remove one of the valves and identify the MANTLE FOLD, the MANTLE CAVITY with LOPHOPHORE, and the posterior mass of internal organs. Using a hand lens, dissect this mass, and with the aid of your text, identify as many of the organs as you can. With what parts of the body does the peduncle connect? What are the function and the internal structure of the peduncle?

IV analysis

1. Describe the structural organization of a planarian. What are its methods of locomotion? What does it have in common with a coelenterate?

2. Where in nature do planaria live? How do they breathe and excrete, and how is internal transport accomplished?

3. Compare the structural organization of flukes and tapeworms with that of planarians. How are the parasitic flatworms adapted to their ways of life? What do you conclude the effect of parasitism to be on structural complexity?

4. Review the life cycle of a fluke, with attention to larval stages and intermediate hosts. Show where transfer from host to host is passive and where active.

5. Review the life cycle of a tapeworm, with attention to larval stages and intermediate hosts. Show where transfer from host to host is passive and where active.

6. Contrast the general acoelomate and pseudocoelomate body organizations. What are the main anatomical differences, and what is the possible adaptive significance of these differences?

7. Describe the structural organization of a rotifer. How does such an animal move, feed, breathe, and excrete, and how is internal transport accomplished?

8. Describe the life cycle of a rotifer. What is parthenogenesis? How do males differ structurally from females, and when do males develop?

9. Describe the structural organization of a nematode. In what respects is this organization like that of a rotifer, and in what respects is it different?

10. Name nematodes of particular importance to man, and show why they are important. Apart from nematodes and rotifers, what other animal types belong to the phylum Aschelminthes, and what characteristics identify this phylum? What phyla other than the Aschelminthes are pseudocoelomate?

11. Describe the anatomical organization of an ectoproct, and show how marine and freshwater types differ. How do these animals (*a*) feed, (*b*) reproduce? Similarly describe the anatomy of a brachiopod. What features differentiate a brachiopod from a clam?

12. Apart from the phyla here studied, which others are (*a*) lophophorate, (*b*) coelomate? Why are entoprocts not classified as lophophorates? Which of the phyla studied in this exercise are the most abundant in terms of species numbers?

exercise 25 metazoa: mollusks and annelids

I materials

Each student

microscope
blank slide
dissecting instruments
dissecting pan, pins
hand lens
Venus, for dissection
Lumbricus, for dissection
Lumbricus, prepared slide, cross section

Class stock

squids, preserved, cut sagittally for study
chitons, snails, clams, other assorted molluscan material, living and/or preserved
Nereis, living, in sea water
leeches, preserved
leeches, whole mounts and/or sections
sipunculids, echiuroids, *Peripatus,* tardigrades, other assorted material of the smaller schizocoelomate groups

II introduction

Among the coelomate animals, one large group (constituting the equivalent of a superphylum) is *schizocoelomate;* that is, the coelom arises in the embryo by a splitting of mesoderm into outer and inner layers, leaving a coelomic body cavity in between. In this superphylum are the phyla Mollusca, Sipunculida, Echiuroida, Annelida, Oncopoda, and Arthropoda. Mollusks and annelids are the principal types to be studied in this exercise.

Mollusks are nonsegmented schizocoelomates, annelids are segmented. The larval development of mollusks typically includes TROCHOPHORE and often also VELIGER stages. The larval development of the aquatic annelids includes a trochophore stage only. Despite the pronounced dissimilarity of a clam and an earthworm, for example, the two phyla appear to be very closely related through a common ancestor. Mollusks today represent the second largest animal phylum; and an ancestral annelid stock has given rise to the largest, namely, the phylum of arthropods, to be examined in the succeeding exercise.

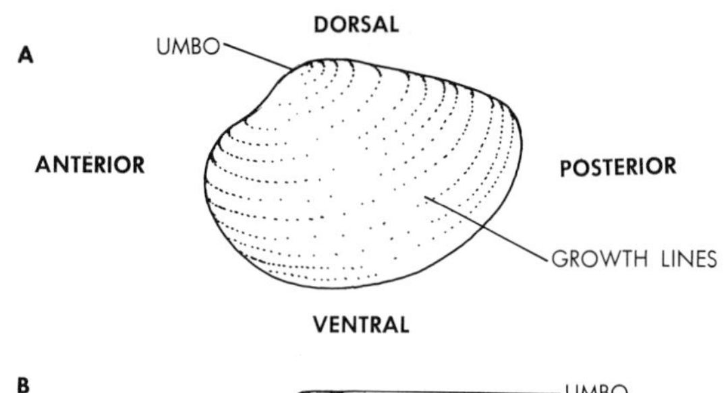

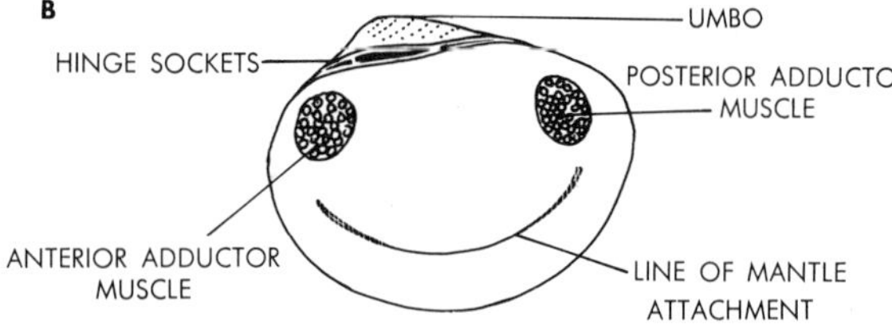

Fig. 25.1 Valve characteristics of a clam. A, *external view of left valve;* B, *internal view of right valve.*

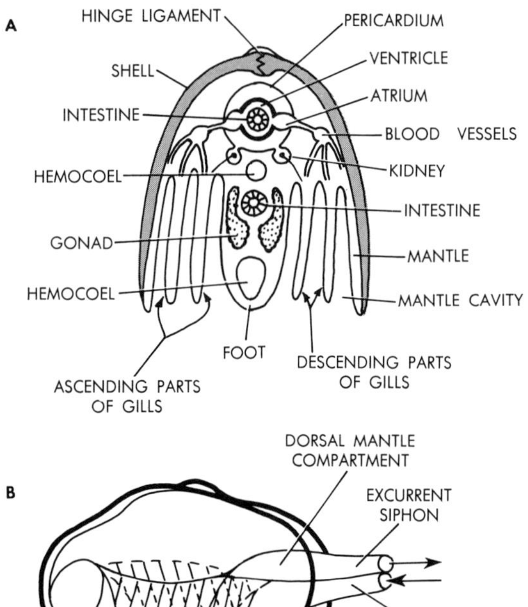

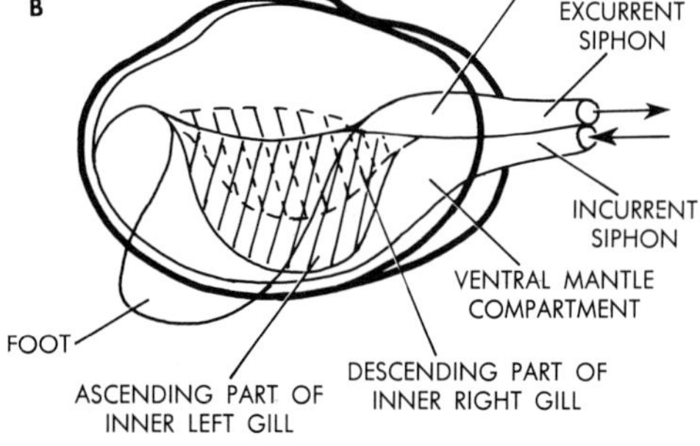

Fig. 25.2 Clam structure. A, *diagram of transverse section;* B, *diagram of lateral view to show interrelations of foot, gills, mantle cavities, and siphons.*

III directions

A. phylum mollusca: mollusks

1. *Class Pelecypoda: Clams*

The clam *Venus* will be used for dissection and study. The exoskeleton of this animal consists of a left and a right VALVE, hinged dorsally by a tough, elastic HINGE LIGAMENT. The more pointed end of the valves marks the posterior end of the animal. Orient the clam accordingly and determine which are the left and right sides.

a. Remove the left valve without injuring any internal tissues. Your instructor may give you supplementary oral directions on how to do this. Carefully separate the MANTLE from the left valve; the mantle is a thin sheet of tissue which normally adheres to the inner surface of the valve. In anterior and posterior regions, you will come to the points where the powerful ADDUCTOR MUSCLES attach to the valve; these muscles pull the valves together. Cut through the anterior and posterior adductors, close to their attachment to the left valve. The valve may then be lifted away carefully and removed from the animal.

Examine the free valve (see also Fig. 25.1). Note the concentric lines of growth on the outside. These lines spread away from the UMBO, the dorsal hump where shell growth starts. On the inside, note the HINGE TEETH, which interlock with corresponding teeth on the right valve when the shell closes. Ascertain how the two valves fit. Note also the positions of the adductor attachments and, running between them and parallel to the margin of the valve, the MANTLE LINE. This line shows where the edge of the mantle tissue has been. Break the shell and examine the broken surface. Note the outer, brown EPIDERMAL LAYER, serving a protective function; the middle PRISMATIC LAYER, composed of minute prisms of calcium carbonate; and the inner, iridescent layer of MOTHER-OF-PEARL. How do pearls form?

b. Study the internal organs of the clam (see also Chap. 12, "The Science of Biology"). Note again the mantle, which lines both valves. Cut the left mantle dorsally, just below its line of attachment, and remove it. This exposes the MANTLE CAVITY and its contents. Among the latter identify the VISCERAL MASS. Extending from it ventrally is the muscular FOOT, and partly overlying it are two pairs of delicate, striated GILLS. Along the posterior margins of the valves, the mantle flaps are grown together and form two openings, a dorsal EXCURRENT SIPHON and a ventral INCURRENT SIPHON. In some clams these siphons are greatly elongated into a muscular tube that can be extended and retracted by the animal (see also Fig. 25.2).

c. Each gill is honeycombed with parallel internal water tubes. PORES on the surface of a gill provide entry into these tubes (see also Chap. 12, "The Science of Biology"). Cut away a small piece of a gill, and with hand lens and/or microscope look for some of these pores. Note too that the external surface of the gill (and also the mantle) is CILIATED. The cilia create a current which draws water into the mantle cavity through the incurrent siphon. Microscopic food particles are strained out by the cilia and are passed over the gill surfaces to the dorsal and anterior part of the animal. Water enters through the gill pores into the water tubes of the gills, and here gas exchange takes place. The water then collects in a chamber within the dorsal edge of the gill. These chambers from all gills unite posteriorly and discharge into the excurrent siphon. Cut carefully along the dorsal edge of a gill and see if you can identify the dorsal water chamber and its posterior exit.

d. Parts of the ALIMENTARY SYSTEM are usually identifiable by their dark contents. Locate the posterior portion of the intestine (along the posterior surface of the posterior adductor muscle) and note that the ANUS discharges into the excurrent siphon. Trace the intestine forward. In the mid-dorsal region of the body, it will be seen to pass into a sac. This sac, the PERICARDIUM, encloses the PERICARDIAL CAVITY, which represents the main part of the coelom of a clam. Slit this sac carefully and examine its contents. The HEART is located in it, consisting of a single VENTRICLE and two thin-walled ATRIA. The intestine passes through the ventricle. The atria lie lateral to and below the ventricle and are attached to the pericardium. They may easily be destroyed in dissection. Leading forward from the ventricle, dorsal to the intestine, is the ANTERIOR AORTA, which supplies the front part of the body; and leading backward, ventral to the intestine, is the POSTERIOR AORTA, which supplies the hind part (see also Fig. 25.3). Follow the

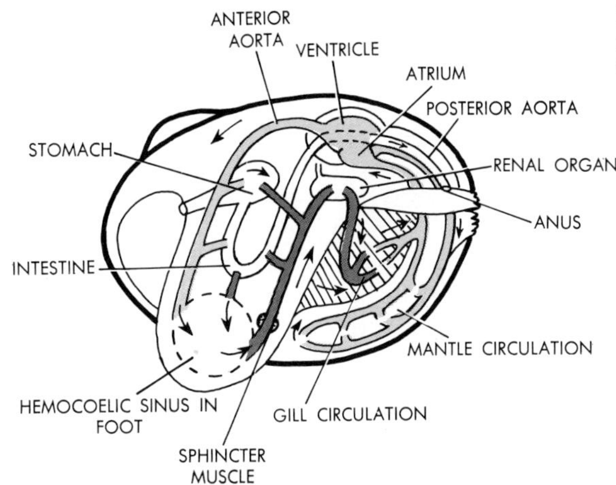

Fig. 25.3 The general pattern of the blood circulation in most clams, diagrammatic. Arterial blood, light-shaded; venous blood, dark-shaded. Oxygenation of blood takes place in the gills and, most particularly, in the mantle. Arrows indicate direction of flow. The sphincter around the vein in the foot accomplishes an accumulation of blood in the foot sinuses and so produces enlargement and stiffening of the foot during locomotion.

intestine a short distance forward, into the visceral mass. Just ventral to the pericardium, on each side, locate the brown KIDNEY. Cut into one and observe that it is a U-shaped tube.

e. Locate the MOUTH, just below the anterior adductor muscle and, between two pairs of ciliated flaps, the LABIAL PALPS. Food strained out by the gill cilia collects in this buccal region and is carried from here into the alimentary system. Find the short ESOPHAGUS, which leads from the mouth to the spherical STOMACH. This organ lies in the visceral mass, which cannot be easily studied. Carefully cut the visceral mass and the foot into exact left and right halves and examine the cut surfaces. The pasty substance consists partly of REPRODUCTIVE ORGANS and partly of DIGESTIVE GLANDS (HEPATOPANCREAS). The latter are greenish brown, and embedded within them is the STOMACH. The intestine emerges from the stomach, forms two loops within the visceral mass, then runs dorsally and through the pericardial cavity. Trace any of the intestinal coils that are exposed.

f. Review the structures of the clam, system by

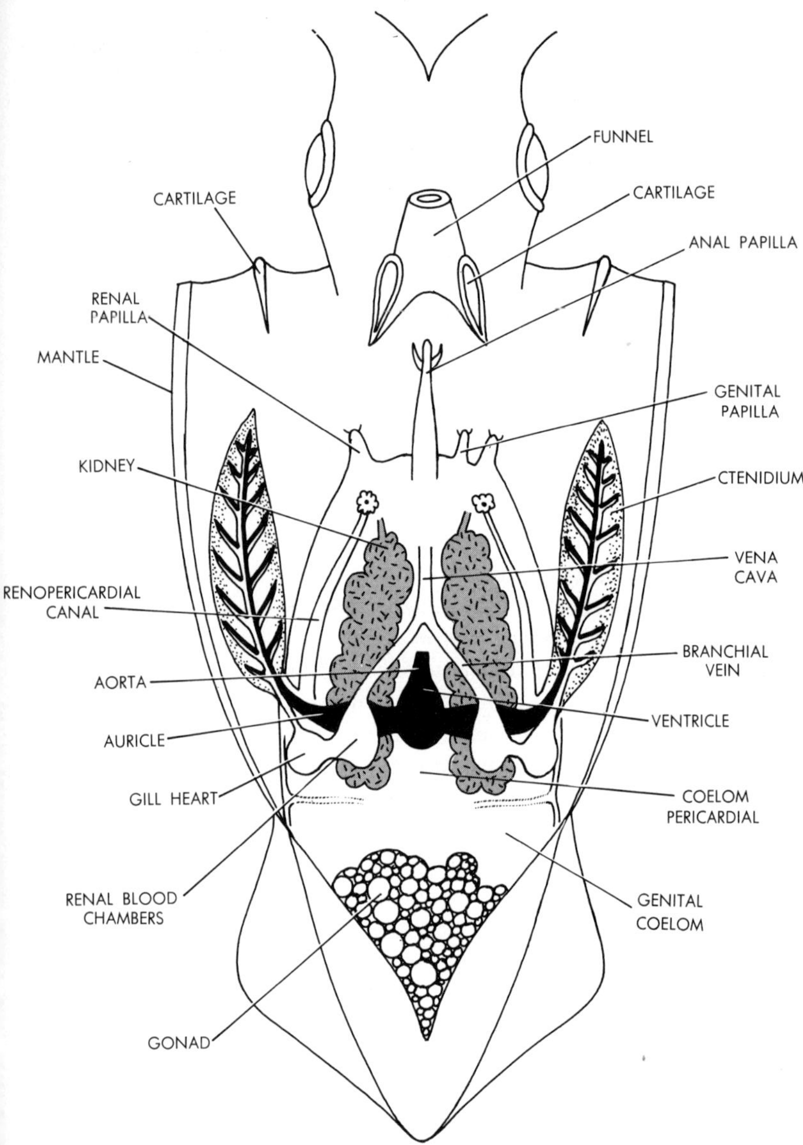

Fig. 25.4 Ventral dissection of a squid, diagrammatic.

system, and make sure that you understand their architectural arrangement and their functioning.

2. *Class Cephalopoda: Squids, Octopuses*

Several preserved squids cut sagittally will be available for study (see also Fig. 25.4 and Chap. 12, "The Science of Biology"). In such a preparation note the HEAD-FOOT, with EYES and TENTACLES. Examine the SUCKERS on the tentacles and ascertain if all tentacles are alike. In the interior of the head, identify the buccal mass, with JAWS and RADULA, and the continuation of the alimentary system as the ESOPHAGUS. Locate the BRAIN GANGLIA within a cartilage CAPSULE. Behind the head note the external muscular MANTLE and the FINS. Underneath the mantle on the upper side lies the chitinous PEN. Locate the COLLAR at the forward edge of the mantle, the FUNNEL just behind the head on the lower side, and the MANTLE CAVITY. The latter communicates with the exterior via the funnel and the mantle collar. Within the mantle cavity identify the GILLS and the ANUS, the latter located on an ANAL PAPILLA. Also opening into the mantle are the reproductive and excretory ducts. In the interior of the visceral hump, trace the U-shaped alimentary tract and note STOMACH, DIGESTIVE GLAND, and INTESTINE. Also locate the KIDNEYS and, in the hind region, the REPRODUCTIVE ORGANS within the COELOM. Portions of the HEART and of other parts of the circulatory system may be identifiable as well.

Check the parts studied on this sectioned specimen against information in your text, and make sure you understand the functions of all organs seen.

3. *Other Mollusks*

Available for examination will be a variety of living and/or preserved chitons, snails, clams, and other mollusks. Study these as directed by the instructor.

B. phylum annelida: segmented worms

1. *Class Polychaeta*

Examine living specimens of the clamworm *Nereis* in bowls of sea water. Note the SEGMENTS of the worms and the lateral segmental appendages, or PARAPODIA. What is their function? Do all segments possess parapodia? Are all parapodia alike? Feel for the BRISTLES on the parapodia.

The pulsing of the DORSAL BLOOD VESSEL may sometimes be observed through the body wall. What is the direction of this peristaltic motion? Is the VENTRAL NERVE CORD visible through the body wall?

Gently hold an animal down to the bottom of the bowl and examine the HEAD (see also Chap.

12, "The Science of Biology"). The first segment, or PROSTOMIUM, carries four EYES, two fleshy lateral PALPS, and two small median TENTACLES. The second segment, or PERISTOMIUM, bears the MOUTH and also possesses tentacles. The PHARYNX may be everted inside out through the mouth, and the pharynx then projects forward under the first head segment. Black JAWS are found anteriorly on the everted pharynx.

Return the animals to the class stock, and study the internal anatomy of annelids in the following section.

2. *Class Oligochaeta: Earthworms*

a. Examine the external features of *Lumbricus*, the familiar earthworm. Locate MOUTH and ANUS, and, by feeling with your fingers, locate the position of the segmental BRISTLES. Using a hand lens, find out how many bristles there are per segment, and where they are. Count the segments from the anterior end, and determine the segmental position of the swollen region, the CLITELLUM. What is the function of this region? On the 15th segment from the anterior end, locate the ventral openings of the SPERM DUCTS, situated in tiny swellings. On the 14th segment, find the minute ventral openings of the OVIDUCTS. And on the 9th and 10th segments, find the paired openings of the SPERM RECEPTACLES.

b. Put the animal into a dissecting pan, dorsal side up, and pin it down at the anterior and posterior ends. With fine scissors, cut through the body wall of the clitellum along the mid-dorsal line, and continue the cut forward to the anterior end and also backward for some distance. Make the cut shallow so that only the body wall is being separated. Note the SEPTA, membranous transverse partitions which separate adjacent segments internally. Cut these septa carefully, and pin the edges of the cut body wall flat to the pan. Cover the worm with water and study the interior, using a hand lens where desirable (see also Chap. 12, "The Science of Biology").

c. In the ALIMENTARY TRACT, identify PHARYNX, ESOPHAGUS, CROP, GIZZARD, and INTESTINE. Determine the function of each part. Trace the DORSAL BLOOD VESSEL along the mid-dorsal line. In the region of the esophagus locate the LATERAL HEARTS, which connect the dorsal blood vessel with the VENTRAL BLOOD VESSEL. How many pairs of hearts are there? Carefully remove the anterior parts of the alimentary tract and note, on each side of the esophagus, three large, rather white SPERM SACS. These store sperms produced in the testes (the latter are small and difficult to find). In mating, mature sperms pass from sperm sacs into the sperm ducts which, as noted in a above, exit in segment 15. Such sperms are deposited into the SPERM RECEPTACLES (segments 9 and 10) of the mating partner. Locate the sperm receptacles along the inside of the ventral body wall. The female parts of the reproductive system are also small and difficult to locate (but see Chap. 12, "The Science of Biology"). Underneath the intestine identify the VENTRAL NERVE CORD and its segmental thickenings, the GANGLIA. Near the head end, try to make out the ring of nerve tissue surrounding the pharynx. The dorsal portions of this ring are the BRAIN GANGLIA.

d. Make a microscopic study of the prepared slide of a cross section through an earthworm. In the BODY WALL, identify the CUTICLE, the EPIDERMIS, and the layers of CIRCULAR and LONGITUDINAL MUSCLES. Find the mesodermal PERITONEUM lining the COELOM between body wall and intestine. Laterally within the body cavity, note the sections through the excretory NEPHRIDIAL TUBULES. Locate the VENTRAL NERVE CORD and the dorsal and ventral BLOOD VESSELS. Study the cell layers of the INTESTINE. Note the TYPHLOSOLE, an inward fold of the intestinal wall. What is the adaptive advantage of this fold? Label Fig. 25.5.

3. *Class Hirudinea: Leeches*

Examine preserved specimens and also slide mounts and sections of leeches. Locate the anterior and posterior SUCKERS, the CLITELLUM, and the external ANNULI, transverse creases in the body surface. Are these equivalent to metameres? Locate the ingestive SAWS anteriorly in the pharynx and trace the alimentary system. Note the extensive diverticula in this system. In a cross section, identify body parts corresponding to those of earthworms.

C. smaller schizocoelomate phyla

Representatives of the phyla Sipunculida,

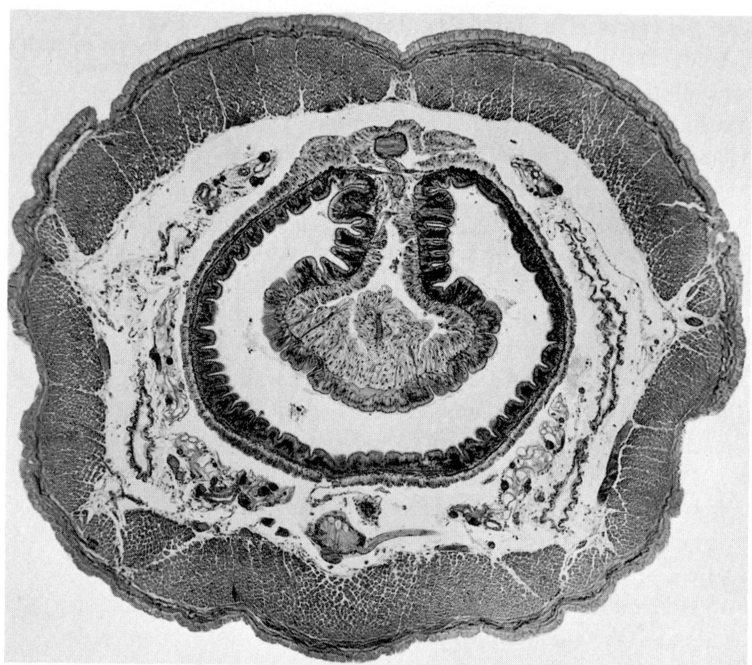

Fig. 25.5 Cross section through an earthworm. Label in detail. (Courtesy of Carolina Biological Supply Co.)

Echiuroida, and Oncopoda (for example, *Peripatus*) may be available. If so, examine these with the aid of your text and as directed by the instructor.

IV analysis

1. Describe the path of water through a clam, showing in detail which structures form part of this path. How and where does gas exchange occur?

2. Describe the structure and architectural arrangement of the alimentary system of a clam, and show how and where ingestion, digestion, and egestion occur.

3. Describe the makeup of the (*a*) circulatory system, (*b*) excretory system, (*c*) nervous system, of a clam.

4. What structural and functional features adapt a clam to its particular way of life? What is this way of life? How does a clam (*a*) move, (*b*) protect itself, (*c*) reproduce, develop, and grow?

5. Describe (*a*) the way of life of a squid, (*b*) the anatomical organization of a squid, (*c*) the manner in which way of life and anatomical organization are correlated adaptively.

6. Name and define the classes of mollusks. Which class probably resembles the presumed molluscan ancestor most? Describe the probable characteristics of this ancestor and show how the structural organization of each class has deviated from the ancestral pattern.

7. Describe the basic body organization of an annelid, system by system. Show how *Nereis* and *Lumbricus* differ in details of organization.

8. How does an annelid (*a*) exchange gases, (*b*) move, (*c*) excrete? How is the blood circulation maintained?

9. What is the adaptive significance of segmentation? Apart from annelids, which other animal groups are segmented?

10. Describe the way of life of an earthworm. What does it feed on? In what respects is its alimentary system adapted to this?

11. Contrast the nervous systems of (*a*) clams and squids, (*b*) clams and earthworms. Correlate the differences with the way of life of these animals.

12. Name the classes of annelids. Show how earthworms and leeches differ in (*a*) structural organization, (*b*) way of life.

13. What is the function of a clitellum? Describe the general organization of the reproductive system of an earthworm, and show how these animals mate and reproduce.

14. What is hermaphroditism? What is the adaptive advantage of this phenomenon, and in which animal groups so far studied in the laboratory is it encountered?

15. Describe the general structure of a trochophore larva. Of which animal phyla is such a larva characteristic? How does this larval form differ from a veliger? Show how mollusks and annelids differ in development after the trochophore stage, and describe the general nature of these developmental events.

exercise 26 metazoa: arthropods

I materials

Each student

dissecting instruments
dissecting pan, pins
hand lens
Limulus, living or preserved, for examination
scorpion, preserved, for examination
crayfish, for dissection
grasshopper, for dissection

class stock

for examination:

trilobites, plaster casts
spiders, assorted, preserved
assorted other arachnids, preserved
brine shrimps, copepods, barnacles, other crustacea, living or preserved
centipedes, millipedes, preserved
assorted insects, preserved

II introduction

Constituting the largest of all phyla, arthropods are schizocoelomates undoubtedly derived from annelid stock. Like annelids, arthropods possess segmented bodies; but the segments here have become diversified greatly in function. It is partly to this segmental specialization and division of labor that arthropods owe their success. Other distinguishing features of the phylum will be encountered in the course of the study below.

Three subphyla are recognized, namely, the extinct TRILOBITES, the jawless and antennaless CHELICERATES, and the jaw- and antenna-possessing MANDIBULATES. Representatives of each of these groups will be examined in this exercise.

III directions

A. subphylum chelicerata

1. *Class Xiphosurida: Horseshoe Crabs*

Study a preserved or living specimen of *Limulus*. The body is subdivided into CEPHALOTHORAX, ABDOMEN, and TELSON (spine). On the dorsal side note the lateral COMPOUND EYES on the conspicuous CARAPACE covering the cephalothorax. On the ventral side, identify the following segmental appendages in anteroposterior sequence (see also Chap. 12, "The Science of Biology"): on the cephalothorax, CHELICERAE, PEDIPALPS, four pairs of WALKING LEGS, and CHILARIA; on the abdomen, OPERCULUM (with reproductive openings) and five pairs of GILL BOOKS. All cephalothoracic appendages are CHELATE, that is, equipped with terminal pincers. The function of the chilaria is unknown; what are the functions of the other appendages? Where is the mouth located? On a walking leg, identify the basal piece, or COXOPODITE, and on it locate the toothed GNATHOBASE. What is the function of the latter? How does *Limulus* swim?

2. Class Arachnida: Scorpions, Spiders, Mites, Ticks

a. Examine a preserved specimen of a scorpion. Note the CEPHALOTHORAX and the ABDOMEN, the last few segments of the latter formed into a "tail" with a terminal, poison-sting–containing TELSON. Identify the following segmental appendages in anteroposterior sequence (see also Fig. 26.1): on the cephalothorax, CHELICERAE (small), PEDIPALPS (large), and four pairs of WALKING LEGS; on the abdomen, OPERCULUM (with reproductive openings), comblike PECTINES, and four pairs of LUNG BOOKS. Are these appendages homologous to those of *Limulus*? Are gnathobases present? What is the function of the pectines?

b. With a hand lens, and drawing on information from your text, study the external features and appendages of a preserved specimen of a spider. What kinds and how many eyes are present? Compare the structural organization with that of a scorpion.

B. subphylum mandibulata: class crustacea class crustacea

1. External Features

In a preserved specimen of the crayfish *Cambarus*, note the chitinous, lime-impregnated EXOSKELETON. Anteriorly it forms the CARAPACE, which covers the dorsal and lateral surfaces of the fused CEPHALOTHORAX. The posterior part of the body, or ABDOMEN, is covered by segmentally arranged chitinous plates (TERGUM dorsally, STERNUM ventrally, a PLEURON on each side).

Note the stalked COMPOUND EYES, the two pairs of ANTENNAE, the MOUTH APPENDAGES, the LARGE CLAWS, the WALKING LEGS, the SWIMMERETS on the abdomen, and, on the last abdominal segment, the broad UROPODS. These latter appendages together with the TELSON form the fan-shaped "tail."

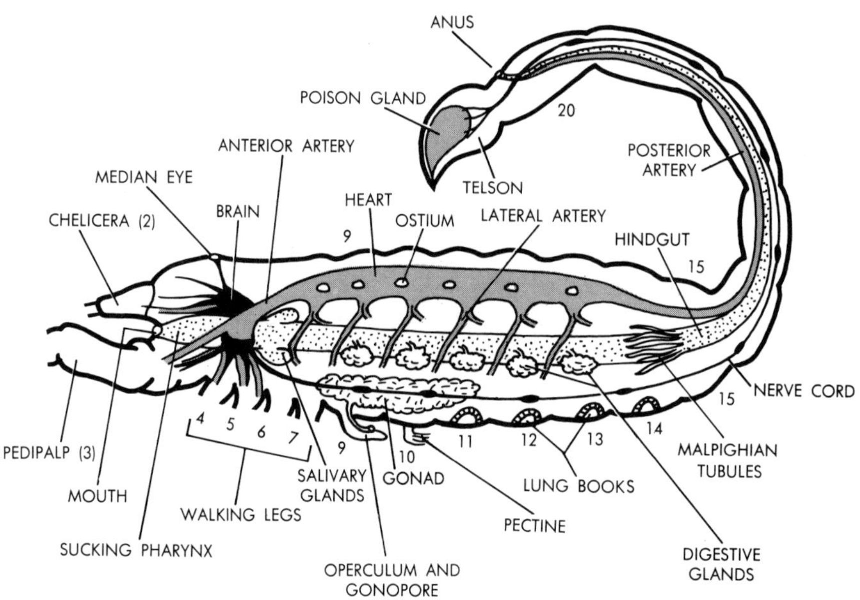

Fig. 26.1 The interior structure of a scorpion. Segments are numbered according to embryonic count.

All appendages are SERIALLY HOMOLOGOUS, that is, in early development and basic adult structure they are all alike, even though they often differ markedly in detailed form and in function. This basic structure may be examined in one of the abdominal swimmerets. The appendage is attached to the body by a basal piece composed of COXOPODITE and BASIPODITE. Jointed to this are two pieces, an outside EXOPODITE and an inside ENDOPODITE. Identify this basic BIRAMOUS (or two-branched) structure also as you study the other appendages below.

Remove the appendages of the left side one by one, starting at the posterior end and making sure that the WHOLE appendage is taken off right at the base. Keep track of both the NUMBERS and TYPES of appendages so removed (for example, lay them out in sequence on a sheet of paper). From the abdomen you should obtain, back to front, one TELSON, one UROPOD, and four SWIMMERETS. In female crayfish, the 1ST ABDOMINAL APPENDAGE is small or absent, and in the male it functions in sperm transfer during mating. Remove it if present. To obtain the thoracic segments, remove the left side of the carapace with scissors. This will expose a GILL CHAMBER and the GILLS, attached to all thoracic segments except the first. The gills represent EPIPODITES, outgrowths from the coxopodites (actually from the body wall near the bases of the coxopodites; see Fig. 26.2). Remove these thoracic appendages with their gills. They are, back to front, four WALKING LEGS, one LARGE CLAW, and the 3D, 2D, and 1ST MAXILLIPEDS. The last named in part serve sensory functions, and in part play a role in handling and tearing pieces of food. From the head segments carefully remove, in backward sequence, the 2D MAXILLA, the 1ST MAXILLA, the JAW (mandible), and the 2D and 1ST ANTENNAE. Note the opening at the base of the 2d antenna. This is the exit of the ANTENNAL GLAND, or GREEN GLAND, the excretory organ of crustacea. The eyes are not segmental structures. Similarly not segmental are the LABRUM (upper lip) and METASTOMA (lower lip) guarding the mouth.

In serial order, review the structure and the functions of all appendages.

2. *Internal Structure*

With a scalpel, carefully loosen the remainder of the carapace and the dorsal exoskeleton of the abdomen from the underlying membranous EPIDERMIS (or HYPODERMIS). Remove the exoskeleton and cautiously slit the hypodermis to expose the internal organs. Whenever muscles are in the way, DO NOT tear them but CUT them with scissors. Cover the animal with water and study the following (see also Chap. 12, "The Science of Biology").

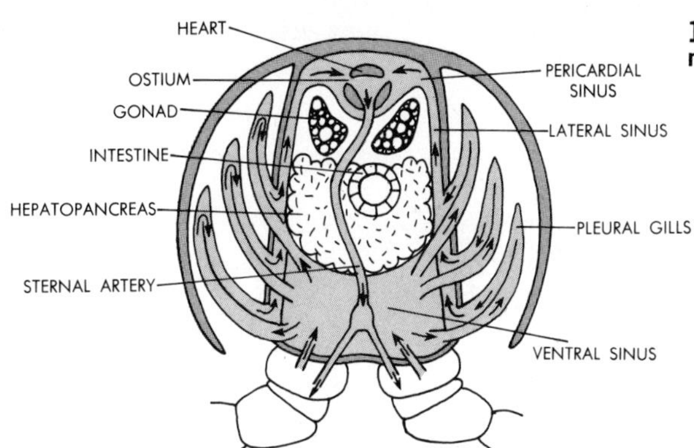

Fig. 26.2 Gills and blood circulation. Arrows indicate direction of blood flow. Blood in the ventral sinus and in parts of the gills is venous; blood in the other spaces shown is arterial.

The small HEART, embedded in the PERICARDIAL CAVITY, is located in the mid-dorsal region. Are arteries visible? Just in front of the heart is the STOMACH, a large sac containing in its wall a grinding structure, the GASTRIC MILL (see also Fig. 26.3). Follow the stomach posteriorly, and trace the INTESTINE to the ANUS, located ventrally in the last abdominal segment. Anteriorly the stomach leads into a short ESOPHAGUS which passes ventrally to the MOUTH. Locate the mouth and probe through it into the stomach. To each side of the stomach are the large DIGESTIVE GLANDS (HEPATOPANCREAS). Behind them, to each side of the heart, are the REPRODUCTIVE ORGANS. Using a hand lens, distinguish their texture from that of the digestive glands. Ducts lead from the reproductive organs to exterior openings on the coxopodites of certain of the walking legs.

Starting in the abdomen and working forward, carefully remove muscles and other structures to expose the VENTRAL NERVE CORDS for their entire

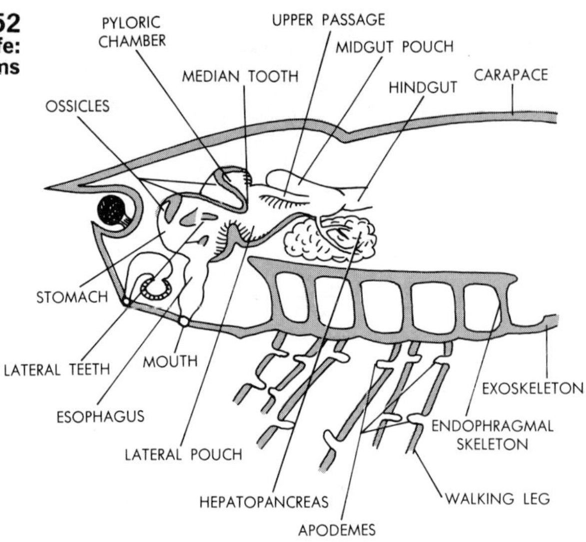

Fig. 26.3 Some of the internal structures of the cephalothorax. Apodemes are breakage planes in the walking legs. The endophragmal skeleton serves for attachment of the leg musculature.

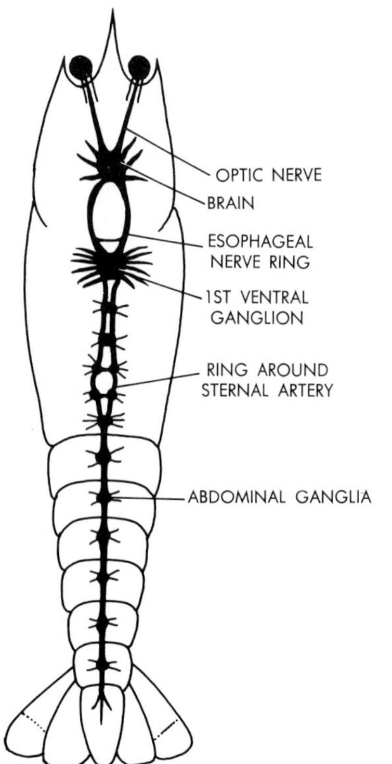

Fig. 26.4 Diagram of the nervous system.

length (see also Fig. 26.4). Note the segmental ganglionic thickenings. Try to identify the ring of nerve tissue circling the esophagus and the BRAIN GANGLIA, which are the anterior portions of this ring. Also locate the saclike GREEN GLANDS near the eyes.

3. *Other Crustacea*

Examine living and/or preserved brine shrimps, copepods, barnacles, and other crustacea as available and as directed by the instructor. Compare and contrast the organization of each form seen with that of the crayfish.

C. subphylum mandibulata: class insecta

1. *External Features*

Study a preserved specimen of the grasshopper *Romalea*. Identify HEAD, THORAX, and ABDOMEN. On the head (see also Fig. 26.5), locate the single pair of ANTENNAE, the pair of COMPOUND EYES, and the three small OCELLI. The mouth parts are the LABRUM, an anterior flap functioning as upper lip; the MANDIBLES, hard biting jaws; a pair of MAXILLAE, each bearing a jointed PALP; and the LABRIUM, which also bears palps and is homologous to the 2d maxillae of crustacea.

In the thorax, composed of three segments, the last two each bear a pair of WINGS. Attached to each thoracic segment is a pair of LEGS. Each leg consists, from the base outward, of a short COXA, a short TROCHANTER, a long FEMUR, a long TIBIA, and a terminal TARSUS, composed of several small joints.

The ten abdominal segments are without appendages. In males, the posterior end of the body is rounded and blunt and curves upward. In females, four curved pointed processes project from the hind end. These are the OVIPOSITORS, used in digging a hole in which eggs are laid. Laterally, in the thin membranes between the thoracic and abdominal segments, find the SPIRACLES, small valve-equipped openings which admit air into the TRACHEAE within the body. How many pairs of spiracles can you identify? The three or four most anterior pairs are inhalatory, piping air directly to all body tissues. The other spiracles are exhalatory (see also Fig. 26.6).

2. *Internal Structure*

Open the thorax and abdomen along the mid-dorsal line and pin down the flaps of body wall (see also Chap. 12, "The Science of Biology"). The HEART, which has probably been damaged during the dissection, lies dorsally in the abdomen. The large REPRODUCTIVE ORGANS fill much of the abdomen. Using a hand lens, can you locate some of the main trunks of the TRACHEAL SYSTEM, leading inward from the spiracles? Find the ALIMENTARY TRACT and identify the short ESOPHAGUS; the large CROP in the thorax; the STOMACH, into which open six pairs of GASTRIC POUCHES; and the INTESTINE, into the posterior portion of which open the excretory MALPIGHIAN TUBULES. Note that only the stomach region, constituting the MIDGUT, is digestive and absorptive; the anterior FOREGUT and posterior HIND GUT are lined with chitin, which is continuous with the exoskeleton. Remove the alimentary system and locate the VENTRAL NERVE CORDS. How many ganglia can you identify?

3. *Other Mandibulates*

Study the external features, including the segmental organization and the appendages, of the various centipedes, millipedes, and other insects set out for examination. Compare with your observations on the grasshopper.

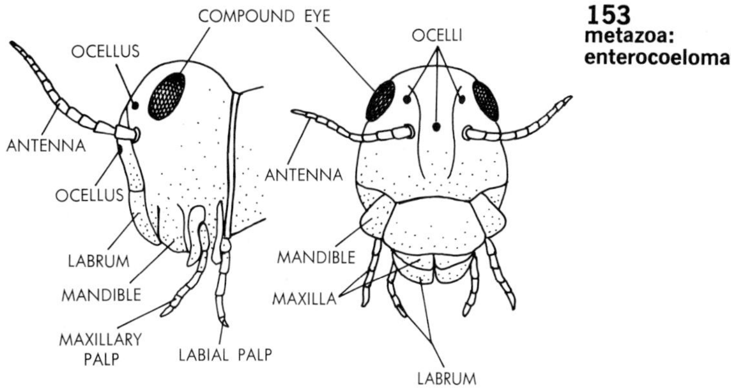

Fig. 26.5 External structure and appendages of the insect head.

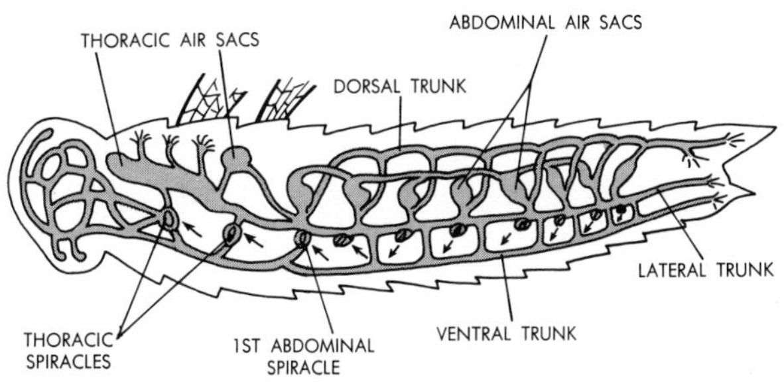

Fig. 26.6 The tracheal breathing system.

IV analysis

1. List the diagnostic characteristics of the phylum Arthropoda. Name the subphyla and classes within the phylum and review the identifying features of each such group.

2. Describe the segmental organization of the chelicerate body. How many segments are there in each body division? Name the appendages of each segment of (*a*) a horseshoe crab, (*b*) a scorpion, and state their functions.

3. Review the basic structure of an arthropod appendage and show how this structure is or is not modified in the appendages of chelicerates, crustaceans, and insects. What different functions do the appendages of arthropods serve?

4. Describe the segmental organization of the crustacean body. How many segments are there in each body division, and name the segmental appendages. Which appendages are not segmental?

5. Describe the blood circulation of an arthropod. Describe the methods of breathing encountered in different arthropod classes. Describe the organs and the patterns of excretion in (*a*) aquatic, (*b*) terrestrial, arthropods.

6. What are the adaptive (*a*) advantages, (*b*) disadvantages, of the arthropod exoskeleton? Show how the exoskeleton contributes to the success of arthropods.

7. Describe the internal organization of a crustacean. Where does a crayfish live, and what is its way of life?

8. Describe the segmental organization of the insect body. How many segments are there in each body division? Name the appendages of each segment of the grasshopper and state their function.

9. Compare the segmental organization of crustacea and insects. Which segments of one group appear to be homologous with which segments of the other?

10. Describe the internal organization of an insect. Show how it differs from that of a crustacean.

11. What is serial homology? Contrast the serial homology encountered in annelids and arthropods. What is the adaptive advantage of serial homology?

12. How can one tell the difference between (*a*) centipedes and millipedes, (*b*) spiders and insects, (*c*) butterflies and moths, (*d*) crayfishes and lobsters? What makes barnacles crustaceans?

13. What is the organization of the arthropod nervous system? Describe the various sense organs encountered in the phylum. What are the structural and functional differences between compound eyes and simple eyes (ocelli)?

14. Describe the processes of development in (*a*) crustacea, (*b*) insects. What are the larval forms of each group, and how do the larvae become adults?

15. Name one or more arthropod types exhibiting (*a*) polymorphism, (*b*) sessilism, (*c*) parasitism. Name some terrestrial crustacea and aquatic insects. List some of the main orders of insects, and for each name a representative animal.

exercise 27 metazoa: entero-coelomates

I materials

Each student

microscope
dissecting instruments
dissecting pan, pins
Asterias, for dissection
tunicate tadpole, whole mount
Ciona, Molgula, or other solitary tunicate for dissection
amphioxus, preserved
amphioxus, whole mount

Each 2 or more students

Sagitta, preserved or whole mount
sea cucumber, preserved (for dissection if possible)
acorn worm, prepared slide, cross section through pharyngeal region

Class stock

sea urchins, living and/or preserved
sand dollars, preserved
ophiuroids, other assorted echinoderm material, preserved
acorn worms, preserved or demonstration specimens

II introduction

Five phyla are enterocoelomate, namely, the Chaetognatha, Pogonophora, Echinodermata, Hemichordata, and Chordata. In all of them, mesoderm typically arises as outpouchings from the embryonic endoderm, and the cavities of these pouches represent the coelom. Echinoderms are bilaterally symmetrical as embryos and larvae but become radially symmetrical as adults. All other groups are bilateral also as adults.

This exercise will deal with representatives of all enterocoelomate phyla except the Pogonophora, but the emphasis will be on echinoderms and on two subphyla of the chordates, namely, the nonsegmented Urochordata and the segmented Cephalochordata. The third and most important chordate subphylum, the Vertebrata, is studied in exercises 1 through 6, at the beginning of this manual.

III directions

A. phylum chaetognatha: arrowworms

Study a preserved specimen or a slide mount of *Sagitta*. Note HEAD, TRUNK, TAIL, and the lateral and tail FINS. In the head region, locate the chitinous GRASPING SPINES and the interior muscles moving these spines. In the trunk note the coelomic BODY CAVITY, the LONGITUDINAL SEPTUM, and the transverse TRUNK-TAIL SEPTUM. Trace the course of the ALIMENTARY SYSTEM. Identify the OVARIES just in front of and the TESTES just behind the trunk-tail septum. With the aid of your text ascertain if any other organs or body parts can be identified. Review the way of life of these animals.

B. phylum echinodermata: spiny-skinned animals

1. *Class Asteroidea: Starfishes*

a. Examine a preserved specimen of *Asterias*. Note the CENTRAL DISK and the five ARMS. What is the symmetry? On the upper or ABORAL SURFACE, locate the MADREPORITE, a brownish circular spot along the edge of the central disk, between two of the arms. (These two are referred to as the BIVIUM; the other three are the TRIVIUM.) Observe the madreporite with a hand lens. What is the function of this structure? With the lens, examine an arm under water. Note the blunt CALCAREOUS SPINES projecting from the surface, and between the spines, the pincer-shaped PEDICELLARIAE. What is their function? Identify also the transparent, tubular SKIN GILLS. At the tip of each arm find the red EYESPOT.

On the ORAL SURFACE, locate the central MOUTH, protected by large spines. Running along the middle of each arm is an AMBULACRAL GROOVE, studded with TUBE FEET. Identify the SUCTION CUPS at the ends of the tube feet. Pluck away the tube feet from one area and determine how many rows of tube feet each arm contains. In the valley of each ambulacral groove, identify the RADIAL NERVE CORD extending to the tip of each arm.

b. Place the animal aboral side up and remove the upper body wall of the trivium and the central disk. To do this, cut off the tip of one of the arms of the trivium, and with scissors cut CAREFULLY through the body wall along each side of the arm. Repeat with the other two arms of the trivium, and let the cuts join at the central disk. Then put the specimen into water, and starting at the arm tips, cautiously lift off the upper body wall. Separate away any internal organs that may be adhering and leave all internal organs intact. Cut off the freed body wall near the central disk. Now cut along the upper margin of the central disk until you come to the madreporite. Here cut around this structure, and carefully lift off and remove the upper body wall of the central disk. Again make sure you do not injure the internal organs. Consult the illustrations in your text to aid in the examination below (for example, Chap. 13, "The Science of Biology").

In the central disk, note the large saclike STOMACH, which fills most of the space. A short INTESTINE joins the stomach to the aboral body wall which you removed. The oral CARDIAC portion of the stomach is thick-walled and can be everted inside out through the mouth. The aboral PYLORIC portion is thin-walled, and into it lead five pairs of large DIGESTIVE GLANDS. Each arm contains one pair of these glands, which fill most of the space within the arm. Remove the glands from one arm, and locate the pair of feathery REPRODUCTIVE ORGANS extending into the arm. These organs lead to the exterior through ducts opening in the angles between the arms. Along the floor of the oral body wall, on each side of the median ridge, find the bulbous AMPULLAE of the tube feet. How many rows of ampullae are there? Split the median ridge lengthwise and locate the RADIAL CANAL, which communicates with the ampullae and the tube feet via short LATERAL CANALS. Follow a radial canal into the central disk and find its juncture with the RING CANAL, which encircles the mouth. Identify also the STONE CANAL, leading from the madreporite to the ring canal.

Determine or review functions of all structures seen.

2. *Other Echinoderms*

a. Class Holothuroidea: sea cucumbers. On a preserved specimen, note the MOUTH, the ORAL TENTACLES, the leathery BODY WALL, and the arrangement of the TUBE FEET. Dissect this specimen by making a longitudinal cut through the body wall, or examine a predissected preparation

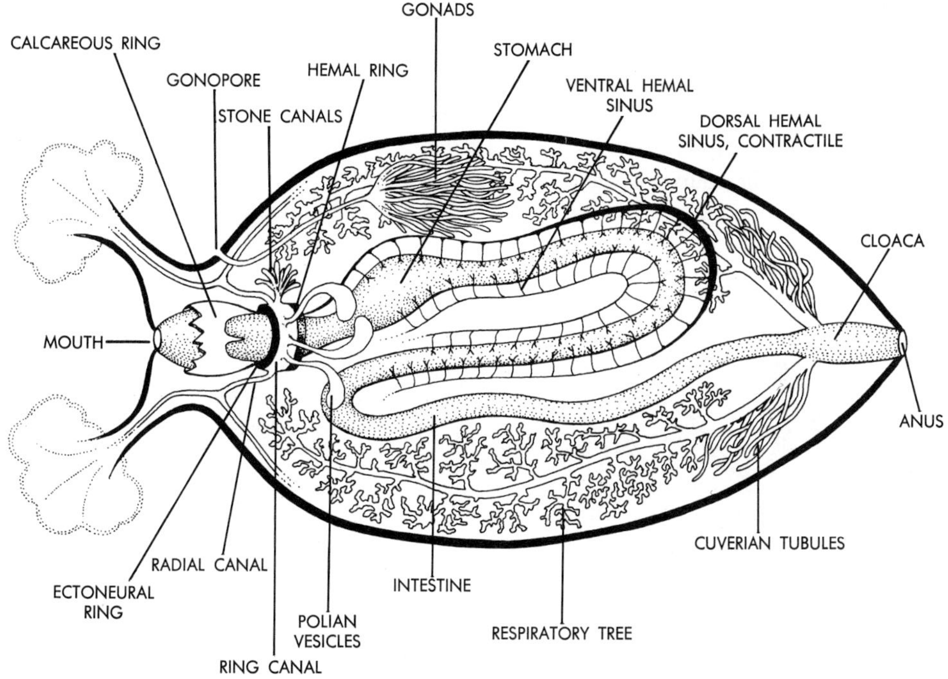

Fig. 27.1 The internal structure of a sea cucumber, diagrammatic.

(see also Fig. 27.1). Note the coiled ALIMENTARY SYSTEM and, attached to the cloacal region, the branched RESPIRATORY TREES, which fill much of the body cavity. Near the oral side, locate the CALCAREOUS RING encircling the pharynx and, near this ring, the RING CANAL of the water-vascular system. Ascertain if you can identify the five RADIAL CANALS emanating from the ring canal. If so trace these into the body.

b. Class Echinoidea: sea urchins, sand dollars. Observe a living or preserved sea urchin and note the MOVABLE SPINES, the delicate TUBE FEET, and, on the oral side, the central leathery ORAL DISK with MOUTH and five TEETH. Examine a dry skeleton of a sea urchin and note the fused CALCAREOUS PLATES. How many rows of such plates are present, and how many of these bear perforations for the tube feet? If the instructor so directs, dissect a preserved sea urchin and identify as many organs and body parts as you can. Examine also a preserved sand dollar and locate MOUTH, ANUS (along the edge of the disk), movable SPINES, and the oral and aboral radial sets of bands along which the tube feet protrude in living animals.

c. If other echinoderm material is set out, examine it as directed by the instructor.

C. phylum hemichordata: hemichordates

Study a preserved or demonstration specimen of an acorn worm. Identify the anterior PROBOSCIS, the COLLAR, and the TRUNK. At the junction between proboscis and collar locate the MOUTH, and on the anterior trunk region note the upfolded GENITAL RIDGES. The paired row of GILL SLITS may be hidden by these ridges.

In a prepared slide of a cross section through the pharyngeal region, find the relatively large central space (see also Fig. 27.2). The ventral part of this space is a portion of the alimentary pharynx, continuous with the esophagus posteriorly, and the upper part is a portion of the breathing pharynx; it communicates via gill slits on each side with the lateral BRANCHIAL SACS, which in their turn open to the outside through anterior gill pores. Identify the epidermis and, immediately underneath it along the dorsal and ventral midline, the dorsal and ventral nerve cords, respectively. Underneath these cords note, if possible, the dorsal and ventral blood vessels. Portions of the reproductive organs will be found in the lateral body regions, extending into the genital ridge on each side of the body.

From these observations and with the aid of your text, review the course of water and food in the interior of the worm.

D. phylum chordata: chordates

1. *Subphylum Urochordata: Tunicates*

a. Examine a prepared whole mount of a tunicate tadpole under the microscope (see also Chap. 13, "The Science of Biology"). Note the prominent TAIL, containing the dorsal (hollow) NERVE CORD and, just ventral to it, the NOTOCHORD.

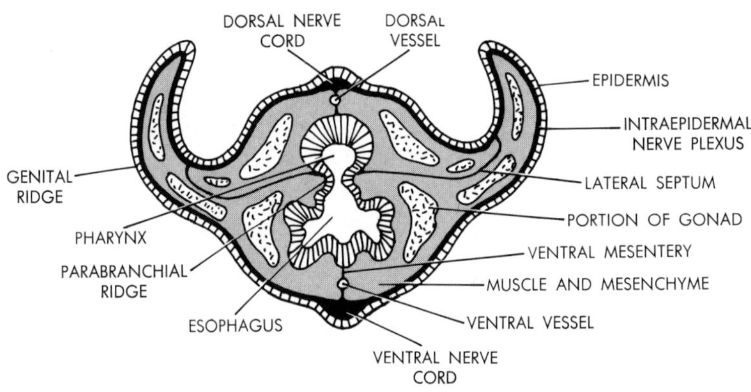

Fig. 27.2 Cross section through an acorn worm at a level just behind the gill slit region.

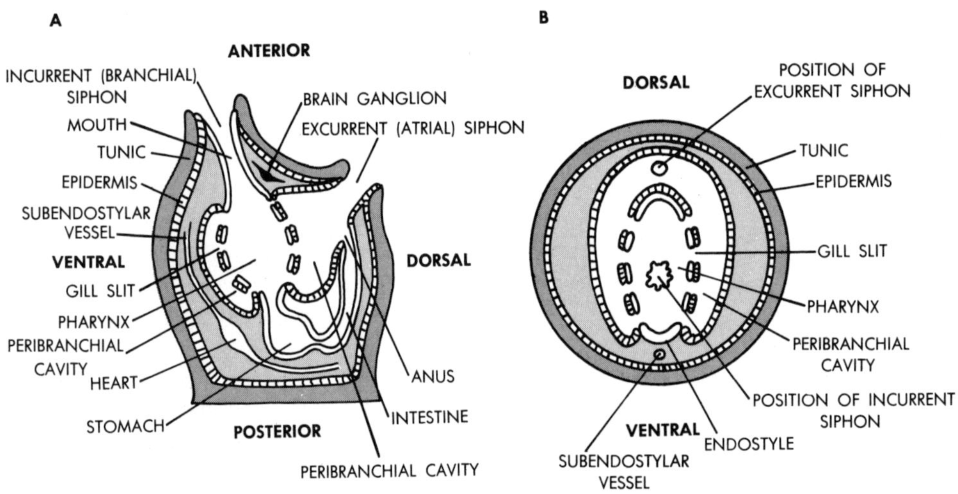

Fig. 27.3 A, *diagram showing anatomical orientations and the ectodermal nature of the lining of the branchial sac. The ectoderm layer is drawn with cross-lines suggesting cells, the endoderm layer is without such lines. Internal organs such as heart and gonads lie in the gray-shaded regions between the epidermis and the branchial lining.* B, *schematic dorsoventral (cross) section at a level just below the excurrent siphon, showing how the branchial sac envelops the pharynx; layers and regions drawn as in* (A).

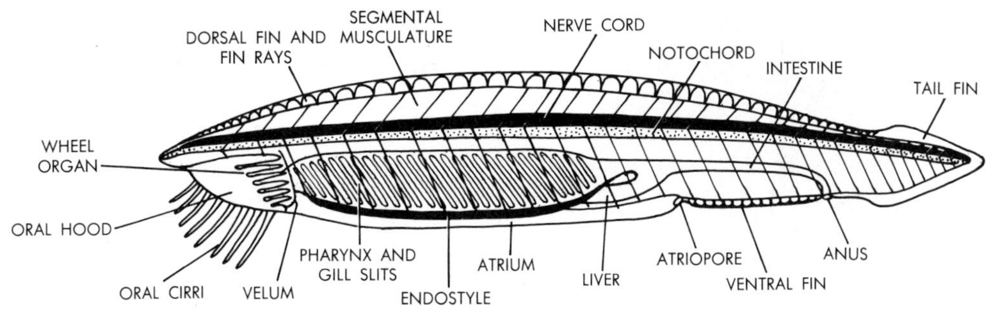

Fig. 27.4 Some anatomical features of amphioxus.

Note also the TAIL MUSCULATURE. In the anterior part of the body identify the BRAIN, an enlargement of the nerve cord. Ventral to it is the still incompletely developed PHARYNX, or BRANCHIAL BASKET, containing pharyngeal GILL SLITS. A cellulose TEST, or TUNIC, envelops the whole larva.

b. Study a preserved adult specimen of a solitary ascidian tunicate. Immerse it in water and note the two upper openings, the INCURRENT and EXCURRENT SIPHONS. The opening directly opposite the bottom base of the animal is the incurrent siphon, also called the BRANCHIAL SIPHON. The other is the excurrent or ATRIAL SIPHON (see also Fig. 27.3).

Pin the animal down with the atrial siphon to YOUR right and carefully remove the tunic. This will expose the transparent body wall, through which most internal organs are visible. The branchial siphon may be seen to lead into the large, ridged BRANCHIAL BASKET which, as in the tadpole, contains pharyngeal GILL SLITS. The pharynx connects near the base of the animal with the ESOPHAGUS. This tube leads into the STOMACH. The INTESTINE, emerging from the stomach, loops forward over the stomach and terminates in the ATRIAL CAVITY, just under the atrial siphon. Visualize the path of water and food through the tunicate body, in at the branchial siphon and out at the atrial siphon. In the basal part of the body, near the looped portion of the alimentary tract, are the REPRODUCTIVE ORGANS. Ovarian tissue is densely packed; testicular tissue is feathery. Ducts lead away from these organs along the intestine, into the atrial cavity. Try to identify the large greenish DIGESTIVE GLANDS and, quite near the base of the animal, the HEART.

2. *Subphylum Cephalochordata: Lancelets*

Study preserved specimens and/or prepared whole mounts of amphioxus. Use hand lens and the low power (only) of your microscope (see also Fig. 27.4.).

Note the V-shaped MUSCLE SEGMENTS covering much of the sides of the animal. Identify the NERVE CORD, the NOTOCHORD, and the dorsal, ventral, and caudal FINS. FIN RAYS form vertical fin supports. Anteriorly, observe the ORAL HOOD fringed with BUCCAL CIRRI. The hood encloses the VESTIBULAR SPACE, bounded posteriorly by the VELUM, a transverse partition. In the center of the velum is the MOUTH, surrounded by small tentacles. The mouth leads into the spacious ciliated PHARYNX, which is perforated laterally by many GILL SLITS. These slits open into the ATRIUM, a chamber bounded laterally and ventrally by the external body wall of the animal. The atrium opens to the outside at the ventrally located ATRIOPORE. Food is swept by the cilia of the pharynx into the INTESTINE. A DIGESTIVE GLAND (liver) discharges into the intestine. The ANUS is located ventrally, some distance behind the atriopore. Visualize the path of water through mouth, pharynx, gill slits, and atrium and the path of food through the alimentary tract. In mature specimens, yellowish REPRODUCTIVE ORGANS may be seen through the body wall.

Label Fig. 27.5.

IV analysis

1. Describe the diagnostic characteristics and the structural organization of arrowworms. Review also analogous data relating to beard worms

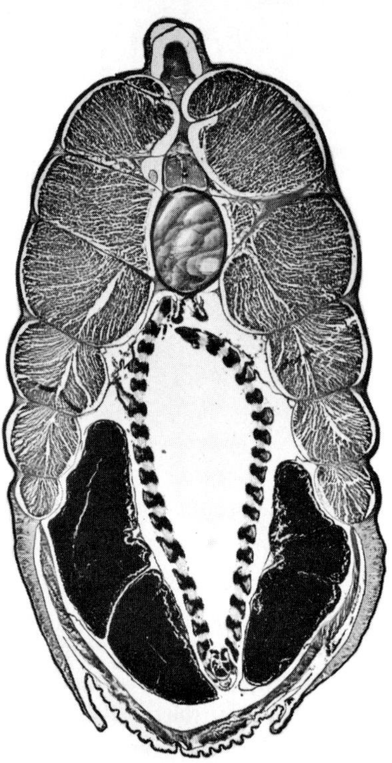

Fig. 27.5 Cross section through amphioxus. Identify the general body level at which this section was made and label the parts as completely as you can. (Courtesy of Carolina Biological Supply Co.)

(pogonophorans), using your text for information. How are enterocoelomates as a whole distinguished from (*a*) other coelomates, (*b*) other Bilateria?

2. What diagnostic features define the echinoderm phylum? List the classes of echinoderms, and show what distinguishes each from the others.

3. Describe the structure and the functions of the water-vascular system of echinoderms.

4. Describe the structural organization of a starfish. Where is the coelom? How does a starfish (*a*) exchange gases, (*b*) excrete, (*c*) maintain internal transport, (*d*) feed? What does a starfish feed on?

5. What structural features of starfishes are direct correlates of the sluggish way of life of these animals? Do echinoderms possess a nervous system?

6. Specifically where are representatives of each of the echinoderm classes found in nature? Contrast the structural organization of starfishes with that of sea cucumbers, sea urchins, and brittle stars. Which echinoderm groups possess ambulacral grooves?

7. Describe the phylum characteristics of hemichordates and the structural organization of an acorn worm. On what grounds are hemichordates regarded to be related evolutionally to echinoderms and to chordates? Name body parts that appear to be homologous in these three phyla.

8. What diagnostic features define the chordate phylum? List the subphyla of chordates, and show what distinguishes each from the others.

9. Specifically where are tunicates found in nature? Where are lancelets found?

10. Describe the structural organization of a tunicate tadpole. Ascertain how the larva transforms into an adult.

11. Describe the structural organization of an adult tunicate. Contrast with the organization of the tadpole.

12. Describe the structural organization of a lancelet. In what fundamental respects is it (*a*) unlike, (*b*) like, a typical vertebrate? How does a lancelet excrete?

13. Describe the process of breathing in tunicates and lancelets, and contrast with the equivalent process in a fish. Do similarly for the process of alimentation. Is the atrium of tunicates homologous with that of lancelets?

14. Do vertebrates possess a notochord? Discuss. Which animals are included in the (*a*) Acrania, (*b*) Craniata?

15. Which chordate groups are segmented and which are not? Which groups other than those studied in this exercise are members of the (*a*) tunicate subphylum, (*b*) cephalochordate subphylum? Name and define the classes of the vertebrate subphylum.

part 5 metabolism

exercise 28 nutrition in plants: transport

I materials

Each student

microscope
dissecting instruments
blank slide, cover slip

Each group of 4 students

millimeter ruler
dissecting instruments
wax pencil
rubber bands
ring stand with clamps
1-ft-long dowel rod or other bar to fit ring-stand clamp
15-ml test tube
10 1-ft-long glass tubes, 2 to 4 mm internal diameter
10 1½-in. pieces of rubber tubing fitting tightly on glass tubes above
2 600-ml beakers
8 250-ml beakers
10 ml distilled water
10 ml 0.4 *M* $CaCl_2$ solution
100 ml 2 *M* mannitol solution
100 ml 0.5% basic fuchsin solution

Class stock

seedlings of bean (preferably) or tomato or sunflower, about 6 in. tall, in sand flats or potted, 17 for every 4 students
petroleum jelly
plasticine or modeling clay
adhesive tape, ½ in. wide
cardboard sheets
Fuchsia plant, potted, disposable (one for entire week of exercise)
glass or plastic tubing, 2 to 3 ft long, 0.5 cm internal diameter

II introduction

Materials absorbed by roots and nutrients manufactured in leaves must be TRANSPORTED to all living tissues of the plant. This process is as essential a phase of "nutrition" as the absorption and manufacture of nutrients. Phloem and xylem play the principal roles in nutrient transport.

You recall that three factors are essential in xylem conduction: push from below, through ROOT PRESSURE; pull from above, through TRAN-

SPIRATION; and uninterrupted continuity of water between roots and leaves, maintained by the COHESION OF WATER molecules. You recall also that external environmental conditions in soil and atmosphere have an important bearing on xylem conduction. These aspects of internal nutrient transport can be demonstrated rather readily and can be measured quantitatively with a fair degree of accuracy. Such experiments on sap flow form the content of this exercise.

Groups of four students will work together as individual teams, the team members sharing and alternating the different types of operations to be performed.

III directions

A. root pressure

The following may be performed by the instructor as a class demonstration of root pressure.

The stem of a potted *Fuchsia* plant is cut through some 2 or 3 in. above the soil and the leafy part of the plant is discarded. A grain of light green dye is placed on the cut surface of the remaining stem and a 2- to 3-ft long glass or plastic tube (internal diameter about 0.5 cm) is connected to the cut stem by means of a piece of rubber tubing. The glass tube is clamped to a ring stand in vertical position; a ruler may also be fastened to the tube to indicate distances from the cut end of the stem. The pot is set into a dish of water such that the water level comes up to not more than about one-quarter of the height of the pot.

Root pressure will drive water up into the glass tube. The height of the water column, recorded at 6- or 12-hr intervals over a period of a few days, provides a measure of the force of root pressure.

B. transpiration

1. *Preliminary Operations*

a. In one of the experiments below you will need a seedling that has been kept in the dark for several hours. The instructor will have put a group of seedlings into a dark chamber some hours before the laboratory started. Dig out one of these dark-adapted plants, quickly wash off the soil, and put the plant into a beaker of water. WORK IN THE DARK as much as possible. Now with scissors held UNDER WATER cut through the stem about 1 in. below the lowest node. MAKE SURE THAT THE CUT SURFACE OF THE STEM DOES NOT COME INTO CONTACT WITH AIR. Remove the root, identify your beaker in some way, and keep the leafy part of the plant in the dark until you need it.

b. Construct a humidity chamber as follows. Cut out or obtain a 3-in.-square piece of cardboard and make a small hole through the center, just large enough to accommodate the stem of a seedling. Take two 250-ml beakers and fill one about half full with water. Around the outer rim of the other beaker attach strips of adhesive tape so that about half of the tape width projects beyond the rim. Now cut off a seedling an inch or so below the lowest node. Pass the cut stem through the hole in the cardboard and immerse the stem end into the filled beaker. With scissors held UNDER WATER, cut off another ½ in. from the immersed stem, and then let the cardboard drop over the rim of the water beaker. Where the stem passes through the cardboard, apply some plasticine or modeling clay to make a reasonably airtight fit. Now invert the beaker with the taped rim over the exposed part of the seedling, and seal the free portion of the tape against the cardboard. Move the whole assembly to a well-lighted spot, and keep it there till needed.

c. Attach clamps to your ring stand and fit a dowel rod or other bar HORIZONTALLY into the clamps. Put nine rubber bands tightly on the rod, and space them out along the rod. (Place one of the bands close to the ring stand; this one should be used for apparatus 10 below.

2. *The Transpirometers*

Assemble a TRANSPIROMETER as follows. Cut off a seedling an inch or so below the lowest node. Put the stem into a large finger bowl or beaker of water (but keep the leaves dry), and with scissors held UNDER WATER, cut off another ½ in. of stem. Now fit half of a 1½-in. piece of rubber tubing tightly over one end of a 1-ft-long glass tube. Immerse the rubber-fitted end into the beaker containing the seedling, and suck the tube one-half or three-quarters full. Press a finger over the sucking end of the tube so that the water will not run out. Then fit the cut stem end of the seedling TIGHTLY into the rubber projecting from the tube. Keep the leaves as dry as you can. See that the node near the cut end of the stem is well into the rubber; it aids in producing a tight fit. If necessary, wind a rubber band around the juncture for added tightness (however, do not crush the stem!).

If done correctly, (*a*) no air bubbles will be present where the cut surface of the stem meets the water column; and (*b*) the water in the tube will not run out when you remove your finger from the end and invert the whole assembly, so that the seedling is upright. The partially filled tube and tightly attached plant represent one of the transpirometers you will need. Mount it vertically on the rod of your ring stand, using one of the rubber bands.

3. *Experiments*

Prepare a total of 10 transpirometers to provide the following experimental conditions:

1: control. No further treatment. (Use the apparatus already assembled.)

2: same as above, except that the water column is LONGER than in (1).

3: same as above, except that the water column is SHORTER than in (1).

4: petroleum jelly applied thoroughly to the UPPER surfaces of ALL leaf blades.

5: petroleum jelly applied thoroughly to the LOWER surfaces of ALL leaf blades.

6: petroleum jelly applied thoroughly around the exposed part of the stem and the leaf petioles.

7: all leaf blades cut off, leaving only stem and petioles.

8: apparatus placed into BRIGHT, DIRECT light. (Make sure that leaves are well illuminated and heat injury to plant is avoided.)

9: apparatus in complete darkness. (Use dark-adapted seedling already prepared in section B1a, and keep assembly in dark chamber.)

10: plant in high humidity. (Use seedling in humidity chamber, already prepared; lift cardboard off lower beaker, and without disturbing plant and upper beaker, fit filled transpirometer tube to cut stem end. Mount on rod close to ring stand, and clamp cardboard to stand for extra support.)

Move all plants except 8 and 9 to a shaded (but not dark) place, and keep them there for the remainder of the experiment.

With a wax pencil mark the water level at the lower end of all 10 transpirometers. Record the time. Let the experiments run for 1 to 1½ hr. During this interval, proceed to sections C and D of this exercise and complete them.

After 1 to 1½ hr, record the time and read the transpirometers. Mark the present water levels, and measure the distance in millimeters between the initial and the terminal water marks. Record in the table on Data Sheet 8, page 000. From the data, calculate the amount of water transpired by each plant in cubic centimeters per hour. Interpret results in the light of the experimental design.

C. influence of external conditions

1. Label four 250-ml beakers A to D. Using a 15-ml test tube to measure approximate volumes, fill the beakers as follows:

A: 60 ml tap water

B: 45 ml tap water, 15 ml 2 *M* mannitol; stir well

C: 30 ml tap water, 30 ml 2 *M* mannitol; stir well

D: 15 ml tap water, 45 ml 2 *M* mannitol; stir well

2. Dig out four seedlings with roots and generous amounts of soil to keep the roots as intact as possible. Dip the plants into water a few times to wash off the soil, then put one plant into each of the labeled beakers.
3. Note the time. Let the plants stay in the beakers for 1 to 1½ hr. In the interval complete section D of this exercise.
4. After 1 to 1½ hr, examine the plants. Feel the leaf blades in your fingers, and roll them gently to test their crispness. Record your observations and interpret the results.

D. xylem conduction

1. Label three 250-ml beakers E to G. Put basic fuchsin into each, to a height of about 1 in.
2. Dig out a seedling with roots as intact as possible wash off the soil, and put the roots into the dye of beaker E.

3. Cut off a seedling 1 in. above the soil and lay it on the table for 2 min. Then immerse the cut stem end into the dye of beaker F.
4. Cut off a seedling 1 in. above the soil, immerse the cut end into the dye of beaker G, and with scissors held INTO the dye, cut off about ½ in. from the immersed stem end. THE NEWLY CUT SURFACE SHOULD NOT COME INTO CONTACT WITH AIR.
5. During an observation period of about 1 hr, examine the plants at 10- to 15-min intervals.
6. Through which of the plants is the dye visibly rising? (Examine the stems thoroughly from all sides before answering.) Explain fully. At the end of 1 hr, cut a thin transverse slice from about halfway up the stem of plant G, and mount this slice on a blank slide with a drop of water. Cover and examine under high power. Describe the location of the dyed tissues. What tissues are these? Cut slices from successively higher regions of the stem, petioles, and leaf veins. Determine how far up into the plant the dye has moved during the allotted interval.

IV analysis

1. Define TRANSPIRATION, ROOT PRESSURE, TRANSLOCATION, and show how these events are brought about in a plant.

2. In the transpirometers you used, the water-lifting power of plants is demonstrated. Does this lifting power vary with the length of the water columns in the glass tubes, that is, with the amount of water available? Compare results in tubes 1 to 3 and explain.

3. To what height will an ordinary water pump lift water? Explain the underlying physical principle. Does the physics of a water pump provide a model for the transpirational lifting power of plants?

4. What conclusions can you reach from the results in transpirometers 4 to 7? What role did the petroleum jelly play?

5. How does illumination influence transpiration? How does light produce this effect? Is there any adaptive significance in this?

6. How does the humidity of the atmosphere influence transpiration? How does humidity produce this effect?

7. From your experimental data, calculate how much water would be released into the atmosphere by a forest of 1,000 trees, each tree possessing 1,000 leaves. On the basis of this, can you estimate if vegetation plays a major or a minor role in determining local weather conditions?

8. What exactly does the wilt test in section C demonstrate? What is the role of mannitol in the beakers? How does the mannitol act, and what is mannitol? What does it affect—root pressure, transpiration, or both? Could some substance other than mannitol have given similar results?

9. Define TURGOR. What maintains it, and what function does it serve?

10. By what process does the red dye rise in some of the plants in section D? Compare results in beakers E and G; what can you conclude? Compare results in beakers F and G; what can you conclude?

11. What groups of substances will a root-hair membrane let through? What groups will it not let through? What physicochemical properties does a root-hair membrane have?

12. How does sap rise in trees in early spring, when leaves have not yet matured? Inasmuch as phloem and xylem conduct up, down, or both ways, how are nutrients transported laterally in a plant?

13. If a transpirometer were set up as in your experiments, if the glass tube were completely filled with water, and if a root system with a piece of stem were fitted to the lower end of the tube, would water rise through such an assembly? What tissue would the glass tube replace? What would happen if the glass tube were incompletely filled? Describe.

14. Suggest appropriate apparatus and experimental procedures by which phloem conduction could be demonstrated and measured.

15. On the basis of the demonstration in section A, how could you measure root pressure quantitatively, as so many pounds (or other units) of pressure generated by the plant per unit amount of living root tissue? How could you measure what fraction of root pressure is due to osmosis and what fraction to metabolic activity of root cells?

exercise 29 nutrition in animals: digestion

I materials

Each group of 4 students

2 doz or more test tubes
test-tube rack and brush
3 beakers, 250 ml
2 beakers, 50 or 100 ml
pipette, 10 ml
bunsen burner plus stand, wire grid
medicine dropper
millimeter ruler
wax pencil
spot plate
20 ml each of pH 9, 7, and 5 buffers (see Appendix)
25 ml egg-white solution (diluted in 5 to 7 volumes of water)
25 ml 1% starch solution, boiled
35 ml 5-10% pancreatin solution
35 ml 5-10% pepsin solution
conc. NaOH, in bottle
30 ml Benedict's reagent
IKI reagent, in dropping bottle

Class stock

eggs, fresh
skimmed milk, fresh
salad oil
distilled water, stock
crushed ice, stock
narrow glass tubes, 1 in. long (3 per team)

10 to 15 ml per team:

phenol red indicator solution
sat. $HgCl_2$
0.2% NaOH
0.2% HCl
0.5% $CuSO_4$
0.5% Na_2CO_3
ammonium oxalate, sat. solution
5% bile salt solution
5-10% rennin solution
2% sucrose solution

II introduction

In this exercise you will duplicate in test-tube experiments some of the digestive processes taking place in the mammalian alimentary tract. Specifically, you will examine oral, gastric, and intestinal digestion by testing the action of salivary, gastric, and pancreatic enzymes on carbohydrates, lipids, and proteins. The saliva used will be your own; digestion in the stomach will be simulated with commercial extracts of pepsin and rennin; and intestinal digestion likewise will be simulated with prepared extracts of the pancreas (called PANCREATIN) and with bile salts. Each of the digestive enzymes will be allowed to act on egg white, which will serve as protein substrate, on salad oil, which will be the lipid substrate, and on starch and sucrose, which will be sample carbohydrate substrates. The effectiveness of the enzymes at different pH levels will be studied as well. The results of digestion can be demonstrated through procedures that include, for example, the biuret, IKI, and Benedict's tests; you have already performed them in exercises 8 and 10, but if necessary reacquaint yourself with them now.

Keep in mind that enzymatic digestion is HYDROLYTIC in nature, similar in certain respects to the acid or alkaline hydrolyses you carried out in the exercises of Part 2. Make sure you come to appreciate the differences between enzymatic and nonenzymatic hydrolyses, and also between hydrolytic and nonhydrolytic decompositions generally.

Oral digestion takes place most rapidly, intestinal digestion least rapidly. For this reason the natural sequence of digestive processes is reversed in the tests below, which begin with preparatory procedures for the experiments on intestinal digestion. Also, protein digestion takes longer than fat or carbohydrate digestion; hence the instructor may advise you to set up the protein tests (sections B1, C1, and D1) before the others. However, notwithstanding these reversed sequences for reasons of expediency, do keep the natural order of alimentary events always in mind.

Groups of four students will again form individual teams. To reduce confusion in labeling and identifying given test mixtures, the experiments below have been numbered consecutively. Note, however, that you will not need as many separate test tubes as there are numbered tests, for many of the experimental runs will have been completed by the time others are started.

III directions

A. preliminary operations

1. The instructor will have prepared a beaker with egg-white solution into which have been placed pieces of narrow glass tubing, each about 1 in. long. The pieces have been allowed to fill with the egg white and the whole has then been boiled to produce a firm coagulum. Obtain three of the glass pieces filled from end to end with the boiled egg white.

2. Set up one large or two or three smaller beakers with water maintained throughout the laboratory period at 37 to 40°C.

3. Clean a 10-ml pipette and use it routinely for measuring out quantities of fluids. Many of the tests below are comparative, and exact measurements are therefore required.

B. intestinal digestion: pancreatin

1. Proteins

Prepare six numbered test tubes and add to each 2 ml of pancreatin solution. Then add the following:

1: 2 ml distilled water, 2 ml pH 9 buffer
2: 2 ml egg-white solution, 2 ml pH 9 buffer
3: 2 ml egg-white solution, 2 ml pH 7 buffer
4: 2 ml egg-white solution, 2 ml pH 5 buffer
5: 2 ml egg-white solution, 2 or 3 drops of phenol red indicator, and 0.2% NaOH DROPWISE (SHAKE after each drop) until the mixture is JUST distinctly pink
6: one of the glass pieces with boiled egg white, 1 ml pH 9 buffer, and enough additional pancreatin solution to cover the glass piece completely

Put all six tubes into the 37°C water bath for 2 hr (or as long as the laboratory period will permit). Shake the tubes from time to time. In the interval proceed with the other parts of the exercise.

After the incubation, examine tube 5 for color change and interpret. Examine tube 6 and determine if and how long a portion of the column of egg white in the glass tube has been digested. Treat tubes 1 to 4 as follows. Divide the contents of each tube equally between two test tubes. On one portion then perform a coagulation test for proteins (for example, heat, or sat. $HgCl_2$), and on the other portion carry out a biuret test. Prepare also controls for tubes 1 and 2 by setting up two fresh tubes exactly like 1 and 2 except that these are not incubated. On half of each of these controls then do a coagulation test, on the other half, a biuret test. Compare results with the experimental tubes and also compare among the experimental tubes. (NOTE: in the coagulation tests, try if possible to distinguish the various AMOUNTS of coagulum formed.) Interpret all data in the light of the experimental design and record them on Data Sheet 9.

2. *Lipids*

Number three test tubes 7 through 9 and put 2 ml of pancreatin solution into each. Boil tube 7 over an open flame for 1 min, then cool under the tap. To tubes 7 and 8 now add 1 ml of bile salt solution, and to all three tubes add 2 or 3 drops of phenol red indicator. Also add to all three tubes, dropwise and with shaking, 0.2% NaOH until each mixture JUST turns pink. Finally add to each tube 5 (equal) drops of salad oil. Shake up thoroughly and place the three tubes into the 37°C water bath. Incubate for 1 to 1½ hr.

Thereafter examine the colors of the tubes (hold them against a white background for comparison). If necessary, set up control tubes identical to given experimentals in all respects except that the incubation has not been performed. Record and interpret the results and explain the significance of all procedural steps.

3. *Carbohydrates*

Number four test tubes 10 through 13 and add 2 ml pancreatin solution to each. Then add:

10: 2 ml starch solution, 2 ml pH 9 buffer
11: 2 ml starch solution, 2 ml pH 7 buffer
12: 2 ml starch solution, 2 ml pH 5 buffer
13: 2 ml sucrose solution, 2 ml pH 9 buffer

Place these tubes into the 37°C water bath for about 3 min. Then, and at successive 3-min (or shorter) intervals thereafter, place a drop of solution from each of tubes 10, 11, and 12 on a spot plate, and test for starch with IKI reagent. When this test becomes negative for tube 10, cease the incubation for all tubes. Is the IKI test also negative for tubes 11 and 12 at this point? Perform a Benedict's test on all tubes, carefully measuring quantities of reagent added. (NOTE: tubes 11 and 12 must be alkalinized with conc. NaOH before testing, tube 12 more so than tube 11; keep track of the amounts of NaOH added to a given tube, and add equal amounts of distilled water to the other tubes to keep the total quantities the same.) Record and interpret the results.

C. gastric digestion: pepsin, rennin

1. *Proteins*

To each of five numbered test tubes add 2 ml of pepsin solution as well as:

14: 2 ml distilled water, 2 ml pH 5 buffer
15: 2 ml egg-white solution, 2 ml pH 5 buffer
16: 2 ml egg-white solution, 2 ml pH 7 buffer
17: 2 ml egg-white solution, 2 ml pH 9 buffer
18: one of the glass pieces with boiled egg white, 1 ml of pH 5 buffer, and enough additional pepsin solution to cover the glass piece completely

Put all tubes into the 37°C water bath for 1½ to 2 hr. Then examine tube 18 and determine if and how long a portion of the column of egg white in the glass piece has been digested. With tubes 14 to 17 proceed as in the corresponding tests for intestinal digestion. Thus, divide the contents of each tube and perform a coagulation test on one portion, a biuret test on the other. Prepare also controls for tubes 14 and 15, equal in all respects except that the incubation is omitted. Then do coagulation and biuret tests on each of these controls. Compare results between and among sets of tubes and record and interpret the data.

2. *Lipids, Carbohydrates*

Put into a test tube (19) in sequence 2 ml pepsin solution, 1 ml bile salt solution, 2 or 3 drops of phenol red indicator, 0.2% NaOH dropwise while shaking until the mixture just turns distinctly pink, and 5 drops of salad oil. Shake thoroughly and keep the tube in the 37°C water bath for 1 to 1½ hr. Then examine the contents for color changes and interpret.

Put into each of two test tubes (20, 21) 2 ml of pepsin solution and 2 ml of pH 5 buffer. To tube 20 then add 2 ml of starch solution, to tube 21, 2 ml of sucrose solution. Keep both tubes in the 37°C water bath. After ½ hr or more make an IKI test with a drop of solution from tube 20 and perform a Benedict's test on the contents of both tubes. Record and interpret the data.

3. *Milk Proteins*

Examine the catalytic effect of rennin as follows. Into each of six test tubes put 5 ml of fresh skimmed milk and add:

22: 1 ml rennin solution

23: 1 ml rennin solution that has been boiled over a flame for 1 min

24: 1 ml 0.5% Na_2CO_3, 1 ml rennin solution

25: 1 ml sat. NH_4-oxalate, 1 ml rennin solution

26: 5 drops 0.2% HCl, 1 ml rennin solution

27: 0.2% HCl slowly until precipitation takes place

Keep all tubes in the 37°C water bath for 15 min. Then invert each tube over a beaker. Record and explain the results and the significance of each of the six tests.

D. oral digestion: saliva

Collect about 10 to 15 ml of your own saliva in a small beaker (if necessary, stimulate salivation by chewing a piece of gum).

1. *Proteins, Lipids*

Put into a test tube (28) one of the glass pieces with boiled egg white and enough saliva to cover the piece. Incubate at 37°C and check for digestion at the end of the laboratory period. Put into another test tube 3 ml of egg-white solution and 2 ml of saliva. Mix and draw off about 1 ml of the contents for an immediate biuret test; save the results of this test (29). Divide the remainder between two test tubes (30, 31). To tube 31 add a drop of phenol red and 0.2% NaOH dropwise until the mixture is just distinctly pink. Then keep both tubes at 37°C for 15 to 30 min. Thereafter do a biuret test on tube 30 and examine tube 31 for color changes. Record and interpret all results.

Put into a test tube (32) 1 ml saliva, 1 ml bile salt solution, a drop of phenol red indicator, 0.2% NaOH dropwise until the mixture is just pink, and 3 to 4 drops of salad oil. Shake up and incubate at 37°C for 15 to 30 min. Then examine the tube for color changes. Record and interpret the data.

2. *Carbohydrates*

Put into a test tube (33) 2 ml sucrose solution and 1 ml saliva. Incubate at 37°C for 10 to 15 min and then subject the contents to Benedict's test.

Examine the polysaccharide-digesting capacity of saliva by putting into a test tube (34) 2 ml of starch solution and 1 ml of saliva. Mix, note the time, and now work rapidly with one of your team members. After 15 sec and at successive 15-sec intervals, put a drop of tube 34 on a spot plate, and test for starch with a drop of IKI reagent. When this test has become negative, add Benedict's reagent to the tube and test for reducing sugars.

If the saliva has acted too rapidly in this first trial, repeat the IKI-testing process with DILUTED saliva and starch solution so that digestion will proceed somewhat more slowly and the endpoint can be determined without undue haste and with an error not exceeding about 20 sec. Then, taking into account such desired adjustments of concentration and making appropriate substitutions below, determine the effectiveness of saliva under the following conditions:

35: 2 ml starch solution, 1 ml pH 9 buffer, 1 ml saliva

36: 2 ml starch solution, 1 ml pH 7 buffer, 1 ml saliva

37: 2 ml starch solution, 1 ml pH 5 buffer, 1 ml saliva

38: 2 ml starch solution, 1 ml pH 7 buffer, 1 ml boiled saliva

39: like tube 37, but all prechilled and tube kept in crushed ice

40: like tube 37, but all prewarmed and tube kept at 37°C

Determine the time required for the IKI test to become negative in the contents of each tube. Record and interpret the results.

IV analysis

1. Review the design and the results of the tests in section B1. What was the objective of test 1? Should you expect digestion to occur in this test? How was tube 5 designed to test for digestion?

2. At what pH did pancreatin prove to be most effective with (*a*) proteins, (*b*) starch? What enzymes does pancreatin contain, and under what conditions do they act in the body?

3. Does pancreatin digest lipids? Sucrose? Explain the design and the results of the tests in sections B2 and B3.

4. On the basis of your results with the glass pieces filled with boiled egg white, compare the protein-digesting capacities of pancreatin, pepsin, and saliva. At what pH did pepsin prove to be most effective? Under what conditions does this enzyme act in the body?

5. What was the objective of test 14? Test 19? Why was a test equivalent to that of 5 or 19 not prescribed in section C1? Does pepsin digest (*a*) lipids, (*b*) carbohydrates?

6. What is the composition of natural (*a*) pancreatic juice, (*b*) bile, (*c*) gastric juice, (*d*) saliva? What is the function of each component in these fluids? What other digestive juices are present in the mammalian alimentary tract?

7. Explain the results, and the reasons for them, of the tests in section C3. Describe the mechanism of action of rennin and show what ingredients must be present for its action.

8. Which test in section C3 approached the normal condition in the stomach most closely? Inasmuch as HCl alone precipitates proteins, how can the coagulation of milk proteins be ascribed to rennin rather than to HCl in the stomach?

9. What is the name of the protein in milk? The sugar? The fat? What is the adaptive advantage of a rennin mechanism in man? What other animals possess such a mechanism?

10. Inasmuch as HCl alone is known to hydrolyze proteins (see your tests in exercise II.3), how can gastric hydrolysis be ascribed to pepsin rather than to HCl in the stomach? In the light of this, differentiate clearly between enzymatic and nonenzymatic hydrolysis.

11. At what (*a*) pH, (*b*) temperature, is saliva most effective? Does this fluid digest (*a*) proteins, (*b*) lipids, (*c*) sucrose? What compounds can it digest? What was the objective of test 38?

12. What is the adaptive advantage of a rapid salivary digestion compared with the slower digestion elsewhere in the alimentary tract? In exercise II.4, starch decomposition was catalyzed by the enzymes phosphorylase and phosphatase; does such a process take place in the alimentary tract? Distinguish between hydrolytic and nonhydrolytic decompositions.

13. List as many hydrolytic enzymes as possible that digest (*a*) proteins or protein-derived substances, (*b*) fats, (*c*) carbohydrates. For each of these enzymes list the original substrate and the compound resulting from enzyme action.

14. What is the advantage of having several enzymes acting on the same type of substrate, as in the alimentary canal? Or do you consider this to be an instance of functional inefficiency?

15. Are digestive enzymes found in plants? Where? What are they? What function do they serve? Describe the structure of the bonds attacked by (*a*) amylases, (*b*) lipases, (*c*) proteinases.

exercise 30 respiration

I materials

Each group of 4 students

millimeter ruler
wax pencil
medicine dropper
pipette, 20 ml
16 large test tubes
20 small (15-ml) test tubes, without flanged rim, fitting snugly into the large test tubes
6 rubber stoppers, for small test tubes
test-tube rack, or beaker large enough to hold 14 of the large test tubes
flask with distilled water
100 ml fresh yeast suspension (5 cakes bakers yeast in 1 liter distilled water)
100 ml glucose solution (25 g/liter distilled water)
40 ml NaF solution, 0.01 *M* (0.4 g/liter)
40 ml NaF solution, 0.03 *M*
20 ml NaF solution, 0.10 *M*
20 ml NaF solution, 0.20 *M*
20 ml $MgSO_4$ solution, 0.20 *M* (24 g/ liter)
20 ml $MgSO_4$ solution, 0.10 *M*
20 ml Na-pyruvate or Na-citrate solution (50 g/liter)
0.05% aqueous methylene blue solution, in small bottle

Class stock

water baths or incubators at 37°C
test-tube brushes
distilled water, stock
2% formaldehyde
2.5% sucrose solution
2.5% lactose solution
2.5% fructose solution
2.5% galactose solution
2.5% pentose (arabinose or ribose) solution
0.2 *M* sodium azide (NaN_3) solution (13 g/liter)

II introduction

In this exercise you will test how well yeast cells are able to utilize various respiratory fuels, how the respiration of a given fuel is affected by various inhibiting conditions, and how effectively dehydrogenation takes place under various experimental conditions.

You recall from your text that, in one step of glycolysis, the 3-carbon phosphoglyceric acid (PGA) is transformed into the 3-carbon phosphoenolpyruvic acid. The conversion requires the enzyme ENOLASE and the participation of MAGNESIUM IONS, Mg^{++}, as cofactors. This circumstance forms the basis for some of the experiments below: since magnesium ions can be precipitated out from a reacting system by fluoride (forming insoluble magnesium fluoride), the action of magnesium (hence glycolysis and respiration as a whole) can be INHIBITED with fluoride ions.

Groups of four students will work together as individual teams.

III directions

A. preliminary operations

1. Make sure that all glassware is THOROUGHLY clean. If necessary, scrub with soap and water, rinse, drain, and rerinse twice with distilled water. NOTE: fluorides are lethal POISONS. At sublethal dosages they cause extreme distress. The concentrations and quantities available to you in this exercise are far below the lethal level. Nevertheless, WASH YOUR HANDS after handling solutions of fluoride. A similar warning applies to sodium azide, used in one of the tests of section B and section C. In general, be CAUTIOUS but do not be alarmed.

2. In the tests to follow, each of 14 small test tubes will be filled with three equal quantities of different fluids. The total amount of fluid per tube (approximately 15 ml) should be the same for all tubes and should fill a tube right to the top. To facilitate the later measuring-out procedure, take one small test tube and fill it to the top with distilled water. Suck up all this water into a 20-ml pipette, note the amount withdrawn, and let exactly one-third of this amount flow back into the tube. With a wax pencil, mark the precise level reached by the water. Next let another third flow into the tube and again mark the exact level. When the last third is then added, it should again fill the tube to the top. Now line up 13 additional small tubes, and as precisely as you can, copy on them the wax pencil marks. It will probably be best here to transpose the marks to one new tube at a time (for example, set the marked tube and one still unmarked side by side on the bench surface and duplicate the marks).

3. The 14 small marked tubes, together with 14 larger tubes, will be used as simple RESPIROMETERS. To practice their assembly and use, fill one of the small tubes with distilled water. Hold one of the larger tubes upside down and slide it over the water-filled small tube. Let the rounded bottom of the large tube come to rest against the open rim of the small tube. Using a pencil or your fingers if necessary to hold the tubes in this position, quickly invert the entire system. The large tube will now be right side up, and in the small tube an air space of varying size (depending on your technique) will have been trapped over the water column. Determine the length of this air space with a millimeter ruler, measuring from the bottom of the water meniscus to the highest (that is, lowest) point of the small tube. In the actual experiments, try to keep these initial air spaces as small as possible.

Dismantle the practice run, empty the water, and number the small test tubes from 1 to 14 (hold the tubes upside down as you label them). Set the tubes into your test-tube rack or holding beaker.

4. Prepare the following solution: into a separate test tube pipette 5 ml of the Na-pyruvate (or Na-citrate) solution. To this add 5 ml of the 0.10 *M* NaF solution. Shake, label this tube PYRUVATE-FLUORIDE (or CITRATE-FLUORIDE), and set it aside; it will be used below (section B, test 10). Rinse the pipette.

5. Prepare the following solution: into a separate test tube pipette 5 ml of the 0.20 *M* NaF solution. To this add 5 ml of the 0.20 *M* $MgSO_4$ solution. Shake, and observe what happens. Write out the chemical reaction that took place. Label this tube PRECIPITATED FLUORIDE and set it aside; it will be used below (section B, test 9). Rinse the pipette.

B. substrates and inhibitors

1. To each of the 14 numbered small test tubes add yeast suspension up to the first mark. Then add, up to the second mark, the solutions listed first for each of the tubes below, and to the top, the solutions listed last.

1: distilled water, distilled water
2: sucrose, distilled water
3: lactose, distilled water

4: fructose, distilled water
5: galactose, distilled water
6: pentose, distilled water
7: glucose, distilled water
8: glucose, 0.10 M $MgSO_4$
9: glucose, precipitated fluoride
10: glucose, pyruvate-(or citrate-) fluoride
11: glucose, 0.01 M NaF
12: glucose, 0.03 M NaF
13: glucose, 0.10 M NaF
14: glucose, 0.20 M sodium azide

Now slide the large test tubes over the filled small ones, as outlined above, invert, and redeposit the so-assembled respirometers into the test-tube rack or holding beaker.

2. In the appropriate spaces of Data Sheet 10, page 000, record the INITIAL GAS READING of each tube,, in cubic centimeters. To do this, measure the height of the air space in each tube with your millimeter ruler and convert this reading into cubic centimeters. You may assume that every 8-mm length of the air column in the test tube corresponds to an air volume of 1 cm^3.

Now place your respirometers into an incubator or water bath held at 37°C. Note the time. Let the assembly incubate for 1 hr or more. During this interval, go on to section C and complete it.

After 1 hr of incubation remove the respirometers and in the table below record the TERMINAL GAS READING for each tube, in cubic centimeters as above. Subtract the initial from the terminal readings, and record the NET GAS VOLUMES per hour.

Note that this series of tubes represents two basic sets of experiments; tubes 2 through 7 test the ability of yeast to utilize a variety of sugars as respiratory fuels, and tubes 7 through 14 test the effects of various inhibiting conditions on yeast respiration. What is the function of tube 1? Interpret the results in the light of the contents of the respirometers.

C. dehydrogenation

1. Methylene blue has the property of being able to combine with hydrogen and becoming colorless in the process:

$$\underset{\text{(OXIDIZED)}}{\overset{\textit{blue}}{\text{Mb} + \text{H}_2}} \longrightarrow \underset{\text{(REDUCED)}}{\overset{\textit{colorless}}{\text{MbH}_2}}$$

You recall that hydrogen is normally removed from fuels during respiration, under the influence of enzymes called DEHYDROGENASES. Such hydrogen is then transferred to various acceptors. In view of the properties of methylene blue, it is possible to introduce this dye into a respiring system and to make the dye serve as the principal hydrogen acceptor. If the dye decolorizes, fuel dehydrogenation, hence respiration as a whole, may be concluded to have taken place. Indeed, by timing the decoloration of the dye, the intensity of respiration under various conditions can be measured.

2. Number six test tubes. Each is to receive three 5-ml amounts of different fluids. Accordingly, mark each tube with a wax pencil to divide off three equal (5-ml) volumes, identically for the six tubes. Use a pipette and distilled water for measuring purposes, as in section B, above. Put yeast suspension into each tube up to the first mark. Then add, up to the second mark, the solution listed first for each of the tubes below, and up to the third mark, the solution listed last.

1: distilled water, distilled water
2: glucose, distilled water
3: glucose, 0.01 M NaF
4: glucose, 0.03 M NaF
5: glucose, 0.20 M sodium azide
6: glucose, 2% formaldehyde

To each tube now add one drop of 0.05% methylene blue, stir or shake, and continue adding dye one drop at a time until the mixture after stirring is recognizably light blue. Stopper the tubes, set them into the rack, and record the time. Continue to observe and record in the table on Data Sheet 11, page 000, if, and after what time interval, decoloration takes place in the tubes. Interpret the results in the light of the contents of the tubes. Note that formaldehyde, as in tube 6, is a preserving agent which fixes and kills living material.

IV analysis

1. Show which of the 14 respirometer runs in section B were experimentals, which controls, and what the latter were controls to.

2. Which of the substrates you tested in section B was yeast best able to utilize as respiratory

fuel, and which not? What do these results suggest about the molecular or structural makeup of yeast?

3. Considering the experimental conditions in section B, did the yeast in the respirometers respire aerobically or anaerobically? What would you expect the results to have been if the substrates added were not carbohydrates but (*a*) fatty acids, (*b*) amino acids?

4. In section B, what do the results in tubes 11, 12, and 13 prove, when compared with the result in tube 7? What does tube 8 show?

5. What did the precipitated fluoride solution contain? Review the chemical reaction that took place when this solution was made. In the light of this, explain the result in tube 9. How could gas production have been greater than zero? Where could unprecipitated magnesium ions have come from?

6. Do any of the experiments of section B show whether the respiratory process might be affected by the sulfate ions of $MgSO_4$ or the sodium ions of NaF?

7. In the light of the result in tube 13, account for the result in tube 10. What is the function of the pyruvate in the pyruvate-fluoride solution?

8. Do you have experimental proof that the pyruvate in the pyruvate-fluoride solution does not merely render fluoride ineffective in some way?

9. Section A above contains a warning about the poisonous nature of fluorides. Can you now explain WHY fluorides are poisons? What makes cyanides and azides poisons?

10. From the experiments in section B and the various considerations above, suggest new respirometer runs that could be done (*a*) to provide additional experimental control, that is, to circumvent any of the inconclusiveness arising from the first 14 runs; (*b*) to elucidate the nature of other intermediate steps in the respiratory process; (*c*) to measure the efficiency of respiration with different fuels or with the same fuel under different conditions.

11. What is the chemical nature of the gas produced in the respirometer tubes? How could you test this? If respiration is aerobic, how many molecules of oxygen are consumed for every molecule of gas given off?

12. In section C, how did NaF influence the speed of dye decoloration? What can be concluded? What effect did sodium azide have? Explain.

13. In section C, did respiration still take place after the addition of formaldehyde? Accordingly, in what sense were the yeast cells "killed"? Are the results of section C consistent with those of section B? Discuss.

14. At what steps in the normal (*a*) aerobic, (*b*) anaerobic, sequence of respiratory reactions is hydrogen liberated? What are the hydrogen acceptors normally functioning at these steps? How is the hydrogen transferred to oxygen?

15. Drawing on information gained in this exercise and on textbook data, what experimental procedures would you suggest for quantitative measurement of the metabolic rate of yeast (that is, amount of energy produced per hour per given weight of yeast under specified environmental conditions)?

exercise 31 photosynthesis

I materials

Each group of 4 students

5 test tubes
2 250-ml beakers
200 ml 95% alcohol
100 ml IKI solution
xylene, in small bottle
medicine dropper
rubber bands
thermometer
ring stand, clamps
finger bowl
electric heater or bunsen burner, connected

Class stock

fresh *Elodea*, stock
phenol red indicator solution
2.5% $NaHCO_3$ solution, stock
1% NaOH solution, stock
0.10 *M* NH_2OH solution
0.10 *M* NaF solution
4% formaldehyde solution
syringes, with fine needles
100- or 150-watt bulbs
red, blue, and green light bulbs or cellophane sheets
crushed ice
large (1-liter) beakers
as many sets of the following as specified by the instructor, based on number of tests of section A to be done and number of work teams in class:
1 large test tube, with two-hole rubber stopper
2 2- to 3-in. lengths of rubber tubing
1 2-in.-long glass tubing
1 6-to-7-in.-long glass tubing
1 10-in. glass capillary tube, internal diameter 0.5 mm
1 pinch clamp, screw type
1 plastic millimeter ruler
ready assemblies for experiments B2 to 7, set up in advance of laboratory according to planned schedule, in sufficient numbers for teams in class; required, aside from glassware and routine chemicals:
geranium plants, potted
silver-leafed geraniums, potted
variegated *Coleus* plants, potted

II introduction

The first part of this exercise deals with experiments designed to test various factors influencing the rate of photosynthesis. The second part describes experiments dealing with the raw materials and the endproducts of photosynthesis. See if, FROM YOUR EXPERIMENTAL DATA ALONE, you can arrive at a reasoned chemical input-output statement showing what materials (and how much of each) enter the photosynthetic process and what materials (and how much of each) result from it.

Groups of four students will again form individual work teams. The instructor will specify if all teams are to carry out all experiments or how the experiments are to be parceled out among the teams in the class. All teams should in any case become familiar with all results obtained by the class.

III directions

A. the rate of photosynthesis

1. *Preliminary Operations*

Set up manumetric assemblies to provide some or all of the experimental conditions described in section 2 below. The instructor will specify which of the experiments are to be carried out by each team or by different teams of students in the class.

The apparatus basic to all these experiments is prepared as follows (see Fig. 31.1). Obtain a large test tube fitted with a two-hole rubber stopper. Into one hole of the stopper insert a short piece of glass tube and to the outside end of this tube attach a short length of rubber tubing to serve as a mouthpiece. Put a screw-type pinch clamp on this mouthpiece. Into the other hole of the stopper insert a glass tube just long enough to reach to almost the bottom of the test tube. To the outside end of this tube attach a 2- to 3-in. length of rubber tubing, and connect this tubing to an approximately 10-in.-long glass capillary tube (internal diameter 0.5 mm). With rubber bands, fix a plastic millimeter ruler to the capillary tube and fasten the tube horizontally to a ring stand.

Put a 3-in. piece of *Elodea,* cut end UP, into the test tube and press the two-hole stopper assembly tightly into the test tube. Close the pinch clamp part way. Dip the free end of the capillary tube into a beaker containing 2.5% $NaHCO_3$ solution, and by sucking on the rubber mouthpiece, fill the whole apparatus with this solution up to about ½ in. below the two-hole stopper (however, note modifications for experiments 5a, b). Then close the pinch clamp completely. Put the test-tube portion of the apparatus vertically into a large beaker of water, so that the water just covers the outside surface of the two-hole stopper. Leave a thermometer in the large beaker and measure the temperature. Let the entire assembly stand for some 10 min to permit temperature equilibration throughout the system, and maintain this temperature subsequently within about 2 deg; if necessary stir the water and/or add small amounts of cooler water. During this time introduce a SMALL air bubble into the capillary tube, at the end where this tube is attached to the test-tube portion. To do this, gently force the (fine) needle of an empty syringe into the rubber tubing which connects with the capillary tube, and inject a bubble of air. Withdraw the needle, and after the period of temperature equilibration, adjust the millimeter ruler so that the position of the bubble in the capillary tube can be measured.

2. *The Basic Rate*

The assembly above may be used for the de-

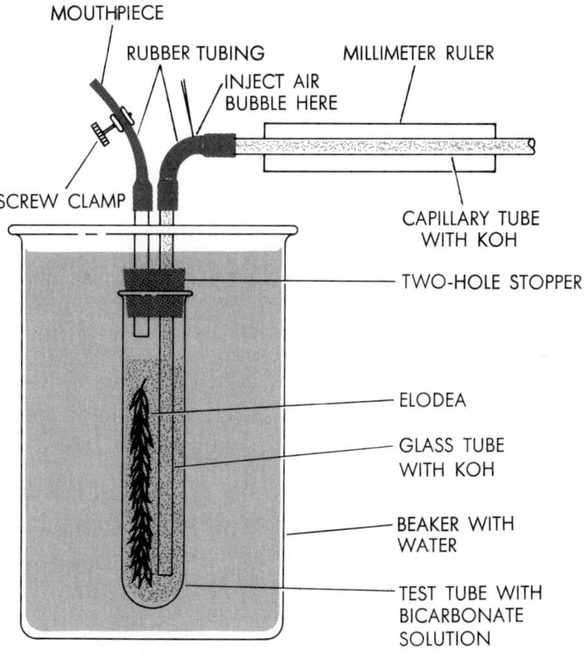

Fig. 31.1 Assembly for experiments on photosynthetic rates.

termination of a basic rate curve of photosynthesis. The data obtained may then serve as controls for the other experiments described below, in which the influence of various environmental factors on photosynthetic rate is tested.

Switch on a desk light equipped with a 100- or 150-watt bulb and from a distance of about 1 ft illuminate the apparatus containing the *Elodea*. Record the time and the exact position of the air bubble in the capillary tube. Reread the bubble position every 2 min, over a period of 20 min. Plot the data. Does gas evolution take place at a linear rate? From the total distance of bubble movement and the internal diameter of the capillary tube, calculate the amount of gas produced per hour.

3. *The Influence of Light Intensity*

Run tests as in expt. 2, except that (*a*) an assembly is placed a considerable distance away from the light source, into dim light (several assemblies may be used here, placed at different distances from the light source); (*b*) an assembly is kept under dark conditions, for example, covered with a dark cloth or put into a closed cupboard.

4. *The Influence of Light Quality*

Run comparative tests with (*a*) red light, (*b*) blue light, (*c*) green light. Use appropriately colored light bulbs or cover standard bulbs with appropriately colored transparent materials.

5. *The Influence of Temperature*

Run comparative tests (using standard lighting) with the test-tube system immersed in beakers containing (*a*) crushed ice, (*b*) water maintained at 30°C.

6. *The Influence of Inhibitors*

Run tests as in expt. 2, except that (*a*) the test tube is half-filled with 0.10 *M* NH_2OH (hydroxylamine) before *Elodea* is put in; correspondingly less $NaHCO_3$ is then added; (*b*) the test tube is half-filled with 0.10 *M* NaF before *Elodea* is put in; correspondingly less $NaHCO_3$ is then added; (*c*) the *Elodea* used is first killed as an organism, either by boiling or by prior formaldehyde treatment for about ½ hr.

Record your measurements, plot the data as graphs where warranted, and obtain the results of experiments performed by other teams in the class. On the basis of all information collected, draw conclusions as to how the rate of photosynthesis can be affected by given conditions. Interpret these conclusions.

B. photosynthesis and food production

With the exception of expt. 1 below, all others have been set up ahead of time. The instructor will specify which experiments are to be performed by each team or by different teams in the class. In every case read the description of an experiment before you carry out the tests.

1. *Light and CO_2*

a. Label four test tubes A through D and fill each about two-thirds full with water. To each add 3 drops of phenol red solution, an indicator dye giving a pink-red color in alkaline media and a yellow color in acid media. Then add, drop by drop with a medicine dropper, 1% NaOH solution to each tube until all yellow coloration has disappeared. Into a separate test tube pour a little of the $NaHCO_3$ solution you used in section A, and dilute it with slightly more than an equal amount of water (to make the concentration roughly 1%). Take up some of this solution in a clean medicine dropper and add it drop by drop to tubes A and C, until the contents of these tubes just become distinctly yellow; a few drops should suffice.

b. Put an approximately 2-in.-long piece of *Elodea* upside down into each of tubes A and B. Hold both tubes close against the lit bulb of your desk lamp (or an equivalent light source). Observe for several minutes or until changes are noticeable. Record the nature of the changes.

c. Transfer the plant of tube A to tube C, the plant of tube B to tube D. Put tubes C and D into a dark chamber and leave them there for about 15 min. Then note any changes and record. Interpret every step of these tests and account for all results obtained.

2. *The Pigment Requirement*

a. *Test design*. Silver-leafed geranium plants possess white-edged leaves. The mesophyll cells along the leaf margins normally lack chlorophyll, but the remainder of the leaf blade is green as usual. For the test below, potted silver-leafed geraniums have been kept under bright illumination for several hours.

b. Experiment. Remove one of the white-edged leaves from the plant, and place the leaf in a beaker containing boiling alcohol. Boil for several minutes, until the chlorophyll of the leaf is completely extracted and the leaf is white. (The alcohol can be used repeatedly; save it for later extractions.) Now put the leaf into a finger bowl containing IKI solution, and test for the presence of starch (see exercise 8). In what regions of the leaf is the starch test positive? What exactly does the experiment show? Is this a controlled experiment?

3. The Role of Nongreen Pigments

a. Test design. Leaves of variegated *Coleus* plants possess three kinds of pigments: green chlorophylls, red anthocyanins, and light-yellow carotenoids. A small area at the base of the leaf blade, where it attaches to the petiole, contains carotenoid pigments only. The green marginal zone of the leaf blade contains both chlorophyll and carotenoids. The bright red central region contains anthocyanin and carotenoids. And the deep purple color of the zone between the central and marginal leaf parts is a combined effect of all three pigments, chlorophyll, anthocyanin, and carotenoids. For the test below, potted variegated *Coleus* plants have been kept in bright light for several hours.

b. Experiment. Remove a leaf from the plant and decolorize it. To do this two separate extractions are necessary, since some of the pigments are water-soluble (which?), and some are alcohol-soluble (which?). Thus, first put the leaf into a beaker with boiling water, for one extraction, then transfer it to boiling alcohol for the second extraction. Test the fully decolorized leaf for starch, in IKI.

Record results. Is there a correlation between pigment localization and starch localization? Which pigments can be concluded to be specifically involved in food manufacture? Is the above a controlled experiment?

4. The Light Requirement

a. Test design. Potted geranium plants were kept in the dark for 2 days. Strips of black light-screening tape were then applied across the blades of some of the leaves. The plants were subsequently kept in bright light for 6 to 7 hr before the laboratory started.

b. Experiment. Remove a taped leaf from the plant, detach the tape, and boil in alcohol to extract the chlorophyll. Then test the leaf for starch, with the IKI test. Record results and interpret the experiment carefully. Is light required for photosynthesis? For starch synthesis? Is the above a controlled experiment?

5. The Gas Requirement

a. Test design. Two potted geraniums were kept in the dark for 2 days. Two large jars were also prepared. Into one was placed a beaker containing concentrated NaOH solution, and into the other a beaker containing $CaCO_3$ crystals and HCl. Both jars were lidded tightly and were left for a few hours. Then one of the geranium plants that had been kept in the dark was placed into each jar, the lids were screwed back, and both assemblies were illuminated in bright light for 6 to 12 hr.

b. Experiment. Working quickly, remove a leaf from each of the two jars and IMMEDIATELY retighten the lids. Label the leaves for identification by notching one with scissors. Boil both leaves in alcohol to extract chlorophyll, then test for starch in IKI.

Record results and interpret carefully. Explain each step of the test design. What exactly does the experiment prove? Compare the data with those obtained in expt. 1 above.

6. The Structural Requirement

a. Test design. Potted geranium plants were kept in the dark for 2 days. Some of the leaves were then treated in one of three ways, the specific way being indicated on marked tapes placed around the petioles of the leaves: in one set of leaves, the upper surfaces were covered thoroughly with a film of petroleum jelly; in a second set, the undersurfaces were similarly covered; and in a third set, both surfaces were covered. The plants were then left in light for 2 to 3 days.

b. Experiment. Obtain one leaf from each of the three sets and remove the petroleum jelly. This can be done chemically, by dissolving the petroleum jelly in xylene, and mechanically, by wiping the petroleum jelly off the leaf surfaces. A combination of both methods will probably be necessary. Do not rush this cleaning procedure, and be meticulous; the accuracy of the experiment depends on how well the petroleum jelly is removed. Extract chlorophyll from the cleaned leaves, then test for starch.

Record results. What do they show? Correlate the data with the test design. What can be concluded from this experiment about leaf structure?

7. Starch Synthesis

a. Test design. Potted geranium plants were kept in the dark for 2 days. Two leaves were then removed for each experiment. One leaf was immersed by its petiole in a 10% glucose solution, the other in plain water. Both leaves were subsequently kept in the dark for 1 day.

b. Experiment. Remove the two leaves from their solutions, boil in alcohol, and test for starch.

Record results. If starch is indicated, where is it localized? Why? Interpret the data carefully. Is light necessary for starch synthesis? For photosynthesis? Compare and reconcile the answers with those for expt. 4.

IV analysis

1. In the experiments of section A, what is the function of the $NaHCO_3$ in the medium for *Elodea*? What would happen if the medium were plain water?

2. From your data, state how the rate of photosynthesis is affected by (*a*) light intensity, (*b*) light quality, (*c*) temperature. Does temperature affect purely photochemical reactions? Explain the theoretical reasons for all correlations you obtained.

3. In expt. 6a, section A, what did hydroxylamine actually inhibit? What step of photosynthesis did it affect? Did it also affect respiration? If so, could not an effect on photosynthesis be explained simply as an indirect result of respiratory inhibition?

4. Explain the effect of sodium fluoride in expt. 6b, section A. Did the compound affect photosynthesis, respiration, neither, or both? What should be expected on theoretical grounds? Account for the results of experiment 6c, section A. Should the molecular machinery of photosynthesis not continue to be operational even if the plant is killed as an organism?

5. What sources of error are inherent in the design of the experiments in section A? Does the solubility of gases in water introduce errors? Does the apparatus actually measure the production of pure oxygen?

6. Explain the design and the results of expt. B1. What can be concluded with respect to (*a*) photosynthesis, (*b*) respiration, on the basis of these tests?

7. What was the reason, in most of the experiments of section B, for keeping the plants in the dark for 2 days before using them?

8. Suggest two reasons for boiling leaves in alcohol before testing for starch. Would an untreated leaf allow aqueous IKI to penetrate?

9. In the light of the result of expt. B7, is it legitimate to use the test for starch as a test of whether photosynthesis has occurred in a leaf or not? Discuss. What is the actual immediate end-product of photosynthesis?

10. In view of the answers to item 9 above, how must the light requirement of starch synthesis be stated? How must expts. B4 and B7 be interpreted?

11. Are cells in the white margins of silver-leafed geranium leaves able to manufacture starch? Are root cells able to make starch?

12. Does a negative starch test in the experiments of section B indicate that starch was not present in the leaves? That photosynthesis did not occur?

13. Which light waves does chlorophyll transmit? Would a plant grown in blue, red, or green light photosynthesize? What waves are used normally in photosynthesis? Is chlorophyll green?

14. What is the function of the reagents that were put into the jars in expt. B5? What did the experiment show? In the CO_2-free jar, could the plant not have used respiratory CO_2 for photosynthesis?

15. Can a plant use respiratory carbon dioxide for photosynthesis and photosynthetic oxygen for respiration? If so, why does a plant continually require fresh supplies of CO_2 and oxygen?

16. What does expt. B6 show? Are stomata the

only pathways over which a plant can receive and replace gases? Reconcile the answers to these two questions.

17. If chlorophyll were made to dissolve in a beaker of carbonated water and the whole were illuminated, would photosynthesis occur? Discuss. In the light of this, list requirements for photosynthesis not dealt with in the experiments of section B.

18. Suppose photosynthesis were a totally unknown process and the experiments in this exercise were performed for the first time. Based strictly and solely on these experiments, what conclusions about photosynthesis could be drawn?

19. Do pigments other than chlorophyll function in photosynthesis? What is the function of anthocyanin and carotenoids in plants?

20. Suggest designs for controlled experiments which would prove that phosphoglyceraldehyde, not glucose, is the principal immediate endproduct of photosynthesis.

part 6 steady states

exercise 32 behavioral responses of plants

I materials

Each group of 4 students

microscope
hand lens
blank slides, cover slips
dissecting instruments, pins
filter paper
cork stoppers
2 large test tubes with one-hole rubber stoppers
finger bowl with glass-plate lid
4 cardboard boxes with lids
red and blue cellophane sheets
camel's-hair brush
petri dish with sterile nutrient agar (1 g agar, 10 g sucrose, 10 mg boric acid, 100 mg Difco yeast extract, water to 1 liter)

Class stock

distilled water, stock
pots, stock
vermiculite, stock
dark chambers
absorbent cotton
balance or weighing scale
drying oven at 80°C or electric heaters and wire racks
red and blue light sources (colored bulbs or glass plates or cellophane)
10% sucrose solution
lanolin paste
lanolin-auxin paste (see Appendix, "Auxin")

Plant material

potted plants for geotropism tests (*Coleus, Iresine, Impatiens,* geranium, bean, or other, 1 to 3 per team)
root-bearing seedlings, just germinated (pea, corn, radish, or other, 12 per team)
lily flowers, fresh (1 per team)
Mimosa, potted (1 plant)
Venus's-flytrap, potted (1 plant)
clover or related legume, some in dark, some in light, to show sleep movements
plants for epidermis stripping (*Sedum, Tradescantia,* or others)
bean seedlings in pots with vermiculite, started 1 week earlier from seeds presoaked for several hours (3 seeds per pot, 3 pots per team)
grass seedlings, rapidly germinating (for example, variety Red Top, see Appendix), grown from

seeds on wet filter paper for 2 days in dark (3 dishes per team plus controls)

lettuce seeds, light-sensitive (for example, variety Grand Rapids, see Appendix); 2 to 3 doz, each soaked for 24 hr in darkness on wetted filter paper in dishes (4 dishes per team plus controls)

for optional experiments (C3, D):

stem cuttings (*Coleus, Iresine, Impatiens,* chrysanthemum, ivy, or other)

Coleus plants, potted, 6 in. high, with 4 nodes (4 per team)

seeds for photoperiodism tests (radish, morning glory, buckwheat, marigold, or other fast-flowering types)

II introduction

This exercise is devoted to an examination of hormonal and behavioral control in plants. More specifically, plants or plant parts will be exposed to given environmental stimuli and the responses of the plants will be studied. The tests are designed to demonstrate tropistic, turgor-produced, light-induced, and optionally also developmental responses of plants.

Inasmuch as a good many of the response capabilities of plants involve growth or development, many of the tests below cannot be completed on the same day they are started; in some cases 24 hr, in others several days or a week, and in still others a month or more must elapse before results can be read. The bulk of the exercise consists of short-term tests that can be terminated either in the same laboratory period or at most by the following period one week later. In tests requiring growth periods of only 1 or 2 days, the instructor may specify that experiments set up by other classes earlier in the week be inspected by you now, whereas the experiments set up by you today will serve other classes later in the week. Longer-term tests are also described below (sections C3 and D). The instructor will inform you which of these, if any, are to be carried out. His decision will be based on whether plant-growing periods of several weeks and daily attention during such periods can be made consistent with the laboratory schedule and/or the caretaking time required by staff and students. For any of the longer-term experiments that are undertaken, set up a calendar schedule for plant maintenance, inspection, and test termination. Also, appropriate time allowances will have to be made during given later weeks of laboratory.

Groups of four students will form individual work teams. Divide the tasks of plant maintenance and checking on experiments equitably among the members of the team.

III directions

A. tropistic responses

1. Geotropism

a. To observe the effect of gravity on stems, a well-watered potted bean, *Coleus, Iresine,* or geranium plant is placed on its side and is kept in a dark chamber. The plant is maintained in this lateral position, is watered every 2 or 3 days, and is examined in the next laboratory period. Record and explain the growth response of the stem.

b. To ascertain if the stem apex plays a role in the geotropic stem response, set up two experiments either with two fresh bean seedlings or with two branches (with leaves) of the *Coleus* or other plant used in expt. a. If bean seedlings are used, cut off the roots under water; and if branch stems are used, analogously recut the stem bases under water. Prepare two large test tubes stuffed loosely with absorbent cotton, filled with water, and fitted with one-hole rubber stoppers. Gently push the cut stem base of an experimental plant through the hole of the stopper, and make sure that the cut surface within the test tube is well in contact with water. Use petroleum jelly to seal any openings between the rubber stopper and the stem. Now cut off the stem apex of each plant. Cover the cut surface of plant 1 with plain lanolin paste, the cut surface of plant 2 with lanolin-auxin paste. Place both assemblies on their sides (for example, tape the test tubes horizontally to a box or block of wood), and keep them in a dark chamber for several days or until the following laboratory period. Then examine the growth responses and interpret the results.

c. To observe the effect of gravity on roots, obtain six recently germinated seedlings of pea, corn, radish, or other plants. Gently pin three of them to a cork stopper in the following orientations: one seedling with the root pointing down, one with the root pointing sideways, and one with the root pointing upward. From each of the remaining three seedlings, cut off (with a sharp razor blade) about 2 mm of the root tip and pin these plants to the cork as well, in the same three different orientations. Place the cork into a finger bowl containing a wet filter paper and some excess water, cover the assembly with a glass plate, and keep it in a dark chamber for 1 to 3 days. Then examine the growth response of each root and interpret the results.

2. Phototropism

a. Rapidly germinating grass seeds have been sprinkled into small petri dishes or finger bowls containing wetted filter paper and a little excess water and have been allowed to sprout in total darkness for 2 days. Three of such dishes are used for the following tests. Prepare three cardboard boxes in each of which a hole is cut into one of the side walls. When the lid is put on such a box, light should enter only through the hole. Near this opening is then positioned a light source, white light for one box, red light for the second, and blue light for the third. Leave the grass seedlings in one-half of each dish intact, and from the plants in the other half carefully cut off varying lengths of the tip portions of the stems. Place one dish into each of the cardboard chambers. To serve as a dark control, the instructor will prepare a similar dish of seedlings and will place it into a completely dark box. One day (or more) later, examine the plants in each dish and record the growth responses. Interpret all results.

b. To determine the phototropic response of roots, prepare a cork with rooting seedlings exactly as in section 1c. Now, however, place the finger bowl with the plants into a box in which white light may enter through an opening in the side. After 1 to 3 days examine the growth response. In this case light as well as gravity has been allowed to affect the plants, hence it is necessary to compare the results with those obtained for gravity stimuli alone. Are there differences in the results that can be attributed specifically to light?

3. Chemotropism

The growth response of plant parts to chemical stimuli can be demonstrated most readily on growing pollen tubes. Pollen grains can be germinated on a nutrient medium on which are also positioned sources of various diffusing chemicals. If such chemicals have an effect on the pollen tubes, the latter will grow either into or away from the chemical gradient.

From a fresh lily flower, carefully dissect out the pistil and cut it transversely into several pieces so that some of the pieces are derived from the ovary, others from the style, and still others from the stigma. With needle and forceps, arrange these pieces 1 in. or so apart on the sterile nutrient agar of a sterile petri dish (see Materials section above for composition of the agar). Also dig a shallow well at one point in the agar and place a little of the auxin-lanolin preparation into it. Then, with the aid of a camel's-hair brush, sprinkle pollen grains from the same lily flower over the agar surface and distribute the grains so that some are present at various distances (2 mm and more) around each of the pistil pieces and the auxin paste. Cover the dish and keep it in the dark. Examine it the next day (and if possible also earlier). Ascertain how the growth of the pollen tubes is influenced by the different parts of the pistil, by the auxin preparation, and by different distances from the chemical sources, and whether the chemotropic responses, if any, are positive or negative.

B. turgor responses

1. Stomatal Movements

In line with oral directions given by the instructor, strip a piece of the lower epidermis off a leaf (*Sedum*, *Tradescantia*, or other, as specified). Immediately put this tissue into water on a blank slide. Trim off any thick leaf parts and cover the thin epidermal layer with a cover slip. Examine under the microscope and observe the stomata. Focus on one stoma, and while continuing to observe, replace the water on the slide with 10% sucrose solution. To do so put a piece of filter paper along one edge of the cover slip and with a medicine dropper add sucrose solution along the opposite edge (in the process do not flood the slide nor dry it out completely). What happens to the stoma? After the effect is established, flush out the sucrose solution with distilled water, using the same procedure as above. How does the stoma change now? Repeat the sucrose substitution at this point and ascertain if the first effect can be reestablished. Explain the results and show under what conditions stomatal movements occur in the intact plant.

2. *Leaf Movements*

a. A sensitive plant of the genus *Mimosa* will be set out. Note the leaf structure and the PULVINI, swellings at the bases of the leaflets and the petioles. Hold a lighted match about ½ in. from the tip of one of the leaflets. How does the plant respond? With a pencil touch the tip of another leaf and again note the response. Time the intervals required for the leaves to reattain their original positions. Explain the nature of these movements.

b. A specimen of the carnivorous VENUS'S-FLY-TRAP plant will be set out. Examine the sensitive leaves, and with a hand lens, locate the sensitive hairs on the inner leaf surfaces. With a pencil lightly touch a point on the outer surface of one of these leaves, where sensitive hairs are absent; then touch a sensitive hair directly. What are the responses in each case? Time the interval required for the leaf to reattain its original position.

c. Some clover or related leguminous plants have been maintained in darkness for 24 hr, and another set of such plants has been kept in the light. Compare the positions of the leaves in the two groups. Place one of the dark-adapted plants into the light and note the response. Also place one of the light-adapted plants into a dark chamber and time the interval required for a leaf response.

C. light-induced responses

1. *Light Intensity*

This test will be performed on bean seedlings that have been grown in the following manner. One week before the laboratory period, seeds were soaked in water for several hours and three seeds each were then planted in pots containing vermiculite. One set of pots (series A) was kept in complete darkness, a second set (series B) was maintained under conditions of minimum lighting, and a third set (series C) was given full lighting. All plants were watered daily.

Obtain one pot from each of these series, gently remove the three 1-week-old seedlings from each, and wash off the vermiculite. For each plant then ascertain the degree of development attained; measure stem length, number of nodes, number and size of leaves, length and extent of root system. Average these data for the three plants in each series and compare the averages among the series. Also, determine the combined weight of the three A plants, to the smallest unit your laboratory scale will permit. Analogously weigh the B and C plants. These measurements represent the gross weights, or wet weights. How do they compare for the three series?

To determine the dry weights, that is, the weight fractions attributable not simply to free absorbed water but to structural plant matter, dehydrate the plants completely in a drying oven set at 80°C. If such an oven is not available, the plants can be put into the meshes of a wire rack and the rack can be placed on an electric heater. This method is inferior to oven dehydration but can be made to work so long as direct contact between the plants and the surface of the heater is avoided. When the dehydration is completed, the plants will be hard and quite brittle. Measure the combined dry weights of the three plants in each series and compare with the corresponding wet weights. Relate the data to the experimental design. What conclusions are warranted?

2. *Light Quality*

The germination of lettuce seeds is known to be influenced differentially by red and far-red light. In seeds exposed to red light (with a wavelength of 660 mμ), one form of a substance called *phytochrome* is produced (P_{660}); and in seeds illuminated by far-red light (with a wavelength of 735 mμ), another form of phytochrome is manufactured (P_{735}). Germination of seeds is promoted by one of these phytochromes but is inhibited by the other. One objective of the following tests is to determine which phytochrome has what effect.

You will use four petri dishes (A through D), each containing several layers of well-wetted filter paper and from 2 to 3 doz lettuce seeds. These dishes have been set up and placed into a dark chamber 24 hr earlier, so that the seeds could soak in the absence of light. Carry out the following manipulations:

A: Expose for 10 min to red light. Place a double layer of red cellophane over the dish and illuminate directly with a desk lamp from a distance of about 1 ft.

B: Expose for 10 min to far-red light. Treat as in A, but use a double layer of blue cellophane over a double layer of red cellophane during the illumination.

C: Expose for 10 min to red light, then for 30 min to far-red light.

D: Expose for 10 min to red light, then for 30 min to far-red light, then once more for 10 min to red light.

Immediately after the light treatment put each dish into a dark chamber and keep it in uninterrupted darkness until the laboratory period 5 days later. To serve as control for the whole class, the instructor will also set aside two analogous dishes; a dish E will be retained in continuous darkness for 5 days, without any kind of light exposure, and a dish F will be illuminated continuously for 5 days by white light.

(NOTE: inasmuch as the required 5-day interval could introduce scheduling difficulties, the laboratory staff may already have carried out all experimental procedures up to this point and you may be supplied directly with 5-day-old preparations.)

After the growth period, ascertain for each dish the percentage of seeds that have germinated. Record the results and interpret them in the light of the experimental design.

3. *Light Duration*

(Optional, as specified by instructor)

The objective of these photoperiodic tests is to grow plants of various species from seeds and to subject some of the plants to short-day light treatment (for example, 10 hr of light in every 24 hr), the remainder to long-day light treatment (for example, long-term uninterrupted illumination). Such treatments are continued at least until clear evidence of flowering (for example, bud formation) is obtained in one of the two experimental groups of a given species. The design of the tests may also be elaborated further by subjecting some of the 10-hr plants to brief, one-time illumination at various points during one of the dark periods and/or at various stages of growth.

Use plants that can be brought to flowering rapidly, for example, within 4 to 6 weeks. Radishes and some varieties of morning glories are in this category, but buckwheat, marigold, and others are suitable as well. Plant the seeds in pots or flats, and ascertain if before planting they should be soaked or nicked with a knife (to crack the seed coat and thus to aid in breaking dormancy). Also, to accelerate germination and growth, cover the seeds very sparingly with soil, and after seedlings appear, thin the number of plants to no more than about three per pot. Identify each plant or pot in some systematic way and keep a complete day-to-day protocol as to light and other treatments given and developmental changes observed. From the results obtained, determine the photoperiodic characteristics of each species and the effects of any additional treatments.

D. developmental responses

(Optional, as specified by instructor)

1. *Apical Dominance*

Obtain three *Coleus* plants each about 6 in. tall and having at least four stem nodes. Keep plant A as an untreated control. On plant B, cut off the stem apex and cover the cut surface thoroughly with plain lanolin paste. On plant C likewise cut off the apex but cover the cut surface with lanolin-auxin preparation.

Make the following measurements on each of the plants: (*a*) stem length, (*b*) length of branch stems (if present), (*c*) leaf number for each node, (*d*) number of lateral buds for each node. Record these data. During the ensuing 2 weeks the plants are to be watered regularly and maintained under otherwise similar conditions. Remeasure the plants as above after 1 week and again after 2 weeks of growth. From the comparative results draw conclusions about the effect of auxin and of the normal stem apex on developmental dominance in the stem.

2. *Root Formation*

Obtain several leaf-bearing stem pieces cut from *Coleus, Iresine, Impatiens,* chrysanthemum, ivy, or other plants. On one-third of these pieces, apply to the lower cut surface of the stem an ample covering layer of lanolin-auxin paste (or a commercial hormone preparation for the induction of roots). Then plant these pieces in a pot with vermiculite or set them into water. Most pieces should be planted with their lower, treated ends in vermiculite or water, but also set up one or more with reversed orientation, the treated end projecting up into air.

Treat another third of the stem pieces similarly, but spread the hormone source over the UPPER cut surfaces of the pieces. Using a separate container, again plant most of the pieces with their lower ends down, one or more with their upper ends down. Keep the remaining third of the pieces as untreated controls; plant them in a third pot and here too set up normal and reversed orientations.

All three containers should then be maintained in minimum light for 2 weeks; water regularly if pots with vermiculite are used. After this growth period, carefully remove the pieces, examine the results, and interpret them in the light of the experimental design.

3. *Abscission*

Carry out the following on an approximately 6-in.-high *Coleus* plant possessing at least four nodes, each with two oppositely placed leaves. Cut the leaf blades off two of these leaf pairs but leave the petioles attached to the stem. On one of each pair of petioles apply plain lanolin paste over the cut surface. On the opposite petiole of each pair apply lanolin-auxin paste over the cut surface.

Water and maintain this plant for 3 to 4 weeks. Each week examine the treated petioles and note their condition. Determine in which of them abscission from the stem occurs or is likely to occur first. Interpret the results.

IV analysis

1. What are tropisms? What kinds are known? Describe the role of auxins in producing a geotropic response in (*a*) stems, (*b*) roots. How can the same hormone produce different responses in different plant regions?

2. Describe the phototropic response of (*a*) stems, (*b*) roots, and show what role auxins play in producing such responses. How did the phototropic responses in stems differ with different wavelengths of light? Explain.

3. How did the joint phototropic-geotropic response of roots differ from the purely geotropic response? What kind of experimental situation could be devised to test purely phototropic responses alone, without simultaneous geotropic effects?

4. Explain the results of your experiments on chemotropism. Which factors have you found to influence the growth of pollen tubes and in what manner? What compound or compounds in a pistil represent the chemical stimulus for a pollen grain?

5. Describe the organization and structure of a pair of guard cells. Also describe the effect of various tonicities on guard-cell movements, as in your tests. By what means are such movements brought about in nature? Are these movements adaptive? Explain.

6. Review the nature of contact movements involving turgor changes in plant tissues. What is the possible adaptive significance of such movements? What specific changes within the plant produce the movements of *Mimosa* leaves?

7. What are nastic movements? Nutational movements? Of what probable adaptive significance are these? Where in a plant and under what conditions do they occur?

8. Discuss the results of your experiments on the effects of different light intensities on plants. How do the wet weights and dry weights of dark- and light-grown plants differ and what conclusions may therefore be drawn?

9. Does red or far-red light inhibit the germination of lettuce seeds? Discuss the experimental significance of the different light-exposure sequences you used and show what conclusions may be drawn from the results.

10. What are the effects of different light durations on a plant? How can plants be classified on the basis of their photoperiodic responses? Review the internal mechanism by which photoperiodic responses appear to be brought about.

11. Partly from the results of your experiments (if done), partly with the aid of your text, describe and insofar as possible explain all known developmental effects of auxins in and on plants. What is the effect of auxin on an individual plant cell? How can such cellular effects produce behavioral responses by the plant as a whole? What plant hormones other than auxins are known and what are their effects?

12. List stimuli not dealt with in this exercise to which plants can respond. Insofar as is known, how do such stimuli produce responses, and what are the responses? List stimuli to which plants appear to be unable to respond and compare with the response capabilities of animals.

exercise 33 blood and circulatory control

I materials

Each student

microscope
blank slide, cover slip
human blood, stained prepared slide

Each group of 4 students

50 ml citrated whole blood
8 small test tubes
thermometer
wax pencil
paper clips
10 ml 0.9% NaCl
10 ml 0.9% $CaCO_3$
bunsen burner plus stand, wire grid
alcohol lamp (optional)

Class stock

turtle, 8 in. long, living
turtle board
turtle-pithing equipment
bone saw
kymograph, smoked paper
inductorium, electrodes, batteries, circuit key, wiring
heart levers, writing points
sewing thread, pins
turtle Ringer solution (see Appendix)
medicine droppers
paper bags
oxygen pressure tank
carbon dioxide pressure tank or dry ice
anti-A and anti-B sera for human blood typing, commercial
disinfectant alcohol
blood lancets
absorbent cotton
toothpicks
frogs, living
frog mounting boards
stethoscopes
hemomanometers
glacial acetic acid
0.1% acetic acid
0.1% adrenalin chloride
crushed ice, stock

II introduction

Circulating blood is the vehicle which, on the one hand, ferries foodstuffs, respiratory gases, and other metabolites to all cells, and on the other, carries waste products from all cells to the excretory organs. In addition to these transportive functions, blood serves importantly in steady-state regulation. Certain blood cells are PHAGOCYTES; that is, they are able to engulf foreign bodies such as bacteria and may even leave the blood stream to do so. Blood can CLOT and so may seal up wounds and prevent excessive loss of body fluid. And blood contains protective proteins, ANTIBODIES, many of which reduce or nullify completely the damaging effect of ANTIGENS, that is, potentially dangerous foreign chemicals. All these functions can be grouped under the heading of "internal defense," and this is a major aspect of steady-state maintenance. One part of the exercise below will deal with this defensive function of blood.

If blood is to serve the body at all, it must circulate. Since the heart is the principal organ which keeps blood circulating, a properly functioning heart is an essential prerequisite for the maintenance of steady state. The heart must pump, and at an appropriate RATE: too high a rate would prevent or reduce interaction between body tissues and blood, since blood would pass given tissues too rapidly; too low a rate would starve the tissues of necessary metabolites and would lead to dangerous accumulation of wastes. The heart is also one of the organs maintaining proper BLOOD PRESSURE: too low a pressure would prevent effective circulation in outlying tissues, and too high a pressure might rupture blood vessels or the thin-walled auricles of the heart itself.

Several kinds of regulating mechanisms adjust heart action to specific environmental conditions. Such control devices operate in part on a nervous, in part on a physical, and in part on a chemical basis. The second section of this exercise deals with these control mechanisms and their influence on circulation.

III directions

A. blood

1. *Blood Cells*

Study a prepared, stained slide of human blood under the microscope. Examine red corpuscles, ERYTHROCYTES, under high power and review your observations on these bodies made some weeks before, in exercise 15.

Survey the slide in low power until you find WHITE BLOOD CELLS, much less abundant than erythrocytes and individually somewhat larger. Then examine some of these white cells under high power. Among them, distinguish between LEUCOCYTES, which contain sausage-shaped, nodulated nuclei, and LYMPHOCYTES, which contain large bean-shaped or rounded nuclei. Examine the cytoplasms of these two types of white cells, and note structural features distinguishing them. Estimate the diameter of white cells (for method consult exercise 13), and compare with the diameter of erythrocytes. Survey 10 different high-power fields and count the number of white cells found. Record the average. Then estimate the number of erythrocytes in each of two different high-power fields, record the average, and estimate the numerical ratio of erythrocytes and white cells. How does this value compare with that obtained from data in your textbook?

Survey the slide until you find blood PLATELETS. These bodies are smaller than erythrocytes and irregular in shape. Do you see nuclei within the platelets? Count the number of platelets found in 10 different high-power fields and compare the average with that calculated for white cells. Check the ratio against that obtained from data given in your textbook.

2. *Blood Groups*

In human blood cells, either, neither, or both of two BLOOD-GROUP PROTEINS may be present. These antigens are designated as A and B, and the four possible "blood types" are A, B, AB, and O. If blood cells of group A come into contact with blood plasma of a person of group B, the A cells will be AGGLUTINATED, that is, clumped together. If this occurs within the body it may be fatal, since clumped blood cells clog up vital arteries. The agglutination reaction is an example of so-called ANTIGEN-ANTIBODY reactions, which are at the root of immunization procedures and of many steady-state functions of blood. The plasma of B-group blood contains a protein antibody, called ANTI-A protein, which combines specifically with A-group blood cells and thereby clumps them. Analogously, plasma of A-group blood contains ANTI-B protein, plasma of O-group blood contains

BOTH anti-A and anti-B protein, and plasma of AB-group blood contains NEITHER antibody proteins. In summary:

Blood group	*Cellular antigen*	*Plasma antibody*
A	A	anti-B
B	B	anti-A
AB	A and B	none
O	none	anti-A and anti-B

Commercial anti-A and anti-B sera are available as class stock. Determine YOUR blood group with these two test media. Proceed as follows: Prepare a THOROUGHLY CLEAN and COMPLETELY DRY blank slide. Mark it into halves with a wax pencil and write "anti-A" into the upper left corner and "anti-B" into the upper right corner. Then put a single drop of anti-A and anti-B sera on the appropriate half of the slide, and put the whole on a piece of white paper, flat on the table.

Now clean the tip of your little finger with alcohol, puncture the skin with an alcohol-cleaned blood lancet or needle, and press out a drop of blood. Quickly take up some of this blood on the end of a clean toothpick and transfer it to the drop of anti-A serum on the slide. Take up a second drop of blood on ANOTHER toothpick and transfer to the anti-B serum. THE SEPARATE DROPS OF FLUID ON THE SLIDE MUST NEVER BE CROSS-MIXED. Pick up the slide and, watching continuously, rotate it gently from side to side so that blood and antiserum in each drop become well mixed. Within a few seconds, clumping of cells will occur on either, both, or neither side. Record the result. On the basis of it, determine what group your blood belongs to.

Put cover slips on the slide and examine the clumped cells under the microscope. Compare with a drop of fresh, untreated blood.

3. *Heme*

Crystals of heme may be prepared from blood hemoglobin as follows. Prick your finger with a blood lancet and put a very small drop of blood on a clean slide. Add a small drop of water and stir with a toothpick to hemolyze the red corpuscles. Now add a small drop of 0.9% NaCl, hold the slide over the low flame of an alcohol lamp (or over the light bulb of your desk lamp), and carefully evaporate the material on the slide to dryness. Put a cover slip on the slide and let a drop of glacial acetic acid run under it. Warm gently until bubbles of gas appear. Run in another drop of glacial acetic acid, let the slide cool, and examine its contents microscopically.

How are heme crystals arranged, and what is the shape of an individual crystal? Would you expect this test to be useful in distinguishing bloods of different species? To check your answer, repeat the test using frog blood or ox blood as available.

4. *Blood Clotting*

Four students will work together as a team.

a. Obtain a 40 to 50 ml stock of citrated whole blood and pour 4 to 5 ml into each of four small test tubes labeled A through D. Treat these tubes as follows:

A: place into beaker of crushed ice
B: keep at room temperature
C: place into beaker with water kept at 37°C
D: place into beaker with water kept at 70 to 75°C

Maintain the tubes at these temperatures for 10 to 15 min, to allow temperatures to equilibrate. In the meantime proceed to section 5 below, and complete it.

b. After the waiting period add 1 ml of 0.9% $CaCO_3$ to each of the four tubes, shake, and record the time. Now each team member pries the end of his dissecting needle through the loops of a paper clip to form a wire paddle. Use these devices to whip the blood in the four tubes by rolling the handles of the needles back and forth between your hands; if necessary, lengthen the needle handles with pieces of rubber tubing. During the whipping each tube should be held firm, for example, in a clamp on a stand. Whip for about 1 min and then return the tubes to their appropriate temperature media. Note in which of the tubes, and after what time interval, clotted fibrin has formed and is adhering to the paper clip. With forceps transfer a little of the fibrin on a paper clip to a drop of water on a slide, stir, add a cover slip, and examine under the microscope. Record your observations.

Maintain the tubes at their experimental temperatures for 1 hr or longer (and during this period proceed with the other parts of the exercise). Then collect data on the degree of clotting and of serum separation in each tube. Account for the results.

c. Place 8 to 10 ml of citrated whole blood into a centrifuge tube, and, together with similar tubes from other teams in the class, centrifuge the blood to sediment the cellular components (an approximately 5-min-long run in a table centrifuge will be adequate). What proportion of the volume of whole blood is cellular? Pour most of the clear supernatant plasma into a test tube and warm it for 5 to 10 min in a beaker of water kept at 37°C. Then add 1 ml of 0.9% $CaCO_3$ and whip the plasma as you did earlier in the case of whole blood (use a clean paper clip). Clotted fibrin threads should appear. How do these differ from the threads you examined earlier?

5. *Hemoglobin and Respiratory Gases*

A team of four students prepares three small test tubes approximately half-filled with citrated whole blood. These tubes are treated as follows:

A: oxygenate the blood by bubbling air or pure oxygen into it from a pressure tank; describe and account for the color change.

B: carbonate the blood by bubbling CO_2 into it, either from a pressure tank or by exhaling into it through a soda straw or by adding a small piece of dry ice; again describe and account for the color change.

C: add carbon monoxide to the blood by letting gas from the city supply bubble through (EXERCISE CAUTION HERE; DO NOT PROLONG THE PROCESS UNNECESSARILY, ARRANGE FOR VENTILATION, AND KEEP OPEN FLAMES AWAY). Describe and account for the color change.

Now oxygenate tubes B and C and subsequently carbonate tubes A and C. Again note any changes and interpret.

6. *Capillary Flow*

With the aid of appropriate supporting boards, the instructor will mount a number of just pithed frogs on microscopes so that the webbing between the toes is in the line of view. Pithed frogs may also be opened and the lungs exposed, and these organs can be examined under the microscope. In either case, focus on capillary blood vessels and observe the flow of blood through them. How large are the blood cells in relation to the width of the capillaries? Does blood flow evenly? Explain. Focus on a point where capillaries branch; relate the width of a branch vessel to the amount of blood flowing through it.

B. control of circulation

1. *Heart Rate*

This part of the exercise will be demonstrated by the instructor. A turtle will already have been pithed and opened from the ventral side. Watch while the heart is being connected up with a kymograph. One hookup will lead from the apex of the ventricles to a writing lever, another hookup from one of the atria to another writing lever. Both levers will be made to contact the smoked paper on the kymograph drum. The instructor will also expose the right vagus nerve in the neck of the turtle, and he will make ready an electricity-supplying assembly consisting of battery, circuit key, inductorium, and electrodes, appropriately interconnected by wires. The following experiments on control of heart rate will then be performed.

a. The normal beat. Observe the rhythmicity of the heartbeat, in the heart itself and in the tracings made by the writing levers on the slowly rotating drum of the kymograph. Note that atrial SYSTOLE (contraction) coincides with ventricular DIASTOLE (relaxation), and that atrial diastole coincides with ventricular systole. Do the peaks or the valleys of the traced curves correspond to the systoles? Note the steady AMPLITUDE of the contraction curves. What does such amplitude indicate about heart function?

b. Vagus inhibition. With electrodes applied against the exposed vagus nerve, continuous electric stimulation will be supplied. Watch what happens to the heart and to the tracings on the kymograph. Watch again when the current is stopped. Record observations. What do you conclude about normal vagus function?

c. The effect of temperature. After a normal beat is restored, iced Ringer solution will be flushed on and around the heart with a medicine dropper. What happens? After a period, Ringer solution warmed to about 40 to 50°C will be flushed around the heart. What happens now? Record observations and interpret.

d. The effect of pH. When the heart beats normally again, a 0.1% solution of acetic acid is flushed on and around the heart. How does this procedure affect heart rate? Record. After the effect of acid is established, the heart will be washed with Ringer solution.

e. The effect of drugs. When the heart beats normally again, a 0.1% solution of adrenalin chloride is flushed on and around the heart. How does this procedure affect heart rate? Record. After the effect of adrenalin is established, other drugs may be tried. The heart is then washed with Ringer solution.

f. Fibrillation. With electrodes applied directly against the ventricular muscle, continuous electric stimulation is supplied. Watch what happens to (1) the ventricles and the ventricular tracing and (2) the atria and the atrial tracing. Watch again when the current is stopped. Then the electrodes will be applied directly against the right atrium, and again current will be supplied. What happens now to the atrial and ventricular beat? Record all observations. From them, what can you conclude about impulse transmission through the normal heart? What is happening in the fibrillating heart?

g. Intrinsic beat. The instructor will cut off a piece of heart muscle (for example, the unconnected atrium or a section of ventricle) and will place it into a dish of Ringer solution. Watch for a few minutes and record what happens. How does the beat differ from that of the intact heart? How can there be a beat at all?

h. Data. The instructor may conduct additional experiments on the turtle heart. Thereafter interpret all observations, and summarize how various nervous, physical, and chemical control mechanisms regulate heart rate.

2. Heart Rate and Exercise

The following is to be done by pairs of students, one of each pair recording and measuring, the other serving as test subject. Alternate these functions. Allow 2 to 3 min recovery between tests.

a. Measure PULSE RATE while sitting at rest. One or several stethoscopes will be available. With the aid of one, measure sitting HEART RATE directly. Record. Listen to the HEART SOUNDS: how many are there, and how are they distinguished?

b. Sit and hold a paper bag tightly over your nose and mouth, so that the same air will be rebreathed. Breathe this way for 2 min. During the second minute measure heart rate, either with a stethoscope or by counting the pulse. Record, and compare with normal sitting rate.

c. Stand at attention for 2 min. During the second minute measure heart rate. Record, and compare with sitting rate.

d. Do 10 deep knee bends within 20 to 30 sec. Then sit and immediately measure heart rate. Compare with normal sitting rate.

e. Compare your data with corresponding ones obtained by a student of opposite sex. Record these also, and by checking with a number of other students, determine if the recorded differences are characteristic for the two sexes. Interpret the data in b, c, and d on the basis of heart-rate control mechanisms.

3. Blood Pressure

One or several *hemomanometers* will be available. The instructor will outline the theory underlying the measurement of systolic and diastolic pressure and the technique of using the blood-pressure apparatus. Then the following group demonstration will be executed by pairs of volunteer students, supervised by the instructor. Other pairs of students may subsequently carry out these tests on their own.

a. Measure systolic and diastolic pressure while the test subject sits at rest. Record.

b. With the rubber cuff fitted to the arm, not inflated but ready to use, the subject makes 15 deep knee bends within 30 sec. Then he sits, and his systolic and diastolic pressure is measured immediately. Record and interpret.

IV analysis

1. Distinguish between blood PLASMA, blood SERUM, and DEFIBRINATED blood. Is blood a tissue? Where are the various cellular elements of blood manufactured, where are they destroyed, and how is their numerical constancy controlled?

2. Describe the functions of the cellular components of blood.

3. Describe the mechanism of blood clotting and various methods by which blood clotting can be prevented. How is blood prevented from clotting if it is to be stored for transfusions? How do heat, cold, and pressure affect clotting time? Explain why.

4. In what ways are oxygen, carbon dioxide, and carbon monoxide transported in blood? How is the color of blood affected by these gases? Name different kinds of respiratory pigments and animal groups in which they occur.

5. Define ANTIGEN, ANTIBODY, AGGLUTINATION. Review the principles underlying the determination of blood groups.

6. In view of your blood type, which types of blood can be safely transfused into you, and which cannot? What is a UNIVERSAL DONOR? A UNIVERSAL RECIPIENT?

7. How would you manufacture anti-A and anti-B sera for human blood typing on a commercial scale? Blood plasma of a person of group A does not contain anti-A antibodies. How is this known?

8. Was the turtle used in the experiments above alive? Discuss carefully. What does pithing involve?

9. Describe the nervous, physical, and chemical steady-state mechanisms controlling heart rate and show how these mechanisms operate.

10. In the light of item 9 and the experiments on the turtle, explain the results of the experiments in B2. Show how exercise leads to increased heart rate, and how rest or sleep lead to decreased heart rate.

11. Conditions bringing about an increase in heart rate often also bring about an increase in breathing rate and blood pressure. Which of your experiments above give evidence of this? Show how heart rate, breathing rate, and blood pressure are functionally geared together.

12. Is the effect of acid on the heart, as in expt. B1d, ever encountered under normal conditions? In the light of your answer, can you suggest an adaptive significance of the known condition that vagus control of heart rate is of greater importance than accelerator control?

13. How would fever affect heart rate? Does the weather have any effect on heart rate (*a*) in the turtle, (*b*) in man? Explain.

14. What can a physician tell from blood-pressure data? Is the amount of difference between the systolic and the diastolic pressure in any way informative? What does the general level of blood pressure indicate?

15. How is the force of the heartbeat controlled? Is there any correlation between force of beat and blood pressure? Explain.

exercise 34 breathing and gas exchange

I materials

Each pair of students

100 ml pyrogallol solution (see Appendix)
50 ml conc. KOH (see Appendix)
6- to 7-in.-long glass cylinder, 20 mm internal width
2 one-hole rubber stoppers, to fit 20-mm glass tube
2 2-in. lengths of glass tubing to fit rubber stoppers
3 3-in. lengths of soft rubber tubing
test-tube holder
2 test tubes
2 pinch clamps
3 beakers, 250 ml
millimeter ruler
medicine dropper

Each group of 10 students

large finger bowl
1-liter beaker
1- to 1½-ft length of rubber tubing
2-in.-square flat piece of wood
small length of candle

Class stock

disinfectant alcohol
neutral red solution
soda straws
limewater (see Appendix)
paper bags
clothespins

II introduction

In this exercise a method of measuring the chemical composition of air will first be examined. This method will then be applied to an analysis of how breathing changes the composition of air. Also, with yourself as the test subject, rates of breathing will be studied both under normal conditions and under a variety of experimental situations.

Students will work in pairs. See that the work is shared equitably with your partner and that specific functions are alternated frequently. Both partners are responsible for all data obtained by the team.

III directions

A. gas analysis

1. The Principle

Pyrogallol, a solution of pyrogallic acid in concentrated KOH, has the property of absorbing both oxygen and CO_2 from a mixture of gases. Potassium hydroxide alone absorbs CO_2 only:

$$2\,KOH + CO_2 \rightarrow K_2CO_3 + H_2O$$

Thus, by using pyrogallol and KOH successively, it is possible to measure the amounts of gases present in a given volume of air. The CO_2 content may be determined directly from KOH-absorption data; the O_2 content is given by the difference between pyrogallol-absorption and KOH-absorption data; and the N_2 content is measured as the difference between total air volume and O_2 plus CO_2 volumes.

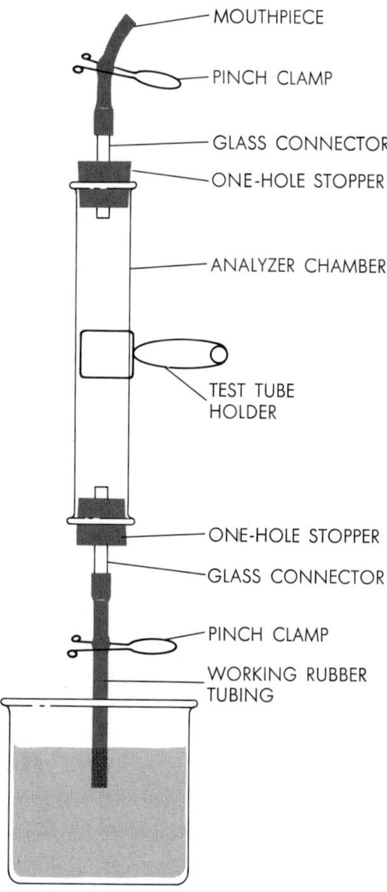

Fig. 34.1 The gas analyzer assembly.

The practical procedure may be illustrated by considering the technique for using pyrogallol. The technique for KOH is exactly the same. If a little pyrogallol is introduced into a sealed container of mixed gases, the reagent absorbs a certain amount of the O_2 and CO_2 present. As a result, the gas pressure falls, since the total absorbed quantity of O_2 and CO_2 no longer contributes its share of pressure. A certain suction potential will therefore exist, and this potential can be used to suck more pyrogallol into the container. The volume of pyrogallol so sucked in will equal the volume of O_2 and CO_2 previously absorbed; then the gas pressure in the container will be in equilibrium with the gas pressure of the external atmosphere. But the newly admitted pyrogallol will absorb more O_2 and CO_2 if more of these gases are present in the container. Hence the pressure will be lowered again, creating a new suction potential. It should be clear that the sucking in of pyrogallol can continue until all the O_2 and CO_2 in the container has been absorbed. At this point the volume of pyrogallol in the container will exactly equal the volume of gaseous O_2 and CO_2 that had been present originally. Thus, by measuring the former, one obtains a measure of the latter.

NOTE: Observe EXTREME CAUTION when handling pyrogallol or KOH. These reagents are exceedingly CAUSTIC and dangerous to living tissue, clothes, and furniture. Keep an ample supply of paper toweling on hand and cover the table surface with paper when you do the work below. DO NOT SPILL any pyrogallol or KOH. If by accident some gets on clothes or hands, wipe off IMMEDIATELY and wash AT ONCE with plenty of water. Be doubly careful to keep these fluids away from the face, yours or anyone else's. Notify the instructor in any and all cases of spillage.

2. The Gas Analyzer

Assemble an analyzer as follows (see Fig. 34.1). Fit a one-hole rubber stopper to each end of a 20-mm-wide glass cylinder. Insert short pieces of glass tubing into the holes of the stoppers so that the ends of the tubes do NOT project beyond the inside surfaces of the stoppers. Attach a 3-in. length of rubber tubing to each of the protruding glass pieces and equip each rubber tube with a pinch clamp (preferably of a type operated by finger pressure). One rubber end will be used as mouthpiece, the other will be the "working end." Clamp a test-tube holder around the middle of the assembly and use it as a handle; during the experiments the analyzer chamber should not be touched by your hands, since their warmth would alter the internal pressure.

The analyzer is now ready for use. To load it with a given sample of gas it is first filled completely with water to expel all the gas (room air) originally present. The water is then replaced with the gas to be tested. Immerse the working end of the analyzer into a beaker of water. Open both clamps and suck water into the apparatus till it is filled beyond the upper clamp. Close the clamps and you are ready to proceed.

3. *The Gas Content of Atmospheric Air*

a. Open both clamps of the analyzer and let the water run into a beaker. Atmospheric air will replace the water. Close the clamps when air has filled the analyzer completely. Half fill a clean beaker with pyrogallol. To get the process of gas absorption started, take up some pyrogallol with a medicine dropper, insert the tip of the dropper into the rubber piece at the working end of the analyzer, open the clamp at that end, and squirt the pyrogallol into the apparatus. Close the clamp, remove the dropper, and rotate the analyzer slowly to let the pyrogallol spread out along the inner glass surfaces. After a minute or so, immerse the working end into the beaker containing pyrogallol. Open the clamp at that end and let the fluid rise into the analyzer. Only a little will probably be sucked in at this point. Close the clamp, rotate the apparatus for a minute, then again allow pyrogallol to be sucked in, as above. Repeat this procedure several times during a 5- to 10-min period, until no more pyrogallol is taken into the apparatus.

Hold the analyzer upright to collect all the pyrogallol at one end. Then measure and record (1) the length of the pyrogallol column and (2) the total length of the gas chamber, from one rubber stopper to the other. Thereafter open both clamps of the analyzer and let the reagent run out into the pyrogallol beaker (fresh reagent can be used repeatedly). Thoroughly wash the apparatus under the tap, refill with water, close clamps, and proceed with the next determination.

b. Fill the analyzer with a fresh sample of atmospheric air as above. Close clamps. Take up some KOH in a clean medicine dropper, insert the tip into the rubber piece at the working end of the analyzer, open the clamp at that end, and squirt KOH into the apparatus. Close the clamp and rotate the analyzer. This procedure will get the process of CO_2 absorption started. After a minute or so immerse the rubber piece at the working end into a beaker containing KOH, open the clamp at that end, and let more KOH be sucked into the analyzer. Continue essentially as in expt. *a* above. Since the amount of CO_2 in air is far smaller than the amount of O_2, do not expect very much KOH to enter the analyzer. Indeed, if too much has been squirted in at the start, the excess will probably be blown out when the rubber piece is in the beaker of KOH and you open the clamp.

When no more KOH is sucked into the apparatus, close the clamps and collect all the fluid at one end. Then measure and record the length of the KOH column. Calculate the percentages of the gases in the air sample as follows:

$$\%\,CO_2 = \frac{100 \times \text{length of KOH}}{\text{length of analyzer}}$$

$$\%\,O_2 = \frac{100 \times (\text{length of pyrogallol} - \text{length of KOH})}{\text{length of analyzer}}$$

$$\%\,N_2 = 100 - \%\,CO_2 - \%\,O_2$$

Thereafter open both clamps of the analyzer and let the KOH run out into the beaker. Wash the apparatus under the tap, refill with water, close the clamps, and proceed with the next determination.

4. *The Gas Content of Exhaled Air*

Fill the analyzer with exhaled air as follows. Hold the working end over an empty beaker and exhale through the mouthpiece into the analyzer, leaving the lips partially open. When you come to the end of your breath, close your lips firmly over the mouthpiece, open both clamps, and let the last fraction of your exhalation go into the analyzer. Close the clamps again. Repeat this procedure several times, until the apparatus is completely filled with exhaled air. Make sure room air is prevented from entering the apparatus; that is, keep clamps closed when you are not actually breathing into the analyzer.

When you are satisfied that the gas chamber is filled properly with exhaled air, proceed with a pyrogallol determination exactly as in expt. 3a. Then repeat with KOH as in expt. 3b. Calculate the percentages of gases in exhaled air, and compare with the data for atmospheric air.

Thereafter let the KOH flow out, wash the analyzer, and refill with water.

5. *The Effect of a Flame on Air*

Fill a large finger bowl with water, and place on it a small wooden float to which a short piece of candle has been attached. Light the candle. Then invert an empty 1-liter beaker over the candle and immerse the rim of the beaker well into water. Determine to the nearest second how long the candle burns. Attach a long rubber tube to the working end of your water-filled gas analyzer. Push the free end of this tube under the beaker and into the gas chamber in which the candle has burned. Hold the analyzer low and upright, open both clamps, and let air from the candle chamber displace the water in the analyzer.

When the apparatus is completely filled with gas, analyze for oxygen and CO_2, as above. Calculate and record the percentages of the gases, and compare with the result in sections 3 and 4.

Thereafter dismantle the gas analyzer and clean all parts thoroughly.

B. gas exchange in animals

1. *Carbon Dioxide in Expired Air*

Half fill a test tube with tap water and add a few drops of neutral red solution. Note the color. Then put a soda straw into the tube and exhale through it, bubbling your breath into the solution for a few minutes. What happens? Record and interpret.

Half fill a test tube with limewater, insert a soda straw, and bubble exhaled air through it. What happens? Record and interpret.

2. *Breathing Rate*

The following exercises demonstrate the effect of CO_2 concentration in blood on the rate of breathing. One partner should serve as test subject, the other should record and keep time. Alternate these functions. In all the following, count one inhalation and one exhalation together as one breath. Allow at least 1 min rest between tests. Record all measurements in the table provided on Data Sheet 12, page 274.

a. Count the number of breaths per minute during normal, unforced, involuntary breathing while sitting at rest. Record the average of three 1-min trials.

b. Take very deep, forced breaths for 1 min, at a faster than normal rate. After such "forced ventilation," breathe as normally and involuntarily as possible and count the number of breaths per minute. Record.

c. Hold a paper bag tightly over your mouth and nose so that you are forced to rebreathe the same air. Do this for 2 min, breathing as involuntarily as possible. During the second minute count the number of breaths. Record.

d. Stand and make 30 knee bends in the interval of 1 min. Then sit quietly and count the number of *unforced* breaths per minute. Record.

e. Repeat each of the above, that is, normal breathing, forced ventilation, rebreathing the same air, and exercise. At the end of each procedure take a deep breath, and hold it as long as possible; count the number of seconds before you are forced to breathe again. Record all data.

f. Repeat all of e, except that you hold your breath not at peak inspiration but at peak expiration. Record all data.

IV analysis

1. Review and discuss the principles on which the gas analyses in this exercise are based. How would you expect the results to vary if you held the analyzer not with a test-tube holder but directly with your hands?

2. When you filled your gas analyzer with exhaled air, what was the reason for using only the last part of your breath? During inhalation, does air entering your lungs consist entirely of fresh atmospheric air? Explain.

3. Since as great a gas volume is inhaled as is exhaled, what takes the place of the used oxygen?

4. How would you demonstrate experimentally that atmospheric nitrogen is not a respiratory gas?

What does air consist of, apart from O_2, CO_2, and N_2?

5. Compare the results of expts. A4 and A5. Which burns more intensely, the candle flame or the respiratory machinery of the body? Would you say, therefore, that one uses a richer energy fuel than the other?

6. Explain the results of the experiments in B1. Inasmuch as CO_2 is constantly produced in the body, how is it that living matter does not become highly acid?

7. Describe the regulating mechanisms in the body which ensure that breathing continues automatically and without conscious effort.

8. In the light of item 7, account for your data on breathing rate after forced ventilation.

9. In the light of item 7, account for your data on breathing rate while rebreathing the same air.

10. In the light of item 7, account for your data on breathing rate after exercise.

11. In the light of item 7, account for your data on variations in breath-holding ability under different conditions. Why is it impossible to hold one's breath for very long under any condition?

12. Is there a correlation between breathing rate and heart rate? Discuss fully. Review the anatomy of the mammalian breathing system.

13. How does breathing differ in aquatic and terrestrial animals? Compare representative breathing systems anatomically and functionally.

14. What is a basal metabolic rate and how is it measured? What factors influence such a rate?

15. What types of animals possess diaphragms? How do those without diaphragms breathe? Discuss specific cases. Does (*a*) an amoeba, (*b*) a plant, breathe? Discuss.

exercise 35 gas exchange and excretion

I materials

Each group of 4 students

1 doz test tubes
2 large test tubes, with two-hole rubber stoppers
test-tube rack and brush
rubber tubing, 4 pieces, 2 or 3 in. long
glass tubing, 2 pieces 2 in. long, 2 pieces 6 or 7 in. long
2 capillary glass tubes, 10 in. long, 0.5 mm internal diameter
2 pinch clamps, screw type
thermometer
millimeter rulers
rubber bands
paper clips
1 beaker, 1 liter
2 or 3 beakers, 250 ml
bunsen burner plus stand, wire grid
spot plate
conc. NaOH, in bottle (14 *N*, or 40%)
20 ml 20% urea solution
30 ml 10% Na_2CO_3 solution
30 ml 5% $HgCl_2$ solution

Team or class stock

approx. 10 to 15 ml per team:

phenol red indicator
ninhydrin reagent
Benedict's reagent
1% glucose solution
2% $AgNO_3$ solution
2% $BaCl_2$ solution
5% $FeCl_3$ solution
5% citric or oxalic acid
pH 7 buffer (see Appendix)
0.1% acetic acid
10% HCl
conc. HNO_3

Class stock

potatoes, fresh
yeast suspension, fresh (2 cakes per liter of water)
whole blood, plasma, or serum (50 ml per team; optional)
10% trichloracetic acid (if blood is used)
urease paper or tablets or powdered enzyme
0.25-ml syringes, with needles

5% KOH solution
0.03 *M* NaF solution (1.2 g/liter)
crushed ice, stock
distilled water, stock
red litmus papers

II introduction

The first part of this exercise is a study of gas exchange in plants, based on indirect measurements of oxygen consumption and direct measurements of CO_2 output by plant tissues. The second part is devoted to an examination of animal excretion, insofar as this function can be tested by determining the composition of urine and comparing it with that of blood. Since blood is the immediate source of urine components, a comparison of the two fluids can show how the kidneys act.

Four students will work together as a team.

III directions

A. gas exchange in plants

1. If living material respires in a fixed volume of air, the cells will gradually use up more and more of the oxygen present and will release CO_2. If conditions are then provided to remove the CO_2 as fast as it appears, the gas pressure within the fixed volume will fall. The amount of falling will be a quantitative index of the amount of oxygen consumed by the living tissue. Carbon dioxide can be removed readily from a mixture of gases by potassium hydroxide (see exercise 34). These principles are made use of in the following experiment.

2. Assemble a manumetric apparatus as follows (Fig. 35.1). Obtain a large test tube fitted with a two-hole rubber stopper. Into one hole of the stopper insert a short piece of glass tube and to the outside end of this tube attach a short length of rubber tubing to serve as a mouthpiece. Put a screw-type pinch clamp on the mouthpiece. Into the other hole of the stopper insert a glass tube just long enough to reach to almost the bottom of the test tube. To the outside of this tube attach a 2- to 3-in. length of rubber tubing; connect the tubing to an approximately 10-in.-long glass capillary tube (internal diameter 0.5 mm). With rubber bands, fix a plastic millimeter ruler to the capillary tube and fasten the tube horizontally to a ring stand.

Close the pinch clamp part way and press the two-hole stopper assembly tightly into the test tube. Dip the free end of the capillary tube into a beaker containing 5% KOH solution, and by sucking slowly on the mouthpiece, carefully draw KOH into the test tube to a height of about 1 in. Then close the pinch clamp completely, and put the test-tube portion of the apparatus vertically into a large beaker of water, so that the water just covers the outside surface of the two-hole stopper. This assembly will serve as the control apparatus.

3. Prepare an experimental apparatus in exactly the same way, but before drawing KOH into the test tube introduce living potato tissue into the air space in the test tube. To do this, cut a prismatic strip of FRESH potato about 2 to 3 in. in length and ½ in. in width and breadth. Quickly weigh this tissue to the nearest gram and record the weight. Using a rubber band and a paper clip bent into a hook, suspend the potato strip securely

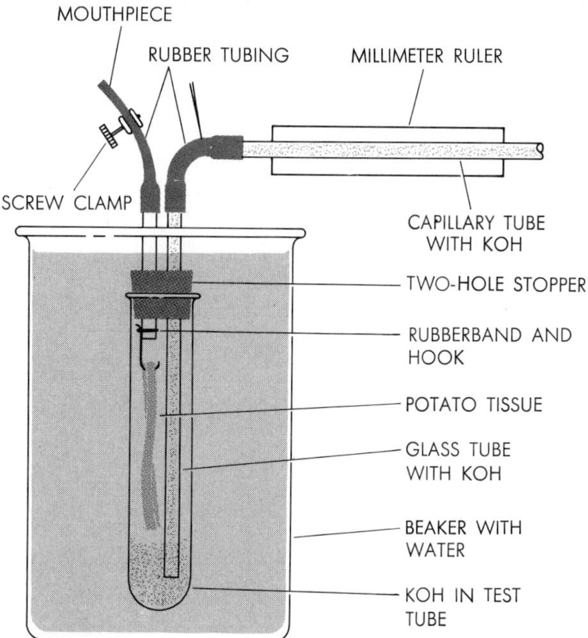

Fig. 35.1 Assembly for experiments on gas exchange.

from the lower end of the short glass tube which leads to the mouthpiece. Then press the stopper assembly with the potato strip into the test tube, and as above, draw KOH into the system. Make sure that KOH never comes into contact with the potato tissue; if it does, the experiment is ruined and must be repeated. Make sure also that the potato strip hangs free within the test tube. Put the assembly into the same beaker of water in which the control apparatus has been put. Add a thermometer to this beaker and measure the temperature.

4. In both the control and the experimental assembly, touch the free end of the capillary tube with a piece of absorbent paper and remove some of the KOH, so that the surface of the solution is well within the capillary tube. Record the time and the position of the KOH level. Reread the position of the KOH level every 5 min, over a period of 30 min. In the experimental apparatus, the KOH level should move progressively farther away from the free end of the capillary tube. In the control system, the KOH level might move in either direction.

At the end of the 30-min run, plot the data. To obtain corrected values for oxygen consumption, SUBTRACT the control values from the experimental values if the KOH level in the control system has moved in the same direction as in the experimental system; ADD the values if the KOH levels in the two systems have moved in OPPOSITE directions.

Does O_2 consumption take place at a linear rate? From the known dimensions of the capillary tube, the total corrected displacement of the KOH level, and the weight of the potato strip, calculate the volume of oxygen consumed per gram of potato tissue per hour.

5. The apparatus may be used to assess the effect of various environmental conditions on oxygen consumption. As specified by the instructor, perform some or all of the following experiments (using the data obtained above as norms for comparison):

a. The effect of temperature. Run 30-min control and experimental tests with the assemblies immersed in a beaker containing (1) crushed ice, (2) water maintained at 30°C.

b. The effect of inhibitors. Soak a fresh potato strip in an inhibitor solution such as NaF, and with this strip then run a 30-min test. Use an untreated or water-soaked potato strip for the control run.

Interpret all data obtained.

B. excretion

Perform the tests below on samples of your own urine. To assess the action of the kidneys further, it is instructive also to run parallel tests on blood. Therefore, if the instructor so specifies, treat whole blood, plasma, or serum with 10% trichloracetic acid and filter off the precipitate. Then, whenever indicated, neutralize or alkalinize the protein-free blood filtrate and use it for the same tests as outlined for urine.

1. *Inorganic Ions*

Determine if the following ions are present by subjecting successive 2- or 3-ml amounts of urine (and blood) to the indicated tests (see also exercise II.1):

a. Chlorides: test with $AgNO_3$.

b. Sulfates: test with $BaCl_2$.

c. Carbonates: test with 10% HCl.

d. Calcium: test with oxalic or citric acid.

e. Phosphates: (1) test with $FeCl_3$; (2) test by alkalinizing a urine sample with NaOH and then gently heating to boiling. If a floccular precipitate appears at this stage, it is due either to the blood protein albumin (indicating inadequate retentive action by the kidneys) or to phosphates. If the latter, the precipitate will disappear on addition of a few drops of dilute acid (an albumin precipitate will persist and increase in acid urine).

f. Ammonium: test by first alkalinizing a sample with NaOH. Then bend a red litmus paper into a U shape and put the bottom of the U well into the mouth of the tube. Place the tube into a boiling water bath. Ammonia will be driven off and will turn the litmus paper blue.

Keep the tube in the boiling water bath for 5 min or so, until a test with fresh litmus paper shows that free NH_3 no longer escapes. Then cool under the tap and add 3 or 4 ml of ninhydrin reagent (ordinarily used as a test reagent for proteins; see exercise 10). The blue color here is due to nonvolatile ammonium salts and compounds containing nitrogen-hydrogen combinations (such as urea). Repeat this ninhydrin test with an alkalinized solution of urea.

2. *Sugars*

a. On an alkalinized sample of urine (and blood) perform a Benedict's test for reducing sugars.

b. A more sensitive test is based on the ability of yeast cells to respire sugars and to produce CO_2, which forms an acid in water. Number two test tubes and put 1 ml of urine into each (use a separate, parallel set of tubes if blood is tested as well). To tube 1 add 2 ml water, to tube 2 add 2 ml of 1% glucose solution, and into each put 2 drops of phenol red indicator. If the mixtures are now pink they are already alkaline and nothing further is required. It is more likely, however, that the urine is originally slightly acid, in which case the mixtures in the tubes will be yellow. If so, add to them DROPWISE 1% Na_2CO_3 until a pink color JUST becomes permanent.

Then put about 6 to 7 ml of yeast suspension into a fresh test tube and add 2 or 3 drops of phenol red indicator. The suspension should now be pink; if not, add 1% Na_2CO_3 DROPWISE until it is and just remains pink. Pour 2 ml of this suspension into each of tubes 1 and 2 and save the remainder as a color control. Place all three tubes into a beaker of hot water (from the tap) and keep them there for about ½ hr. Then record any changes of color, interpret the procedural steps, and account for the results.

3. *Proteins*

Normal urine contains at most only minute traces of proteins (largely albumin), not detectable by the usual tests. Put 3 or 4 ml of conc. HNO_3 into a test tube, incline it and, with a medicine dropper, run 1 or 2 ml of urine down the side of the tube so that the urine layers over the acid. A white zone of precipitation formed slowly at the interface between the fluids is indicative of protein.

Note that, even when proteins are absent, such a white zone may appear in concentrated urine due to the formation of nitrates of urea or uric acid. Test this by layering over conc. HNO_3 in a fresh tube 1 or 2 ml of 20% urea solution. Observe the growth of urate crystals. In the tube with urine, the gradual development of a narrow zone of color (often red) is due to bile pigments and urine pigments.

4. *Urea: Urease Test*

One method of demonstrating urea is to allow the enzyme urease to decompose urea into NH_3 and CO_2. The ammonia so formed may then be detected by its alkaline properties; for example, it may be driven off from the alkalinized solution and tested for with litmus. The technique can also be used quantitatively, for the total amount of NH_3 formed from a given quantity of urine (or blood) can be measured by letting it neutralize an acid of known strength. The amount of urea present can then be calculated by making a separate determination for free NH_3 in urine (or blood) and subtracting this value from that for the total NH_3.

Into each of two test tubes (1, 2) place 2 ml of urine, and into a third tube (3) put 2 ml of 5% urea solution (use separate, parallel sets of tubes if blood is tested as well). To tubes 2 and 3 add a few drops of pH 7 phosphate buffer and to tube 1 add 2 drops of phenol red indicator. The latter mixture should now be yellow, that is, just acid; if it is not, add 0.1% acetic acid DROPWISE until a permanent yellow is JUST established. Now put into each tube either a piece of urease paper or a knife-tip amount of powdered, commercial urease. Keep all three tubes in a beaker of hot water (from the tap) or in a 40°C water bath for ½ hr.

Then add NaOH to tubes 2 and 3 until they are distinctly alkaline, bend a piece of red litmus paper into the mouth of each, and heat the tubes in a boiling water bath. What is the result? Examine tube 1 for color change. Interpret all data.

5. *Urea: Mercury Test*

a. Mercuric chloride, $HgCl_2$, reacts with sodium carbonate by forming a distinct red-brown precipitate (of mercuric oxychloride). However, the mercuric ion may combine preferentially with a number of other compounds, for example, proteins and also urea. In that case, subsequent addition of Na_2CO_3 will not yield a red-brown precipitate, unless $HgCl_2$ is present in considerable excess. Indeed, a quantitative technique of measuring amounts of urea may be based on these reactions. Thus, to a fixed quantity of a urea-containing sample may be added more and more $HgCl_2$ until a test drop of this mixture just gives the red-brown precipitate with Na_2CO_3. The amount of $HgCl_2$ so added provides an index of the mercury-combining power of the sample, hence a measure of the urea content. Alternatively, the same measurement may be made if to a fixed quantity of $HgCl_2$ is added progressively more of a urea-containing sample until a test drop of this mixture NO LONGER gives the precipitate with Na_2CO_3.

Familiarize yourself with the characteristics of these reactions by mixing a little $HgCl_2$ and Na_2CO_3 in a test tube. Then put some $HgCl_2$ into a fresh tube, add several drops of urea solution, and now add a little Na_2CO_3. Note that a slight reaction of $HgCl_2$ and Na_2CO_3 produces only a milky-white turbidity. With stronger reactions the turbidity becomes increasingly yellow, then deep yellow, and only a complete reaction produces the red-brown color. The latter should be taken as the endpoint in the following determination.

b. Collect 5 ml of your own saliva in a test tube and demonstrate the presence of excreted urea in it as follows. Prepare a spot plate containing in each depression a few drops of 10% Na_2CO_3. Mark the level of saliva in the test tube with a wax pencil. Put a few drops of 5% $HgCl_2$ into the saliva, mix and let a coagulum form, then take up a drop of the clear fluid in a medicine dropper and put it into the first depression on the spot plate. Note the reaction. Then add several more drops of $HgCl_2$ to the saliva, mix, and again withdraw a drop for a test with Na_2CO_3. Continue adding more $HgCl_2$ and testing successive drops with Na_2CO_3 in this manner until a definite red-brown precipitate is formed. At this point make another mark on the test tube to indicate the final fluid level. Pour out the mixture, and by measuring water into the tube with a pipette, determine the amount of saliva used and the amount of $HgCl_2$ added. From these data calculate the saliva-urea index, that is, the total mercury-combining power of saliva:

$$\text{Index} = \text{ml } HgCl_2 \text{ used}/100 \text{ ml saliva}$$

The normal value of this index usually lies between 30 and 50. Values above 50 indicate inadequate urea excretion from the kidneys.

c. Perform two parallel tests with urine and accurately made up 0.5% urea solution (or three parallel tests if a blood determination is made as well). Dilute a little of the urine with exactly twice the amount of water (and in later calculations do not forget this dilution factor). Put 7 ml of 5% $HgCl_2$ into each of two (or three) numbered test tubes, and prepare a spot plate containing Na_2CO_3 in the depressions, as above. With a medicine dropper add 1 drop of the diluted urine to tube 1, mix, and withdraw a drop for a Na_2CO_3 test. Add a second drop of the urine to the tube, mix, and again withdraw a drop of the mixture for testing. Continue adding diluted urine, 1 drop at a time and COUNTING the drops, until a test with Na_2CO_3 JUST ceases to produce a distinctly yellow precipitate (white precipitates are formed long after this endpoint has been reached).

Repeat this procedure with the urea solution (undiluted) and tube 2 (and with diluted blood filtrate and tube 3). In each case determine the number of drops required to reach the endpoint with Na_2CO_3.

Determine how many drops of solution make up 1 ml. Then, from the amounts of sample solution added to $HgCl_2$, calculate the mercury-combining indices of urea and urine (and blood). Express the results as milliliters of $HgCl_2$ per 100 ml of sample. Then, from the known absolute concentration of urea in the urea solution, estimate the concentration of urea present in urine (and in blood). Contrast with the value obtained for saliva.

IV analysis

1. In the experiments of section A, what is the role of the KOH in the test tubes? If control assemblies had not been used, what error would have been introduced into the experiments? What errors are inherent in the experimental design even if controls have been used?

2. Given specified constant environmental conditions, is oxygen consumption by living tissue in any way regular? Describe. Compare the rate of oxygen consumption in potato and animal tissue (obtain pertinent information from your textbook). Account for any differences.

3. What factors normally influence rates of oxygen consumption? Explain why and how for each.

4. If it were not possible to measure the gas exchange during the respiration of potato tissue, could respiratory rates be measured in other ways? Discuss. How could the apparatus you used be employed to measure other environmental effects on respiratory rates?

5. In what structures within potato cells does aerobic respiration occur? Does anaerobic respiration take place in the same structures?

6. Which of the inorganic ions you tested for in section B were (*a*) present, (*b*) not present, in urine? Ascertain from your tests (if done) or from the text which of the ions are present in blood, and draw conclusions regarding the role of the kidneys with respect to these substances.

7. What is the metabolic source of the ammonia and the ammonium ions present in urine? What is the source of urea? What accounts for the excretion of nitrogen in the form of different compounds?

8. Describe the results of the Benedict's and yeast-respiration tests on urine. Under what (*a*) normal, (*b*) abnormal, conditions should sugar be expected to be present in urine?

9. Write out the equation for the decomposition of urea by urease. Would you expect urease to be present in urea-excreting organisms? What is the source of commercial urease, and what role would the enzyme play in such source organisms? Account for the procedures and the data of section B4.

10. On the basis of your data and information in your text, which of saliva, blood, and urine contains the highest urea concentration? What can you therefore conclude about kidney action with respect to urea? Would you expect urea to be present in (*a*) sweat, (*b*) tears?

11. Describe the pattern of nitrogen excretion in (*a*) plants, (*b*) aquatic animals, (*c*) terrestrial animals. Which organisms excrete principally uric acid? What is the structure of this compound, and what is the adaptive advantage of excreting uric acid instead of urea?

12. Construct a comprehensive comparative table to show, for each constituent present in blood, whether this constituent is or is not also present in urine and, if it is present, whether it is equally or more or less concentrated than in blood.

exercise 36 neural receptors

I materials

Each student

shark head, preserved in formaldehyde
sheep eye, preserved in formaldehyde
dissecting pan
dissecting instruments

Each pair of students

2 250-ml beakers
wax pencil
6 large metal nails
10 ml 5% sucrose solution
10 ml 10% NaCl solution
10 ml 1% acetic acid solution
10 ml 0.001% quinine solution

Class stock

absorbent cotton
applicator sticks
crushed ice
heating units

II introduction

This exercise is devoted partly to anatomical, partly to experimental work. In the anatomical part, the structure of the vertebrate eye and ear, the two most complex neural receptors, will be examined. In the experimental part, tests on a variety of other receptors will be carried out with yourself as test subject.

Keep in mind that neural receptors are NOT organs with which sensations are experienced. Receptors are what their name implies, namely, stimulus receivers. They are sensitive to certain incoming energy, and they transform such energy into nerve impulses. Thus, eyes do not "see." Eyes are sensitive to light energy, which is transformed into nervous signals; the latter in turn are transmitted to the brain. Sensing of any kind always requires receptor AND sensory path AND modulator.

Moreover, sensing does not necessarily involve the nervous system. For example, the control sequence of pituitary gland (receptor) → blood (sensory path) → thyroid gland (modulator) plays an important sensory role in the control of metabolism. Many organisms possess neither nervous, circulatory, nor any other organ systems, yet they sense very well. For example, in a population of protozoa placed into an environment which is half dark and half light, all organisms will before long have moved into the dark region; the organisms have sensed the light and have responded to this stimulus by moving away. Cytoplasmic molecules function as receptors here.

Receptors evidently vary in structure, complexity, and specific sensitivity to different energy forms. Regardless of their variations, however, all receptors function in steady-state control. For as a result of given sensations, receptor-mediated EFFECTORS are brought into action, through which the cell, the organ, the whole organism, etc., may counteract the environmental stimulus and so may maintain a STEADY state.

III directions

A. the vertebrate ear

1. Put the head of a shark into a dissecting pan, dorsal side up. Along the mid-dorsal line, behind the level of the eyes and roughly at the level of the SPIRACLES (the small, most anterior gill openings), locate a pair of tiny openings. These are the entrances to the ENDOLYMPHATIC DUCTS, canals leading into the ears. In this respect sharks are primitive; early endolymphatic connections between the ears and the outside have disappeared during the later evolution of vertebrates. Remove skin and muscles from the region of the endolymphatic openings, until the cartilage of the skull is revealed. The ears are embedded in this region of the skull. Exercise great care in the dissection to follow. Ear tissue is thin and membranous, and structural relationships are easily destroyed by inadvertent cuts. Use Fig. 36.1 as a guide.

2. With a scalpel, shave away thin slices of cartilage of not more than 1 mm thickness. After a few such slices are cut away, the most dorsal portions of two SEMICIRCULAR CANALS will come into view: the LEFT ANTERIOR and the RIGHT ANTERIOR canals. Note the orientation of these canals with reference to the shark head as a whole. Note also how the skull cartilage is tunneled out to make room for the canals. As will be seen presently, all semicircular canals connect at both ends to the UTRICLE, a median, fluid-filled chamber. Without damaging the canals, carefully chip away cartilage around and under them, using forceps. Also remove cartilage more posteriorly, until two other semicircular canals come into view: these are the LEFT POSTERIOR and RIGHT POSTERIOR canals. Note their relative position. Continue chipping away cartilage, piece by piece. The following (paired) structures will appear in the order given: the UTRICLE, a thin-walled chamber connecting with the endolymphatic duct dorsally and with both ends of each semicircular canal; the HORIZONTAL CANAL, the posterior end of which connects with the utricle just where the lower end of the posterior canal also makes connection; the AMPULLA, the bulbous enlargement found at one end of each semicircular canal; and the SACCULE, the most ventral part of the ear, a fairly large, thin-walled sac in which EAR STONES may be found. If the dissection is carried out carefully, virtually the whole ear can be removed in one piece.

3. The ear of the shark is primarily a balance receptor; utricle and semicircular canals contain receptors for motion (DYNAMIC BALANCE), and the saccule contains receptors for posture (STATIC BALANCE). These structures are present also in the ear of man, and there serve similar functions. The shark lacks a COCHLEA, which in man functions as a receptor for sound. Study the positional relations of the parts of the shark ear, reidentify the parts, and make sketches as desired.

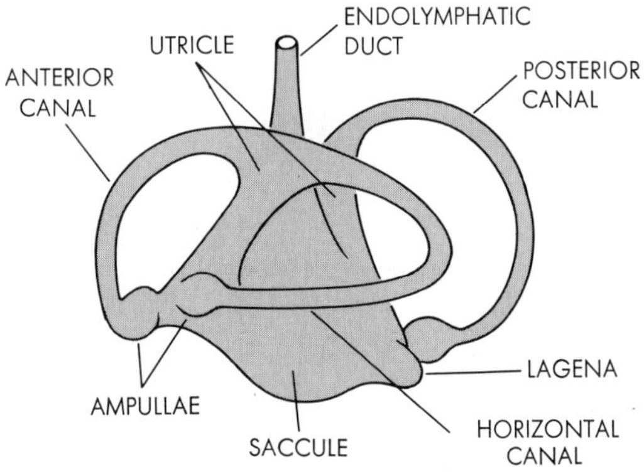

Fig. 36.1 Diagram of the left ear of a shark (anterior is at left side of drawing). The lagena is the region from which, in other vertebrates, a cochlea has evolved.

B. the vertebrate eye

1. The Orbit

Cut away the skin and some cartilage around one of the eyes of the shark. Remove the jellylike substance in which the eyeball is embedded. Then, by examining the space between eye socket (or ORBIT) and eyeball from all sides, note the seven strands of tissue which connect the eye to the socket; six of these are eye muscles and one is the optic nerve. The latter is white in color, eye muscles are pink or yellow. Find the points of attachment of the eye muscles on the eyeball; if necessary cut away more cartilage from the rim of the orbit. Cut through the muscles and the optic nerve and remove the eye. Note the many nerves in the orbital wall; some of these will be examined in detail during the following exercise. Note also the arrangement of the eye muscles. They attach to the socket in two groups, one of two muscles anteriorly and one of four muscles posteriorly. Try to determine how contraction of each muscle would turn the eyeball. Move your own eyes analogously and see if you can deduce the position of the six eye muscles in your own orbit.

Retain the eye of the shark for the next section. Tag the shark head and return it to its preserving container. It will be used again in the next exercise.

2. The Eyeball

The main work in this section will be done on the sheep eye. The shark eye should be dissected in parallel for comparison (see also Fig. 36.2).

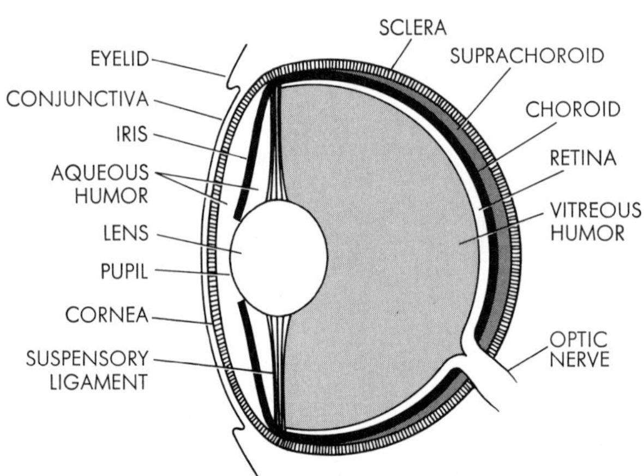

Fig. 36.2 Diagram of a sagittal section through the eye of a shark.

Find the stumps of the optic nerve and the eye muscles on the sheep eye. Then examine this eye from the front and identify the CORNEA, transparent when living but cloudy after formaldehyde preservation; the SCLERA, the white cartilaginous (in sheep) coat covering the whole outside, cornea excepted; the PUPILLARY OPENING, with a horizontal long axis; the IRIS (how pigmented?); and the LENS, partially visible through the pupil.

Carefully bisect the eye with a sharp scalpel, in a plane parallel to the front surface, so that all of cornea, iris, and lens will be in one half and the back portions of the eye in the other half. The jellylike material filling the main cavity of the eye is the VITREOUS HUMOR, which aids in maintaining eye shape.

Examine the back half from the inside. The pale, loose tissue is the RETINA. Note the central BLIND SPOT, where nerve fibers from the retina join the OPTIC NERVE and where the RETINAL BLOOD VESSELS pass into the eye. Lift the retina and examine the underlying CHOROID coat, pigmented black. Note the shiny, greenish material covering part of the choroid layer. This is the so-called TAPETUM LUCIDUM, which acts as a mirror reflecting incident light back into the retina. A tapetum is not present in man. Describe the position of the tapetum. Scrape off some of the choroid layer and note that the choroid lies to the inside of the SCLERA, the outer eye covering already identified above.

Examine the front half of the eye from the inside. Identify the LENS, and note its attachment to the SUSPENSORY LIGAMENTS. The latter are contained in the fine, radially striated membrane which surrounds the lens. The suspensory ligaments are attached peripherally to the CILIARY BODY, a ring-shaped muscle pigmented black on its surface. Remove the lens and look through it. Is the curvature of the lens surface the same in front and back? Describe. Follow the choroid coat toward the front and note that it continues forward as the IRIS. Probe through the PUPIL into the chamber containing the AQUEOUS HUMOR, a space bounded in front by the CORNEA.

Examine the structures corresponding to the above in the shark eye. Compare LENS SHAPE in shark and sheep. In the shark, ciliary muscles attach directly to the lens, and, in focusing, the lens is moved farther away from or nearer to the retina, just as in focusing a photographic camera. Mammals focus by changing lens shape.

Review and make sketches as desired; then dispose of the dissected eyes.

C. experiments on receptors

1. The Blind Spot

On a sheet of paper draw a black circle, about ¼ to ½ in. in diameter, and some 4 in. to the right of the circle, draw a heavy black cross of about the same size. Hold the sheet 20 in. away from your face and cover your left eye with the free hand. Direct your gaze on the circle and SLOWLY move the paper nearer. At a certain distance, the cross will disappear from view; light from the cross is now falling on the blind spot. Move the sheet still nearer and note the reappearance of the cross.

2. Taste Discrimination

Obtain four applicator sticks and roll a small swab of absorbent cotton around one end of each. Rinse your mouth with water. Dip one of the applicators into a 5% sucrose solution, and then touch the following regions of your tongue (or that of a partner) with the sucrose-moistened cotton: tip, front side edge, upper front center, upper back center, back side edge, lower center.

Record where a sweet sensation is most distinct, less distinct, or not registered at all. Rinse your mouth.

Using separate applicators, repeat the above test with each of the following solutions, in the order given: 10% NaCl, 1% acetic acid, 0.001% quinine. Rinse your mouth thoroughly after each series of tests. Record as above for salty, sour, and bitter sensations. TABULATE all data and interpret.

3. Touch Discrimination

This and the following experiments are to be carried out by pairs of students, one of each pair serving as subject, the other as experimenter and recorder. Alternate these functions.

This test estimates the distribution density of touch receptors in various parts of the skin. With the points of fine scissors held a specified distance apart, a given skin area of the blindfolded subject is touched either with one of the scissor points or with both simultaneously. The subject responds by saying "one" or "two," depending on how many distinct touch sensations he experiences. The experimenter tests each spot on the skin several times with one and two scissors points, but in a random order unknown to the subject. The subject is also not told in what order various distances between scissors points are tested. In the table on Data Sheet 13, page 275, are given the skin areas to be explored and the distances to be used. Record a minus sign wherever two points are felt as one and a plus sign where two points are actually felt as two. From the data, estimate the comparative distribution densities of touch receptors.

4. Temperature Discrimination

Prepare a beaker of crushed ice and a beaker of boiling water. Put several long metal nails into each beaker. With a wax pencil draw a square of 1-in. side length on the palm and on the back of the hand of the subject. Subdivide each square with grid lines so that at least 16 or 25 smaller squares are marked off. Draw two similar but larger grids into your notebook, for recording purposes. Blindfold the subject. With his hand resting on the table, explore the marked skin area for cold receptors. To do this, apply the point of an iced nail lightly against a point on the skin. The subject responds by saying "cold" if such a sensation is actually experienced; otherwise he remains silent. It is important here to discriminate well between touch and cold sensations. For every positive response the experimenter marks a plus sign on the grid in his notebook, at a point corresponding to the tested point of the skin; negative responses (that is, points tested that do not elicit a "cold" response) are recorded with a minus sign. Explore the skin in orderly fashion. Start at some corner and proceed to examine the small squares in sequence. Decide beforehand how many points in each small square you will test, for example, nine points arranged like this ⁙ or in some other pattern. Whatever pattern you adopt, use it consistently in each square. Change nails frequently, so that they are really cold when you test. If the nails are wet, wipe the points quickly on absorbent cotton before using.

Map the cold receptors on palm and back of hand. Then repeat the procedure for heat receptors, using the nails kept in boiling water. Determine the relative ratio of cold and hot points for each skin area tested, and compare.

5. *Pain Discrimination*

The same skin grids used above for temperature tests should be used. Draw new recording grids into your notebook. Using a sharp-pointed needle, test the marked skin areas for pain-receptor distribution. Adopt the same testing and recording conventions used above for temperature. The subject is again blindfolded, and he must carefully distinguish between touch or pressure and pain. The needle points, of course, should not be plunged deep into the subject; light pricks are called for. Proceed slowly, for if a pain response is given at a certain point, it may take a second or two before the sensation wears off; another prick during this interval may elicit wrong responses.

IV analysis

1. Review the structure of the shark ear, particularly the position of the pairs of semicircular canals. How do these canals function as receptors of dynamic balance? What is the internal structure of the ampullae?

2. Show what happens in specific semicircular canals when you carry out the following motions: turning the head to the left, nodding the head down, falling forward to the right.

3. How does the saccule function as receptor of static balance? What is the function of the ear stones?

4. Where is the human cochlea in relation to the parts of the shark ear? Describe the structure of the cochlea.

5. What groups of vertebrates possess a cochlea? Do any of the other vertebrates or other animals generally hear? Discuss.

6. Name the sensory paths leading away from the ear. Where specifically are the modulators for the sense of balance and for hearing?

7. What is the position of the long axis of the pupil in the eyes of (*a*) sheep, (*b*) cats? Relate the difference to the different ways of life of these animals.

8. Review the parts of the mammalian eye and discuss the function of each part. What is the "white of the eye" technically?

9. The cornea is one of the few structures of the body that does not contain blood vessels. What is the adaptive advantage of this? How is the cornea nourished? Is it living tissue?

10. Do the eyes of cats possess a tapetum lucidum like those of sheep (and what other vertebrates?)? Discuss the adaptive significance of this layer, considering the ways of life of these animals. Compare with man.

11. Describe the focusing mechanism of mammals. How is this different in sharks? Relate the different lens shapes of sharks and mammals to the different conditions of light refraction in water and land environments.

12. Which groups of vertebrates possess (*a*) stereoscopic vision, (*b*) color vision?

13. Describe the control mechanism which regulates the intensity of light received into the eye.

14. What are the sensory paths leading away from the eye? Where specifically are the modulators of vision?

15. What are the obvious differences between insect and vertebrate eyes? Obtain text information on the structure of insect eyes. To what are they better adapted than vertebrate eyes? To what are they less well adapted?

16. Review the distribution of taste buds on the tongue. What kinds of experiments could be performed to show that different taste sensations are not due to differences in the function or fine structure of different taste buds?

17. Discuss your data on touch discrimination. How does the density of touch receptors vary in different regions of the skin, as tested? Are these differences adaptively significant?

18. How do the absolute frequencies of pain, cold, and heat receptors compare? How do the relative frequencies compare in the various areas tested? What is the structure of these receptors?

19. What other neural receptors, not dealt with in this exercise, does man possess? What potential stimulus energies of our environment are not directly sensible by us? Would it be advantageous to have receptors for such presently nonreceivable stimuli? Discuss.

20. What is meant by SENSORY ADAPTATION?

Give examples from your everyday experience. Relate this kind of adaptation to the so-called WEBER-FECHNER LAW. It states that, within certain limits, the smallest perceptible change in the strength of a stimulus bears a fixed relation to the whole stimulus. For example, if a person can tell the weight difference between 1 lb and not less than 1.1 lb, he will be able to tell the difference between 100 lb and not less than 110 lb.

exercise 37 the nervous system

I materials

Each student

shark head (from exercise 36)
frog, freshly killed by chemical means
dissecting pan, pins
dissecting instruments
hand lens

Class stock

human brains, whole and bisected, preserved
other mammalian and vertebrate brains, whole and bisected, preserved

II introduction

In this exercise the structural organization of the vertebrate nervous system will be examined. Neural functions will be dealt with in the following exercise.

For the principal study of the brain and the cranial nerves the head of the shark will be used. The choice of this animal entails a number of important advantages. Not only is a cartilaginous skull easier to dissect than the bony skull of other vertebrates, but the shark also is a comparatively primitive vertebrate; hence its brain provides a remote, indirect glimpse into the ancestry of the human brain. Indeed, the principal parts of the brain of sharks and primitive fishes generally form the common foundation on which the brain of virtually all vertebrates is built. In later vertebrates additional brain parts have evolved, and some of the original parts have expanded in relative size. These later acquisitions have become superimposed dorsally over the original components present in the ancestral vertebrate brain. Thus, deep inside the human brain may still be found structures that guided our piscine forebears through early seas; functions have partly changed, but the structures have remained virtually the same.

Such close correspondence is in evidence also with regard to cranial nerves. Throughout vertebrate evolution each cranial nerve has continued to innervate the same body parts, regardless of the animal. Functions of many of these parts have changed drastically. For example, portions of the primitive jaw have become portions of the later middle ear; portions of the original gills have become components of the lower face and the neck. But despite such functional changes, the same nerves still provide signal paths to and from the structures in question.

III directions

A. brain and cranial nerves: sharks

1. The same shark head you used in the preceding exercise will be dissected. Put the head into a dissecting tray, dorsal side up, and cut away skin and muscles from the top so as to expose the BRAIN CASE, made of cartilage. The brain, under the dorsal plate of cartilage, extends from a level just anterior to the eyes back to the level of the first gill slits. Carefully shave away dorsal cartilage from this region and expose the BRAIN. Do not damage nervous tissue in the process. Carry your dissection sufficiently far back to expose also the anterior portion of the SPINAL CORD and its connection with the brain. In the following examination make use of text information where warranted (for example, Chap. 21, "The Science of Biology").

2. Study the dorsal aspect of the brain *in situ*. The most anterior structures are the large OLFACTORY LOBES, containing modulator centers for the sense of smell. A very shallow groove marks the separation of these lobes from the CEREBRAL HEMISPHERES, which on superficial view seem to be merged entirely with the olfactory lobes. Note that the cerebrum is relatively small in sharks. This is the structure that has enlarged most during brain evolution. In man, the cerebral hemispheres cover over most of the primitive parts of the brain, which in the shark are freely visible posteriorly. Each cerebral hemisphere contains a central cavity (to be examined later), the so-called first or second BRAIN VENTRICLE. Cerebrospinal fluid normally fills these spaces.

The olfactory lobes and the cerebral hemispheres together represent a brain region called the TELENCEPHALON. Immediately behind it is a narrow, depressed region, the DIENCEPHALON. In the shark it functions in sensory coordination. The diencephalon is covered dorsally by the membranous CHOROID PLEXUS, a dense network of blood vessels which nourishes the forward part of the brain. The choroid plexus forms the roof of the THIRD VENTRICLE; the sides and bottom of this chamber are formed by the diencephalon. The third ventricle communicates anteriorly with the first and second and posteriorly with the fourth (to be examined presently). Note that the brain is fundamentally a hollow structure. The ventricular cavities are continuous posteriorly with a spinal canal running the length of the spinal cord.

Telencephalon and diencephalon together make up the FOREBRAIN. This division merges posteriorly with the MIDBRAIN, or MESENCEPHALON. The latter consists largely of the OPTIC LOBES, a pair of rounded structures containing, in the shark, modulator centers for visual and auditory (that is, balance) sensations. Partly overhanging the optic lobes is the CEREBELLUM, grooved transversely and longitudinally, and representing the METENCEPHALON, that is, the anterior part of the HINDBRAIN. The cerebellum contains centers for motor coordination. The posterior part of the hindbrain, and the most posterior portion of the brain as a whole, is the MEDULLA OBLONGATA, or MYELENCEPHALON, an elongated structure tapering imperceptibly into the spinal cord. The medulla is covered dorsally by another CHOROID PLEXUS, made up of blood vessels supplying the hind portions of the brain. Medulla and choroid plexus enclose the FOURTH VENTRICLE, already referred to above.

Review and label Fig. 37.1.

3. On the side where the eye has been removed during the preceding exercise, cut away CAREFULLY the thin cartilage wall between the brain and the orbit. Chip away pieces around and under the CRANIAL NERVES without damaging these. Do not hurry this dissection; care is essential here. Remove also tissue anterior to the olfactory lobes. From each lobe emerges a strand of tissue, the OLFACTORY TRACT, which enlarges anteriorly into the OLFACTORY BULB. Expose these structures.

Study the individual cranial nerves *in situ*, as outlined below. Most of these nerves emerge from the ventral or ventrolateral side of the brain, so that the brain will have to be lifted cautiously to obtain a good view of the origin of each nerve. After a nerve is identified, trace it away from the brain as indicated below. When the *in situ* examination is completed, cut through each cranial nerve on both sides of the brain, leaving generous stumps attached. Then carefully lift out the whole brain and reidentify the cranial nerve stumps, in a ventral examination of the isolated brain.

The names, functions, and positions of all cranial nerves are given below, in anteroposterior

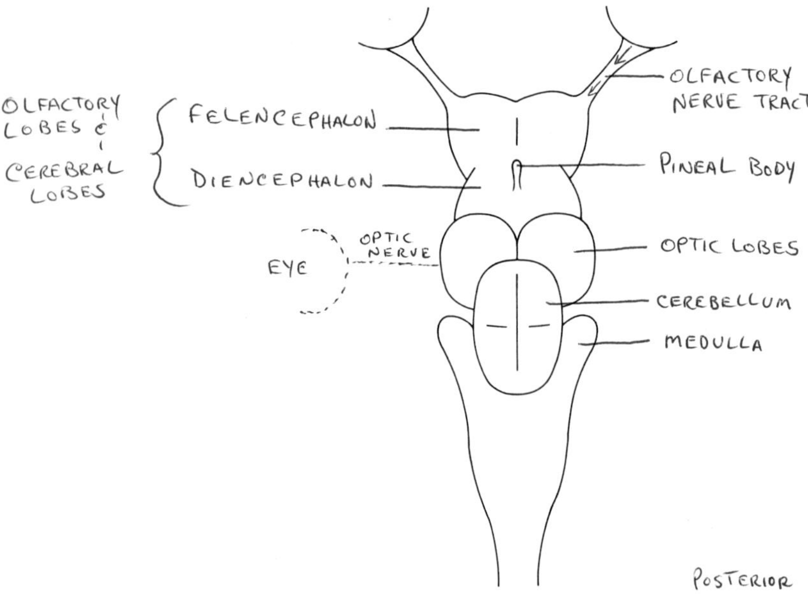

Fig. 37.1 Label this sketch of the dorsal side of a shark brain.

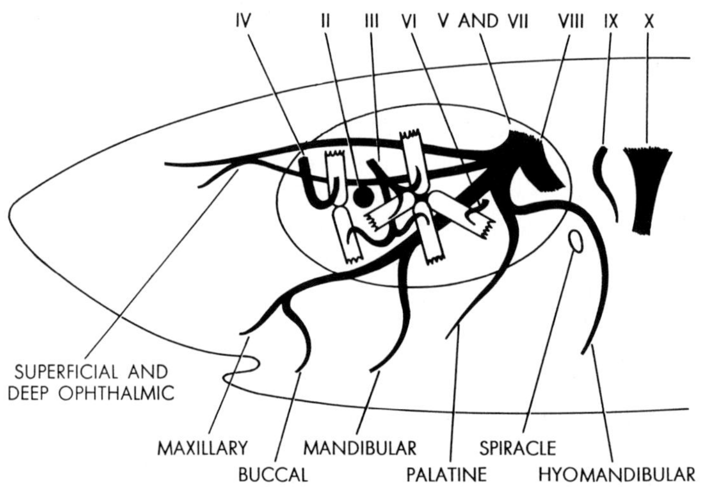

Fig. 37.2 Diagram of the cranial nerves and some of their branches in sharks. ***All nerves named along the bottom of this figure are branches of the trigeminal (V) and/or facial (VII) nerves.***

sequence. Some of these nerves are small and you may not find them, especially in the ***in situ*** examination. Try nevertheless to identify as many as possible (see also Fig. 37.2).

OLFACTORY: sensory. Numerous short, practically invisible nerves connecting the olfactory bulbs and the nasal organs, situated just anterior to the olfactory bulbs. Cut through the olfactory tracts to facilitate lifting the brain when examining the nerves below.

OPTIC: sensory. A large nerve from the retina to the midbrain (optic lobes). The nerve enters the brain from the ventral side.

OCULOMOTOR: motor. It leaves the midbrain behind the optic nerve, passes into the orbit, and innervates four of the six eye muscles.

TROCHLEAR: motor. It leaves the midbrain, passes into the orbit, and innervates one of the six eye muscles.

TRIGEMINUS: mixed sensory and motor. The origin of this large nerve is inextricably mixed with the origins of the seventh and eighth nerves. All three arise as a conspicuous bundle from the anteroventral part of the medulla oblongata. The trigeminus passes into the orbit where it divides into four main branches. Two of the latter run along the median wall and two along the floor of the orbit. The nerves innervate the snout and jaw region. In man, trigeminal branches carry sensory impulses from the lower parts of the head, including teeth, and motor impulses to muscles of the mouth.

ABDUCENS: motor. It arises close to the origin of the fifth nerve, passes into the orbit, and innervates the remaining one of the eye muscles.

FACIAL: mixed sensory and motor. The origin of this large nerve has already been described. Two of its three main branches travel with branches of the fifth nerve and innervate structures in the same areas of the head. A third facial branch passes ventrally into the mouth cavity, tongue, and the anterior gills. In man, the facial nerve supplies the muscles of the face and the salivary glands and carries sensory signals from some of the taste buds.

AUDITORY: sensory. This nerve innervates the ear. It enters the brain where the fifth and eighth nerves leave.

GLOSSOPHARYNGEAL: mixed sensory and motor. A small nerve from the medulla oblongata, inner-

vating the tongue and pharynx region (as the name of the nerve indicates).

VAGUS: mixed sensory and motor. This large nerve is the most posterior cranial nerve in the shark. Its branches supply most of the gills, the heart, and the stomach. In man, this nerve innervates the whole breathing system, the heart, and most of the digestive system. You have already encountered it before, in exercise 33.

Mammals possess 12 pairs of cranial nerves. The first 10 are the same as the above. The 11th (SPINAL ACCESSORY) is a branch of the vagus which has acquired a separate origin, and the 12th (HYPOGLOSSAL) is the first spinal nerve of the shark, which in mammals has come to be included within the limits of the skull.

Review the nerves in the isolated shark brain, and make sketches as desired.

4. Study the ventral aspect of the isolated shark brain. Identify the ventral limits of forebrain, midbrain, and hindbrain. Note the OPTIC CHIASMA, where the two optic nerves meet and cross before entering the brain. Just behind the optic chiasma find the PITUITARY GLAND and note the stalk which attaches the gland to the brain.

With a sharp scalpel bisect the brain into left and right halves. Examine the folded construction of the cerebellum and the continuity of the ventricular cavities. Make sketches as desired. Save the bisected brain for comparison with mammalian brains.

B. brain structure: mammals

1. Examine the external features of human and other mammalian whole brains. On the ventral side, identify the OLFACTORY LOBES anteriorly, the OPTIC CHIASMA, the PITUITARY, and the ventral aspect of the MEDULLA OBLONGATA. Note that these mid-ventral structures correspond precisely to similar ones in the shark brain. Examine the stumps of the CRANIAL NERVES; identify as many as possible.

Dorsally and laterally, identify the large CEREBRAL HEMISPHERES, separated along the midline by a deep fissure; the CEREBELLUM, with its surface pattern of ridges and grooves; and the MEDULLA OBLONGATA, merging posteriorly with the spinal cord. On the surface of the cerebrum, locate the following areas; the FRONTAL LOBE, the large anterior portion of each hemisphere, containing centers for memory, intelligence, and other higher functions (note that in man the most anterior portion forms a PREFRONTAL LOBE); the TEMPORAL LOBE, rather prominent along the side of each hemisphere, containing control centers for hearing, balance, and speech; the PARIETAL LOBE, posterior to the frontal and dorsal to the temporal lobes (and separated from these lobes by distinct surface grooves), containing control centers for most of the skeletal musculature; and the OCCIPITAL LOBE, the most posterior part of each hemisphere, containing control centers for vision. The last-mentioned lobes are sometimes called OPTIC LOBES, but they are not homologous to the optic lobes of the shark. Primitive fishlike optic lobes are present in man, deep inside the brain (see below). The visual centers in mammalian occipital lobes are newly evolved and have largely taken over the functions of the primitive lobes.

2. Examine sagittally bisected human and other mammalian brains from the medial side. Note first the section through the white CORPUS CALLOSUM, a thick curved band of nerve tracts interconnecting the left and right cerebral hemispheres. Tissue above and anterior to the corpus callosum, that is, all of the cerebrum and the olfactory lobes, corresponds to the anterior portion of the forebrain of the shark. Somewhat posterior to the corpus callosum, find a faintly demarcated circular area, the INTERMEDIATE MASS. It interconnects the right and left THALAMUS, which corresponds to the diencephalon of the shark brain. Just behind the intermediate mass is a rounded hillock, covered over by the tissue of the cerebrum. This hillock is the equivalent of part of the midbrain of the shark; that is, these are the primitive optic lobes. Fiber tracts from the optic nerves lead into this region, as they do in the shark, but newly developed tracts in the mammalian brain connect these primitive optic lobes with the occipital lobes of the cerebrum. Just behind the primitive optic lobes find the small, stalked PINEAL BODY.

Reidentify the MEDULLA OBLONGATA. It is largely covered over by the CEREBELLUM. In the latter note the branched white fiber tracts, parts of the so-called WHITE MATTER of the brain. From its gross appearance, brain tissue is classified as white matter and GRAY MATTER, and the latter is usually

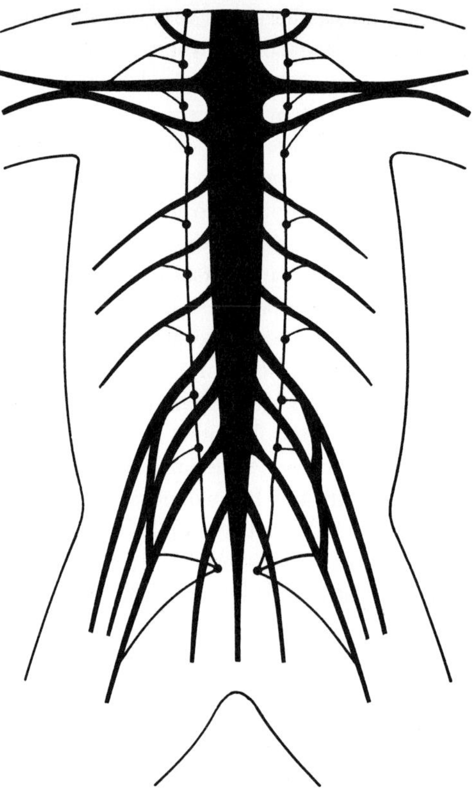

Fig. 37.3 Label this sketch of the spinal nerves and the autonomic chain of a frog.

on the outside of the white matter. This is true for the cerebellum, and also for the cerebrum (for example, the white corpus callosum). What accounts for these two different colors?

Review once more the correspondence between the fish brain and the mammalian brain. Visualize how differential growth of one has given rise to the other. Make sketches of mammalian brains as desired.

C. spinal cord and spinal nerves: frogs

1. Open the body of a freshly killed frog from the ventral side, and carefully remove heart, lungs, digestive tract, reproductive system, kidneys, BUT NOT THE DORSAL AORTA, so that the vertebral column and the dorsal body wall are exposed.

Identify the 10 pairs of SPINAL NERVES as described below (see also Fig. 37.3). How many pairs does man possess? Spinal nerves are all mixed sensory and motor, the sensory components entering dorsally into the spinal cord, and the motor components leaving the cord ventrally. In each spinal nerve, sensory and motor fibers travel together outside the vertebral column.

The first spinal nerve of the frog is small and difficult to see. It is called the HYPOGLOSSAL nerve (which in man is the 12th cranial), and it runs forward from the spinal cord into the lower jaw, where it innervates muscles in the floor of the mouth and in the tongue. A small branch of the 1st spinal also contributes to the 2d spinal nerve.

The 2d and 3d spinal nerves are very prominent. They are complexly united into a fiber network, the so-called BRACHIAL PLEXUS. Locate this plexus in the shoulder region, and trace the nerves into the forelimb. An analogous plexus is present in man, where it also innervates the arms. Inasmuch as man possesses a definite neck, the brachial plexus here is not formed by the 2d and 3d spinal nerves as in the frog, but by the 4th to 8th spinals, lower down along the vertebral column. Branches of the 4th and 5th spinals in man form the PHRENIC nerve, which innervates the diaphragm.

The 4th, 5th, and 6th spinal nerves of the frog are small, but easily visible in the mid-region of the trunk, along the dorsal body wall. What muscles do they innervate?

The large 7th, 8th, and 9th spinal nerves form the prominent SCIATIC PLEXUS innervating the pelvic region and the hind limbs. Trace the large SCIATIC NERVE, formed by the 8th and 9th spinals, into the leg, as far as the knee. An analogous sciatic plexus is present in man, where it supplies corresponding structures.

The 10th spinal nerve of the frog is small. It runs posteriorly into the caudal region, innervating parts of the urogenital system.

2. In the mid-region of the trunk, on each side of the dorsal aorta and parallel to it, locate a fine nerve (use a hand lens to obtain a good view). This is the AUTONOMIC CHAIN, made up of ganglia and fiber tracts of the sympathetic portion of the autonomic nervous system. Trace this chain posteriorly. It will be seen to bend away from the dorsal aorta and to follow the course of the 9th spinal nerve. Trace the chain anteriorly. It leaves the aorta at the level of the 4th vertebra, intersects the brachial plexus and the 1st spinal nerve, and continues toward the base of the skull, where

it intersects the vagus nerve (the 10th cranial) as the latter emerges from the skull. The autonomic chain passes farther into the head, intersecting other cranial nerves, but this cannot be well seen.

Where the autonomic chain intersects a cranial or a spinal nerve a tiny swelling may be found. This is a CHAIN GANGLION. A fairly large VAGUS GANGLION can be identified, for example. Similarly, the 1st, 2d, 7th, 8th, and 9th ganglia, at the intersections with corresponding spinal nerves, can be made out quite well. The other ganglia are too small to be seen.

You recall that the autonomic portion of the nervous system controls involuntary activities, impulses being carried from and to spinal cord and brain by special fiber paths, distinct from fiber paths of the central nervous system. The autonomic chain ganglia serve as relay stations in the fiber tracts of the autonomic system. The ganglia are interconnected one with the other, as has been noted, and also with the spinal cord. Fiber tracts from the ganglia lead to the organs which the autonomic system (specifically the sympathetic portion of this system) controls.

3. Cut off the head of the frog at the base of the skull. Insert scissors into the severed end of the vertebral column and cut through the bone longitudinally, to expose as much of the spinal cord as possible. Be careful here not to damage the cord. If properly done, it is possible to dissect out the whole cord, with spinal nerves still attached (larger ones at any rate). Note the general shape of the cord, the thicker diameter at the pectoral and pelvic levels (where the brachial and sacral plexuses originate), and the tapering at the posterior end. In good dissections it may even be possible to make out the DORSAL and VENTRAL ROOTS of the spinal nerves.

Review and label Fig. 37.3. Then dispose of the dissected shark heads and frogs as directed.

IV analysis

1. Describe some of the major structural and functional differences between vertebrate and invertebrate nervous systems.

2. Describe the parts of the vertebrate brain in detail, comparatively for fish and mammals, and state the control functions of each part.

3. Compare the relative size of sensory control areas in the brain of shark and man. On the basis of this, estimate in which of these two animals a given sense plays a more important role, and relate this to way of life.

4. Considering the functions of the cerebrum, would a decerebrated vertebrate be able to remain alive? How would its behavior differ from that of a normal animal?

5. Differentiate carefully between the central and autonomic parts of the nervous system, as regards structure, location, and function.

6. Describe the anatomy of the autonomic nervous system, and indicate the specific functions of the various parts.

7. Describe the course of a reflex arc in the central nervous system (*a*) involving spinal nerves, (*b*) involving cranial nerves. Then describe the course of reflex arcs in the sympathetic and parasympathetic portions of the autonomic nervous system.

8. Does the right or the left cerebral hemisphere control the actions of the right hand? Discuss. Are the control functions of given cerebral regions unalterably fixed? Discuss.

9. How can the control function of a given brain region be determined experimentally?

10. Review the names, points of origin, and functions of the cranial nerves. Do likewise for spinal nerves.

11. Which sensory nerves would carry impulses if the following body regions were stimulated: finger tip, toe, eyelid, scalp, tongue, pharynx, gums, nose skin, shoulder, abdominal skin?

12. Which motor nerves would carry impulses if the following effectors were to be activated: salivary glands, heart, diaphragm, finger, toe, eyelid, tongue, pharynx, mastication musculature, nose skin, shoulder, biceps, stomach muscles?

13. List different control areas of the human brain containing modulator centers of the (*a*) central, (*b*) autonomic, nervous system.

14. Describe the structural organization of the spinal cord and the spinal nerves in frogs and in mammals (use your text for information, if necessary). How many pairs of spinal nerves are present in frogs and in man? What kinds of nerve fibers do such nerves consist of?

15. State succinctly the general function of a nervous system. Keep in mind that nervous systems are not present in plants. What animal groups do not possess nervous systems?

exercise 38 reflex behavior

I materials

Each group of 2 students

2 live male frogs
2 finger bowls with covers
dissecting pan
dissecting instruments
medicine dropper
ring stand, clamps, bar
2 beakers, 250 ml
10 ml 25% acetic acid
50 ml 0.05% sulfuric acid
1 filter paper

Class stock

frog-pithing needles
water tanks
inductoria, electrodes, batteries, keys, connected
wooden boards, about 6 by 9 in.
string
hypodermic syringes (2-ml), with needles
0.005% strychnine sulfate solution
1% acetic acid

II introduction

This exercise involves experiments on frogs and on yourself. In the tests on frogs, groups of four students will work as individual teams; pairs of students will carry out the human experiments.

You recall that control activity of any kind involves at least five structural components: receptor, sensory path, modulator, motor path, effector. You recall also that nervous reflexes represent a particular kind of control activity, in which sense organs function as receptors, muscles and glands as effectors, brain and spinal cord as modulators, and nerves as sensory and motor pathways. The sum total of nervous reflex activity and the effector responses produced by it account for much of animal behavior, internal as well as overt.

In each control action, and so in reflex activity, a feedback is normally operative. Through it, the response to a stimulus is prevented from going too far in amount and duration. A feedback may take many different forms, but in all cases it is a new stimulus resulting from the first response. This feedback stimulus affects the original receptor, thereby initiating a new control action. The latter continues or halts or reverses the first response, depending on the information supplied via feedback and receptor. As a result of such action sequences, an environmental change can be counteracted and a steady state may be maintained.

In each of the experiments below keep this general pattern of events well in mind. Although many of the experimental conditions will be abnormal and unnatural, the specific reflexes examined are of great importance under natural conditions, and you should attempt to see how this is so.

III directions

A. preliminary operations

1. Prepare a SPINAL frog, one in which the entire brain has been destroyed, but the spinal cord is intact. With your right hand, pick up the animal by its hind legs and hold tight. Put the frog dorsal side up into the palm of your left hand, and clamp the head between your left index finger and middle finger. Hold your left thumb firmly over the trunk of the animal. Release the hind legs now and pick up a pithing needle with the free hand. Draw the needle point lightly along the mid-dorsal line of the frog, in the anterior region. Where the head joins the trunk, a mid-dorsal depression will be felt. This is the juncture of skull and vertebral column. Plunge the needle point vertically into this depression until you can feel that the bone has been penetrated and the spinal cord has been pierced. Now move the handle of the needle from side to side to sever the spinal cord. Still leaving the needle in the puncture, hold it exactly in line with the longitudinal axis of the frog, lower the handle toward the back so that the needle points forward, bend the head of the frog slightly down with your holding fingers, and push the needle point into the brain. If properly executed, no bony obstruction will be encountered, and the needle will go in as far as the anterior end of the brain case. Move the needle handle from side to side to destroy the brain. Then withdraw the needle and place this spinal frog into its finger bowl. Leave it undisturbed for at least ½ hr to allow recovery from the shock of the operation. Prepare a second spinal frog in the same way.

2. While you wait for the animals to be ready, do two things. First, review the anatomy of the nervous pathways in frog and man, as studied in the preceding exercise. Thorough knowledge of these pathways will be essential for proper interpretation of the experiments below. Review also the information obtained in the dissection of the shark head: it can be applied directly to the frog.

Secondly, proceed to section B of this exercise and complete it. The experiments on the frogs are described in section C.

B. reflex activity in man

These tests will be performed by pairs of students, one of each team serving as subject, the other as experimenter and recorder. Alternate these functions.

1. Knee Jerk

The subject sits on a table, with legs hanging freely. The experimenter strikes the patellar tendon, just below the kneecap. The tap should be sharp but not painful and should be delivered with the edge of the hand.

Repeat, the subject this time attempting to inhibit the response by force of will. Can it be done?

Repeat once more, the subject clenching his fist and doing some mental arithmetic at the time the knee is tapped. How does the response vary?

Record all observations, determine the specific neural pathways involved, and interpret the data.

2. Pupillary Reflexes

The experimenter faces the subject and watches his pupils. The subject closes his eyes and covers them with his hands. The experimenter now shines a desk lamp into the subject's face, and at a signal, the subject opens his eyes and looks into the light. What happens to the pupils? Carry out this test by having the subject look first toward a dark part of the laboratory, then toward a bright part. Record observations, and describe the neural pathways involved in this reflex.

The subject holds the edge of a piece of cardboard or several sheets of paper along the midline of his face so as to divide his field of vision. Test the pupillary reflex of one eye, using the desk lamp as above, and determine if a parallel reflex occurs in the nonilluminated eye. Do the pupils adjust independently or together? Record results and interpret.

Carefully watch the pupils of the subject when a third person unexpectedly pinches the skin at the back of the subject's neck. What reflex pathway is involved here? This pupillary response usually accompanies pain stimuli.

Watch the pupils of the subject when he (*a*) looks at a near object and then (*b*) looks at a far distant object. Repeat with reversed sequence. Record responses and interpret.

3. Blink Reflex

The experimenter feints a sudden punch with his fist at the face of the subject and watches the subject's eyelids. Describe the neural pathway of the observed reflex. Repeat the test, the subject this time anticipating the feint and attempting to inhibit the reflex by force of will. Can it be done? Record observations.

4. Salivation Reflex

Obtain a small sample of 1% acetic acid in a clean beaker. Make your saliva flow copiously by "psychic" stimulation. Then put a few drops of the acid into your mouth. What effect does this have on salivary secretion? Record, and describe the reflex pathway involved. Rinse your mouth.

C. reflex activity in the frog

Two students will work together on one frog.

1. General Behavior Reflexes

Record all responses and other pertinent observations in the table on Data Sheet 14, page 276. In interpreting the data, identify first the complete reflex pathway specifically involved in each test, then relate the result to the conditions of the experiments.

a. Posture and breathing. Note the posture of the frog in its finger bowl. What is the position of the hind legs? Count the frequency and intensity of the breathing movements in head and trunk. Record observations.

b. Croak reflex. Hold the frog in your hand, and with a blunt instrument scratch the skin of the animal along the anterior half of the spinal cord. Note the number of scratches required to elicit croaks. Record and interpret. What normal function of the cerebrum can be inferred?

c. Righting reflexes. Deposit the frog in a dissecting tray, in normal sitting position. How does the animal adjust its hind legs? Pull one of the hind legs back, then release it; what happens? Turn the animal over on its back; what happens? Record all observations and interpret.

d. Balance reflexes. Put the frog on a wooden board and tilt the board gradually. Record the balancing movements carried out by the frog. By careful management, try to make the animal climb up the inclined board, perch on the edge, and, as you continue to turn the board, climb down head first on the opposite side. Record observations and interpret.

e. Swimming reflex. Place the frog in a large tank of water, and observe for some minutes. Note posture and swimming responses. Record and interpret.

f. Jumping reflex. Put the spinal frog in sitting position on a clear space of floor or on a long table, and (1) prod the animal from behind, (2) pinch its toes or thigh lightly with forceps. Note if the frog jumps, and if so, how much stimulation is required to produce this response. Record responses and interpret.

2. Some Properties of Reflexes

Push a bent pin through the lower jaw of the spinal frog, and suspend the animal with string from a bar clamped into a ring stand. The frog should hang free. Wet the animal down from time to time. Allow at least 1 min recovery between tests.

a. Unilateral and bilateral reflexes. Note the position of the hind legs in the suspended spinal frog. Are they completely limp? Test their degree of relaxation by raising the palm of your hand against the legs from below and judging the amount of resistance encountered.

Pinch one of the right toes GENTLY with forceps, and observe the response in BOTH legs. Repeat, testing at the same time the degree of relaxation of the left leg. Record observations.

Now pinch the right toe HARD, and again observe the response in both legs. Record, and compare with the first test.

Finally, pinch the right toe once more, but this time continue to hold it so that the leg cannot be withdrawn. What happens? Record.

Determine which neural pathways were involved in these reflex actions, and from the results draw conclusions (1) about the effect of the strength of a stimulus and (2) about the influence of the stimulated side on the nonstimulated side of the body.

b. The effect of stimulus level. Carefully note the response when different parts of the frog skin are stimulated with forceps (for example, belly, forelimb, flank, etc.). For each test, keep records at what anteroposterior level of the animal the skin was stimulated. From the results, determine whether a more pronounced response is obtained in body regions above or below the level of stimulation. (Also collect additional data on the influence of the stimulated on the nonstimulated side of the body.)

c. The effect of strychnine. With a hypodermic syringe, inject 2 ml of a 0.005% solution of strychnine sulfate into the abdominal cavity of the spinal frog. After a few minutes, touch the skin of the animal anywhere and observe what happens. Note that reflexes are paroxysmal, that is, the response is greater and more prolonged than that normally warranted by the stimulus given, and also note that extensor muscles overcome the flexor muscles. Since this is a spinal frog, the action of strychnine evidently does not involve the brain. To determine more precisely the site of action of the drug, remove the frog from its suspension, insert a pithing needle into the neck puncture made originally when the brain was destroyed, and push the needle all the way down into the vertebral column. This will destroy the spinal cord. Resuspend the frog, and stimulate the skin as before. Is a typical strychnine response given again? Record observations and interpret.

d. Direct stimulation of nerve. Take down the strychninized frog from its suspension, open the body from the ventral side, and remove all internal organs so that the vertebral column and the spinal nerves are exposed. Do not touch these nerves. Resuspend the frog. Stimulate the nerves of the sciatic plexus by pinching with forceps or by applying electrodes and sending current through them. What is the response of the legs? Record. Does this confirm or alter your above conclusion regarding the site of action of strychnine? Also, does nervous activity always require the participation of a whole reflex arc, with receptor, modulator, and effector?

Discard the animal just used, and carry out the next series of tests on your other spinal frog.

3. *Purposive Reflexes*

Make sure the suspended animal is kept moist. Allow at least 1 min recovery between tests. Prepare several small pieces of filter paper about 5 mm in diameter.

a. With forceps, dip a piece of filter paper in 25% acetic acid and place the paper on the mid-dorsal skin surface of the frog, in the pelvic region. Note results and record. Wash the skin IMMEDIATELY and THOROUGHLY (raise a beaker of water over the frog several times).

b. Repeat the above test, applying acid-soaked filter paper successively against the following regions (and washing thoroughly after each test): left flank in pelvic region, inside of right thigh, left foot, right forelimb, mid-ventral belly skin. Record results for each case, determine the specific reflex pathways involved, and account for the "purposeful" nature of the responses (keeping in mind that a brain is not present).

c. With forceps hold the right leg firmly extended, then place acid-soaked filter paper on the inside of the right thigh. Result? Record and interpret. Wash the animal.

d. Take down the animal from its suspension, put it into a dissecting tray dorsal side up, and slit the skin at the base of the left leg. Then gently push the thigh muscles apart and find the sciatic nerve. It runs parallel and close to the femur. Cut through this nerve with scissors. Resuspend the animal, and place an acid-soaked piece of filter paper on the left foot. What happens? Compare with the control experiment carried out in (b). What does this experiment prove? Record all observations.

Use this frog to repeat any of the earlier tests, if desired, or to perform others that might be suggested by the instructor.

IV analysis

1. Describe the general composition of a reflex arc. What is a nerve impulse? What is a synapse? How are impulses transmitted across synapses? Discuss in detail.

2. Can you consider a spinal frog as being alive? Is such a frog conscious? What vital functions do such frogs not carry out?

3. Review and discuss your data on general behavior reflexes. What can you conclude about the general control function of (*a*) the cerebrum, (*b*) the brain as a whole, (*c*) the spinal cord? Take your results on the croak reflex into particular account.

4. Suppose the brain of an experimental frog were left intact but the spinal cord were destroyed. How would the behavior of such an animal differ from that of a normal frog? Suppose BOTH brain and spinal cord were destroyed?

5. What is the speed of a nerve impulse? Is this consistent with the normal reflex time you measured? Explain.

6. What experimental evidence do you have that reflexes not only may be inhibited but may also be augmented? Where in a reflex arc does an inhibiting or augmenting stimulus act?

7. Is the possibility of inhibiting or augmenting reflexes adaptively useful to an animal? Discuss. Are there reflexes that cannot be inhibited or augmented? Is this adaptively significant?

8. In diagrammatic form, draw complete reflex pathways from and to each of the hind legs of a frog, via spinal cord, considering that each leg possesses extensor AND flexor muscles, innervated individually.

9. In the diagram of item 8, show from your data what reflexes (affecting both legs) must have occurred (*a*) when one leg was pinched lightly, (*b*) when one leg was pinched hard, (*c*) when the stimulated leg was held.

10. Account for the observation that we do not fall unceremoniously when we accidentally step on a sharp object with one foot. Draw a diagram of the reflex actions occurring under such conditions, taking into account also that we become conscious of the misstep.

11. From your evidence, where in the nervous system does strychnine act? Name other poisons affecting the nervous system and show how and where these act.

12. When a nerve is stimulated directly somewhere along its course, in which direction does an impulse travel? Suppose the sciatic nerve of a spinal frog were stimulated directly. What response would be obtained?

13. What response would be obtained if the dorsal roots of the 8th and 9th spinal nerves of a spinal frog were stimulated directly? If the ventral roots were similarly stimulated? Discuss fully.

14. Describe the specific reflex pathway involved in the adjustment of pupil size when the gaze is directed on a near or a far object. What is the adaptive significance of this reflex?

15. What can a physician tell about the nervous system by testing the knee jerk of a patient?

16. When the leg of a spinal frog withdraws upon stimulation, why does this leg not stay withdrawn permanently? Discuss fully. The answer involves a consideration of feedbacks.

17. Preferably for all, but for at least five of the reflexes examined in this exercise, show what feedbacks were operative, and how they contributed to steady-state maintenance.

18. What are conditioned reflexes? How do they differ from the ones dealt with in this exercise? How are conditioned reflexes related to learning?

part 7 reproduction

exercise 39 mitosis and meiosis

I materials

Each student

microscope
Allium, longitudinal section of root tip
whitefish blastula, mitotic stages
Ascaris, comprehensive slide of oviduct showing meiotic stages

Class stock

Drosophila, salivary gland smears, stained

optional:

onion roots, living, on bulbs grown in water-filled beakers for 3 or more days
acetocarmine stain, in dropping bottles (see Appendix)

II introduction

Some of the microscopic details of mitosis and meiosis will be examined in this exercise. You recall that mitotic cell division is the standard method of cellular multiplication in all organisms except the Monera. Through this process, unicellular organisms REPRODUCE vegetatively, fertilized eggs GROW into adult multicellular organisms, adult organisms REPLACE cells lost or destroyed through normal wear and tear, and injured organisms may REGENERATE lost body parts. Mitotic cell division requires energy and raw materials, is preceded or followed by intracellular reproduction of molecules, and is therefore preceded or followed by cell growth.

Mitosis itself is a process of NUCLEAR duplication, characterized by an exact duplication of chromosomes. Through mitosis a dividing HAPLOID nucleus becomes two haploid nuclei, and a dividing DIPLOID nucleus becomes two diploid nuclei. Mitosis is usually accompanied by cytoplasmic cleavage, the overall result then being "mitotic cell division." But note that mitosis may take place without cytoplasmic cleavage.

Meiosis too is a specialized NUCLEAR process. It results in a halving of chromosome numbers and is a response to the chromosome-doubling effect of fertilization. During meiosis, TWO nuclear divisions usually accompany ONE chromosome duplication. Thus, a nucleus divides twice and produces four nuclei; at the same time, a diploid chromosome set duplicates once and produces two diploid, or four haploid, sets. The net result of meiosis, therefore, is the transformation of one diploid nucleus into four haploid nuclei. In many cases meiosis is accompanied by cytoplasmic cleavage, the result then being four CELLS, each containing a haploid nucleus.

Meiosis occurs at different points in the life cycles of different organisms. In animals, for example, meiosis is a phase of gamete production. In male animals, all four haploid cells produced by meiotic divisions become sperms. In female animals, only one of the haploid cells matures into an egg; the others degenerate and are known as POLAR BODIES. This animal meiotic pattern will be studied in this exercise.

III directions

A. chromosomes

1. Examine stained preparations of giant chromosomes in salivary gland cells of *Drosophila* (low and high power). Each of these unusual and atypical elongated filaments is actually not a single chromosome but a whole bundle of like chromosomes fused together into a large broad strand. The existence of such giant chromosomes is a great boon in genetic work, since they allow the study of internal chromosome structure in fine detail, both under normal conditions and after experimental manipulation (for example, X raying of fruit flies and production of mutations through chromosome breakage).

In low power, cell and nuclear boundaries will not be seen. They have largely been broken in the manufacture of the slide. Note, however, the darkly stained chromosome masses, each representing the genetic content of one cell. In such a mass, identify the long filaments trailing out from the common center. Each filament is a giant chromosome.

In high power, note the conspicuous dark and light banding of the giant chromosomes. This banding is thought to be a visual representation of the line-up of genes. In view of the makeup of giant chromosomes, each transverse band would contain several identical genes (arranged like a disk in three-dimensional view), equal in number to the number of individual chromosomes composing the giant filament. Note that the (transverse) thickness of the giant chromosome varies from region to region and that the (longitudinal) thickness of the crossbands varies also. Such structural landmarks are specific, that is, they occur identically in corresponding chromosomes of other salivary gland cells. This permits the researcher to pinpoint precisely the chromosome locus which may have been affected by experimental treatment of fruit flies. Giant salivary chromosomes have aided significantly in the construction of GENE MAPS.

2. If so directed by the instructor, prepare an acetocarmine-stained squash preparation of onion root tips. The procedure is outlined in exercise 13, section C2, and you may already have made such a preparation in that earlier context. A repetition at this point will permit you to reexamine chromosomes of plants and allow you also to observe cells and nuclei at the various mitotic stages to be studied in the next section. Compare the appearance of onion and salivary gland chromosomes, and use the slide as a supplement in section B1 following below.

B. mitosis

1. *Plant Mitosis: Onion (Allium) Root-tip Slide*

In low power, locate the ZONE OF DIVISION, some distance behind the APICAL ROOT MERISTEM. Note the large number of dividing cells, containing densely stained, filamentous chromosomes. Switch to high power, and by moving the slide as necessary, find each of the mitotic stages described below. Study each stage carefully and make sketches if desired. Keep in mind that the staging is necessarily arbitrary to some extent, since mitosis is a continuous, uninterrupted process in which one phase merges imperceptibly into the next.

a. "Resting" stage. The nondividing cell. It is "resting" only from the standpoint of mitosis, not in any metabolic or functional sense. Review your observations on these cells made in exercises 13 and 14, and reidentify the cellulose CELL WALL, the CYTOPLASM, the well-defined NUCLEAR MEMBRANE, and within the nucleus, the NUCLEOLUS and the granular CHROMATIN. In killed and stained nondividing cells, the genetic substance usually appears in the form of chromatin granules. In the living state, fine filaments can be found which become thicker as cell division approaches.

They are then known as CHROMOSOMES. Duplication of chromosomes usually occurs during the resting stage (this is not demonstrable in all types of killed tissues). The chromosome pairs so produced are held together at one point, the so-called CENTROMERE.

b. Prophase. Distinct chromosomes (actually chromosome pairs) are now visible, still more or less grouped together in the center of the cell. The nuclear membrane has dissolved. A SPINDLE of gelated cytoplasmic fibrils is beginning to form, but it may not yet be visible at this stage.

c. Early metaphase. A fully formed spindle is now in existence, with fibrils ranging from one end of the cell to the other. The point at each end where the spindle fibrils converge demarcates a spindle POLE, and an imaginary line through both poles marks out a spindle AXIS. The chromosomes (more precisely, the centromeres of the chromosomes) have lined up in the so-called METAPHASE PLATE, a plane which bisects the spindle axis at right angles. Spindle fibrils connect the centromeres of the chromosomes with each of the spindle poles. These specific fibrils may not be distinguishable from spindle fibrils generally.

d. Late metaphase. The centromeres have divided, and the pairs of chromosomes are well visible. Gelated fibrils form between the centromeres of each pair of chromosomes.

e. Anaphase. One set of chromosomes migrates toward each spindle pole. Each set contains one of each original pair of chromosomes. The fibrils between the centromeres lengthen, and those between centromeres and spindle poles shorten. Find various stages of anaphase, with chromosome sets farther and farther apart.

f. Telophase. The spindle begins to subside and it eventually disappears altogether (that is, the gelated cytoplasm of the fibrils reverts to a sol state). A DIVISION PLATE is laid down across the cytoplasm, cutting through the cell (and the spindle) at right angles to the spindle axis and halfway along it (that is, in the plane formerly occupied by the metaphase plate). The division plate consists of pectic material which is later fortified with cellulose, thus forming new boundaries between the daughter cells. The chromosomes have clustered together near the spindle poles, where a new nuclear membrane develops around them. The chromosomes subsequently revert to a fine filamentous state, and they again appear as chromatin granules in stained preparations. Mitotic cell division is now completed.

If you have made an acetocarmine squash preparation above, find in it mitotic stages corresponding to the ones just studied in the prepared slide.

2. *Animal Mitosis: Whitefish Blastula Slide*

A blastula is an early developmental stage of an animal embryo, produced by successive cell divisions of a fertilized egg. The cells composing a blastula are still fairly large, and the division rate is high. Thus, many dividing cells are usually found in cross sections, and various mitotic stages are represented.

Study animal mitosis in detail, using the whitefish blastula slide. Make item-by-item comparisons with plant mitosis, and sketch as desired. The stage descriptions above may be used for general sequence, but the following points of difference should be carefully noted:

a. In view of the regular, patterned arrangement of root-tip cells, and the longitudinal plane in which the tissue is cut when a slide is made, most mitoses in the root tip will be seen "side on"; that is, the plane of cutting will reveal the whole longitudinal extent of a mitotic figure from one spindle pole to the other. In the whitefish blastula, cells are oriented in less orderly fashion. When a section is cut here, therefore, some mitotic figures will be revealed *in toto,* as in the root tip, but others will be cut through obliquely or even transversely. Hence many mitotic figures you see will have an unfamiliar or atypical appearance. Disregard these, and concentrate on those which can be seen in full "side-on" view as in root tips.

b. Animal cells in resting stage possess a CENTRIOLE, a small granule situated in the cytoplasm just outside the nucleus. During prophase, this granule divides and a spindle arises between the two centrioles so formed. In all subsequent stages, the two centrioles represent the spindle poles. By early metaphase, the centrioles have migrated to opposite ends of the cell, and the spindle fibrils range between them. In whitefish cells, centrioles will appear as small, circular, clear areas.

c. Beginning during the division of the centriole in prophase, an ASTER develops and grows around each of the daughter centrioles. Asters are made up of gelated cytoplasmic fibrils (as are spindle fibrils), and these are arranged radially around the centriole. Maximal growth of asters is attained during late metaphase. Thereafter they subside, disappearing from view when the spindle also disappears.

d. Cytoplasmic cleavage in animal cells is accomplished through a CLEAVAGE FURROW, not a division plate as in plant cells. The cleavage furrow is a constriction which, during telophase, cuts through the cell (and the spindle) in a plane at right angles to the spindle axis and halfway along it.

e. When at the end of telophase a nuclear membrane forms around the clustered chromosomes, the centriole remains outside in the cytoplasm, recreating the typical resting-stage condition.

With the exception of the points mentioned here, all other features of mitotic division are generally alike in plant and animal cells.

C. meiosis

1. Background

The parasitic roundworm *Ascaris megalocephala* (see exercise 24) is ideal for a study of meiosis. First, the chromosome number in this worm is small ($n = 2$), so that chromosome counts are made very easily. Secondly, the females possess long, fairly straight oviducts in which may be found eggs at all stages of maturity, depending on how far down along the oviduct the examination is made. At the anterior end of the oviduct, eggs are still immature and diploid, having just been released from the ovary. Sperm entrance takes place in this region. In this species, sperm entrance into the egg is the specific stimulus for egg maturation; meiosis occurs as the eggs continue to be propelled along the oviduct. In the middle portion of the oviduct will therefore be found eggs at various meiotic stages, the more posterior oviduct levels containing the later stages. During meiosis, the sperm remains dormant in the egg cytoplasm. When meiosis is completed and the egg is haploid, the sperm nucleus (which is haploid already, having matured in the male) fuses with the egg nucleus; that is, fertilization occurs. Cleavage then begins, through which the fertilized egg is transformed into a many-celled embryo. In the most posterior portion of the oviduct, therefore, MITOTIC cleavage divisions will be found.

Your slide contains a continuous longitudinal section through virtually the whole length of the oviduct, but the elongated slice of tissue has been cut into shorter strips, for easier assembly on the slide. If the slide is placed so that the label is on the left, a series of vertical tissue strips can be seen with the unaided eye. The upper part of the first strip on the left represents the most anterior end of the *Ascaris* oviduct. Progressively posterior parts are found by passing down the first strip, continuing at the UPPER end of the second strip (to the right of the first strip), passing down along it, continuing at the upper end of the third strip, etc., and ending at the lower end of the first strip on the right. Carry out your microscopic examination in this sequence.

2. Egg Maturation

Use low power to orient and to position the slide but high power to study individual eggs. The description below is not detailed, but rather emphasizes the main stages to be studied. Make notes and sketches for each stage, as desired.

a. Eggs and sperm entrance. In the most anterior portion of the oviduct find its tubular walls, and note the mass of EGGS filling the interior. Examine the individual immature eggs. Note their thin bounding membrane and the vacuolated cytoplasm. Egg nuclei are barely visible. At this level of the oviduct, a profusion of SPERMS will be found. Sperms are darkly stained, cone- or nail-shaped, and readily identifiable. Most sperms lie free in the cavity of the oviduct, outside the eggs, but some have already penetrated into the cytoplasms of given eggs. Move down a bit along the oviduct and note that practically all eggs are soon equipped with sperms (why are sperms not visible in some eggs?). Note also that one egg contains only one sperm.

b. First prophase. Slowly continue down the oviduct until you reach a level where all eggs possess SHELLS of appreciable thickness. These are secreted soon after sperm entrance, and provide protective capsules for the later embryos. In the shelled eggs, reidentify the sperms. They are found in the center of the eggs, and they remain there until fertilization. Their characteristic conical shape has largely disappeared, and they may not stain as deeply as before. But the darkish tangled mass of the paternal chromosomes may be identified right up to fertilization.

Some of the eggs will be found to contain not only the central darkly stained spot of the sperm, but also a deeply stained spot near the egg surface, excentrically situated. This is the EGG NUCLEUS, or rather, the bunched mass of the egg chromosomes. At this level of the oviduct they already take a dense stain, the membrane of the egg nucleus may already have dissolved, and the chromosomes may be in prophase. Pass along the oviduct a bit until you see that most of the eggs contain darkly stained egg nuclei or prophase chromosomes (as well as shells and sperm chromosomes).

c. First metaphase. As you slowly continue along the oviduct, the egg chromosomes will become very distinct and will be found to be arranged in a regular pattern. Close examination will also reveal a very nicely formed spindle and spindle poles. This stage is the first metaphase of meiosis. The chromosome number in diploid *Ascaris* cells is four, representing two distinct pairs. In metaphase of MITOSIS, these four chromosomes would line up in "single file," that is, within the same plane ( ). But in metaphase of meiosis they line up in PAIRS ( ). This is the first key difference between the two processes. At metaphase, moreover, each chromosome is actually a double chromosome, duplication having occurred at earlier stages. The doubles are at first held together at the centromere (as in mitosis), but soon the centromeres divide. Late during meiotic metaphase, therefore, there will be an overall total of eight chromosomes. Move your slide until you find eggs showing these eight chromosomes, arranged in the following pattern: . Visualize how this pattern arose from the original diploid condition. Note that now $4n = 8$; that is, four complete sets of chromosomes are present, each set containing ( ).

d. The first polar body. As in mitosis, metaphase is followed by anaphase and telophase. In meiosis, four chromosomes (two sets) migrate to each spindle pole, and a nuclear membrane forms around each of the groups of four. In view of the excentric position of the whole spindle, the cleavage furrow in telophase will cut the original cell into two very unequal daughter cells: one will be very large, one very small. The large one, with two sets of chromosomes, will give rise to the mature egg. The small one, also with two sets of chromosomes, degenerates, and is referred to as the FIRST POLAR BODY. In *Ascaris,* this body is constricted off the main cell at the end of the first telophase, and then becomes attached to the inside of the eggshell, where it remains visible for a considerable length of time. Continue along the oviduct until you find darkly stained polar bodies at points along the inner shell surfaces. Note here also that distinct, excentrically located telophase egg nuclei with formed bounding membranes may be visible and that sperm chromosomes are still present in a central position within the egg.

e. The second meiotic division. The egg now divides once more, passing through second prophase, second metaphase, etc. The whole process parallels the first meiotic division, except that the chromosomes (two sets) do not duplicate again but remain as they are. They again line up pairwise ( ) in the second metaphase plate, and one set migrates to each spindle pole during anaphase. Thus, telophase constriction will produce two cells, each containing one full set ( ) of chromosomes. Since the spindle is excentrically located, the two cells will be of unequal size, as before. The large cell represents the mature egg, now haploid ($n = 2$). The small cell, also haploid, degenerates and forms a SECOND POLAR BODY.

The second meiotic division occurs rapidly after the first, and all stages may not be clearly identifiable. Moreover, different stages may be found together at the same level of the oviduct. Move along the oviduct and identify the breakup of the membrane of the egg nucleus (that is, second prophase); the second metaphase, chromosomes here being more faintly stained than in the first metaphase; and the second telophase in which the haploid egg nucleus (with membrane) is clearly visible, and in which the sperm nucleus may already be stationed close by the egg nucleus. The second polar body is not easily found.

f. Fertilization and cleavage. During the later stages of the second meiotic division, the sperm nucleus, haploid from the start, rounds up and begins to migrate toward the egg nucleus. Move your slide along until you come to a level where most eggs contain two distinct nuclei side by side.

One is the egg nucleus, the other the sperm nucleus. Still farther down the oviduct, fertilization will be in progress: the membranes of the nuclei have broken up, and the nuclear contents are mixed. Here the diploid condition characteristic of *Ascaris* cells is restored. All chromosomes now line up in single file and the first cleavage division takes place. Find this MITOTIC division in the slide. All subsequent divisions are mitotic in nature also. Move the slide to the most posterior levels of the oviduct, and note that the fertilized egg is in the process of constricting into two EQUAL daughter cells. The two-cell stage of the embryo is so produced.

Review your examination of meiosis from the beginning, and make sure you understand the key features of this process of nuclear division.

IV analysis

1. Describe the key events of each stage of mitosis, and state the function of the process as a whole.

2. What different categories or types of mitosis occur in different organisms? What type of mitosis is typical in (*a*) Metaphyta, (*b*) Metazoa?

3. Review what is known about the stimulus required to initiate cell division. Can the occurrence of cell division be experimentally (*a*) prevented, (*b*) stimulated?

4. Cells of the human adult normally do not always contain precisely 46 chromosomes: in any given cell, the chromosome number is usually some even multiple of 23, twice 23 being the most frequent number. Discuss how such differences of ploidy might arise.

5. Many human liver cells (and cells of other tissues too) do not contain 46 chromosomes, but sometimes have 47, sometimes 45; that is, they have accidentally lost or gained one (or more) chromosomes. As far as can be determined, such cells are quite healthy and normal. How is this possible?

6. Review what is known about the frequency of cell division in tissues. What kinds of cells divide at a high rate, and what kinds at a low rate?

7. Would you expect varying gene dosages (due to different degrees of ploidy) to affect the functioning of cells in any way? Discuss. Does the state of ploidy of a cell affect the size of the nucleus or the size of the cell as a whole? Consider here the giant salivary chromosomes of *Drosophila*.

8. Describe the key events of each stage of meiosis, and state the function of the process as a whole.

9. Contrast mitosis and meiosis. Show through what different steps different end results are obtained. Also compare the first meiotic division and mitosis, and the second meiotic division and mitosis.

10. Sketch the chromosomes as they would appear late during the first metaphase of meiosis in an organism where (*a*) $2n = 10$, (*b*) $n = 7$. For each of these, sketch also the appearance of the mitotic metaphase.

11. Show that the formation of polar bodies is adaptively advantageous in egg maturation, but that it would be disadvantageous if it occurred in sperm maturation.

12. Describe the CYTOPLASMIC specializations accompanying (*a*) sperm maturation, (*b*) egg maturation, in animals.

13. State the haploid or diploid chromosome content of cells in the following tissues: wall of oviduct, germinal epithelium of testis, apical root meristem, blastula, membranes between shell and albumen of unfertilized chicken egg.

14. From your text, review the stages in the life cycles of various organisms at which meiosis occurs, and on this basis describe the nature of haplontic, diplontic, and diplohaplontic life cycles.

15. Describe the biochemistry of chromosomes, so far as known. Can the cross-banding in the giant chromosomes of *Drosophila* be described in chemical terms?

exercise 40 reproduction in protista

I materials

Each student

microscope
hand lens

Each 1 or 2 students

prepared slides of:

Spirogyra, conjugation
Oedogonium, with gametes
Ulothrix, with sporangia and gametangia
Vaucheria, with sexual branches and with zygospores
Chara, with sex organs
Ectocarpus, sporophyte with sporangia
Ectocarpus, gametophyte with gametangia
Fucus, section of antheridial conceptacle
Fucus, section of oogonial conceptacle
yeast, budding cells
Saprolegnia, with antheridia and oogonia
Rhizopus, with gametangia and with zygospores
Rhizopus, with sporangia
Penicillium, with conidia
Penicillium, section of fruiting body
Peziza, section of fruiting body
Coprinus, section of whole fruiting body
Paramecium, stained, showing fission
Paramecium bursaria, stained, showing conjugation

Class stock

Fucus, fresh or preserved, with receptacles
Rhizopus, fresh, with sporangia
Stentor coeruleus, rich living cultures containing dividing individuals
Paramecium aurelia, 2 mating-type cultures for demonstration of mating reactions (see Appendix)

II introduction

The objective of this exercise is to examine some of the characteristic protistan life cycles and some of the processes of reproduction and sexuality associated with such cycles. Keep in mind here that an important theme of the exercise is underscored by the word PROCESS; yet in most cases you will be studying only a series of isolated and fixed stages selected from a continuous process. Consequently, to achieve understanding of the meaning of such fixed stages, you will have to connect them in your mind and come to appreciate them as fleeting points within a moving process. For every stage you observe, ask yourself by what living events this stage has been reached and what living events normally follow.

Keep in mind also that REPRODUCTION designates a process of increase, on any level of living organization. By contrast, SEX refers to the joining of relatively unrelated gene sets. This process often does not occur in conjunction with reproduction, especially in Protista; it has the function of furthering the adaptation of individuals to the environment and thus increasing survival potentials. Reproduction and sexuality typically are elicited by specific environmental conditions, reproduction being a response to favorable environments, sexuality, a response to environmental stress. As a result of fertilization, sexuality leads to a doubling of chromosome numbers, which sooner or later is followed in turn by a halving of chromosome numbers via meiosis. The nature of the life cycle of Protista is determined in large measure by WHEN meiosis actually occurs in relation to fertilization (see Chap. 24, "The Science of Biology").

III directions

A. algae

1. *Gametes and Zygotes*

a. Examine the prepared slide of conjugation in *Spirogyra*. Note the tubular BRIDGE of cell-wall material linking two GAMETANGIA, the empty gametangium on one side of the bridge and the gametangium containing the ZYGOTE on the other side. If the zygote has already secreted a hard CYST WALL around itself, it is known as a ZYGOSPORE.

In what respects are the two types of gametes of *Spirogyra* different? Can any two cells of any two filaments function as gametangia and undergo conjugation? At what life-cycle stage does meiosis occur? Does *Spirogyra* sporulate? Carry out vegetative reproduction?

b. Study the prepared slide of *Oedogonium* showing gametangia (see also Chap. 25, "The Science of Biology"). Locate a sperm-containing gametangium, or ANTHERIDIUM, and an egg-containing gametangium, or OOGONIUM. Describe the structure of SPERMS and EGGS. How are such gametes formed? How do they meet? Are ZYGOSPORES present in your slide? At what life-cycle stage does meiosis occur? Is *Oedogonium* separately sexed or hermaphroditic? How and where are spores formed? How is vegetative reproduction carried out?

2. *Gametangial Specializations*

a. Examine the prepared slide of *Vaucheria* showing sexual structures (see also Chap. 25, "The Science of Biology"). Identify a short, rounded OOGONIAL BRANCH and a longer ANTHERIDIAL BRANCH. How are sperms and eggs formed, and how does fertilization occur? Are ZYGOSPORES present in your slide? Is *Vaucheria* separately sexed or hermaphroditic? At what life-cycle stage does meiosis occur? How and where do spores form?

b. Examine the prepared slide of *Chara* showing sex organs (see also Chap. 25, "The Science of Biology"). In the male organ, or ANTHERIDIUM, identify the outer STERILE SHEATH and the inner tissue, which includes ANTHERIDIAL FILAMENTS. In a female organ, or OOGONIUM, identify the outer STERILE SHEATH, the circlet of cells (CROWN) on the uppermost part of the sheath, and the EGG in the interior. How do sperms meet eggs? At what life-cycle stage does meiosis occur? Are stoneworts separately sexed or hermaphroditic? In what respects are the reproductive structures of stoneworts unique among those of Protista generally?

3. *Life Cycles*

a. Study the prepared slide of *Ulothrix* and examine first the structure of the vegetative cells. How does vegetative reproduction occur? Next find SPORANGIA, that is, cellulose housings in which anywhere from 2 to 32 oval cellular bodies may be present. These are SPORES which, when mature, carry four flagella each. The spores escape from a pore in the sporangia. Through what processes do spores develop? Are the spores mitospores or meiospores? Can any vegetative cell become a sporangium?

When vegetative cells come to function as GAMETANGIA, up to 64 gametes may form in each gametangium. Gametes are biflagellate. Are those of opposite sex types visibly different? How and where does fertilization occur? At what life-cycle stage does meiosis occur? Is *Ulothrix* separately sexed or hermaphroditic? What is the developmental fate of the zygote? The life cycle of *Ulo-*

thrix is HAPLONTIC. Review the course of this type of cycle (see also Chaps. 24 and 25, "The Science of Biology"). Which other algae examined above have such a life cycle?

b. Examine the prepared slide of an *Ectocarpus* sporophyte bearing SPORANGIAL BRANCHES. Describe the structure of both the vegetative organism and a reproductive branch. By what processes do SPORES form? Next examine the prepared slide of an *Ectocarpus* gametophyte bearing GAMETANGIAL BRANCHES. How does the vegetative structure of the gametophyte differ from that of the sporophyte? What is the structure of a gametangial branch? By what processes do GAMETES form? What is the structure of a gamete? Is *Ectocarpus* isogamous or anisogamous or oogamous? Review the DIPLOHAPLONTIC life cycle of this organism, with attention to haploid and diploid phases, the timing of meiosis, and the occurrence of mitospores and meiospores (see also Chap. 25, "The Science of Biology").

c. On a fresh or preserved specimen of *Fucus*, identify a swollen terminal RECEPTACLE, and with a hand lens locate the openings of the numerous CONCEPTACLES present within a receptacle. Then examine the prepared slide of ANTHERIDIAL CONCEPTACLES. Note the LINING TISSUE of a conceptacle and the PARAPHYSES growing out from this lining tissue. Some paraphyses will be seen to project through the OSTIOLE, the opening of the conceptacle to the exterior. Distinguish between FERTILE paraphyses, that is, those bearing ANTHERIDIAL BRANCHES, and STERILE paraphyses, that is, those without lateral branches. What is the structure of an antheridial branch? What portion of such a branch forms an ANTHERIDIUM? By what processes are SPERMS produced?

Examine the prepared slide of OOGONIAL CONCEPTACLES. Again note the paraphyses. Also identify the conspicuous OOGONIAL BRANCHES. Where do they grow out from? What is their structure? What portion of such a branch forms an OOGONIUM? By what processes do EGGS form? How does fertilization take place? What is the developmental fate of the zygote? At what life-cycle stage does meiosis occur? Does *Fucus* sporulate? Is the organism separately sexed or hermaphroditic? Review the DIPLONTIC life cycle of the organism (see also Chaps. 24 and 25, "The Science of Biology").

B. fungi

1. Budding

Examine the prepared slide of budding yeast and identify cells with BUDS. By what process does such a bud form? What type of reproduction is illustrated here? Do yeasts undergo sporulation and gametic reproduction? Describe the life cycle of yeasts (see also Chap. 25, "The Science of Biology").

2. Gametic Reproduction

a. Examine the prepared slide showing sexual structures of *Saprolegnia*. Identify an ANTHERIDIAL HYPHA and an OOGONIAL HYPHA. What is the structure of mature gametes? Can you locate FERTILIZATION TUBES leading from a male gametangium into an oogonium (which is enveloped by the male gametangium)? How does fertilization occur? What is the fate of the zygote, here called OOSPORE? Does *Saprolegnia* also sporulate? At which stage of the life cycle does meiosis take place?

b. Examine the prepared slide showing ZYGOSPORES of *Rhizopus*. Note the two SUSPENSOR HYPHAE between which a zygospore is held (see also Chap. 25, "The Science of Biology"). How do gametangia form? How does fertilization occur? At which life-cycle stage of *Rhizopus* does meiosis occur?

3. Sporulation

a. Examine fresh specimens and prepared slides of *Rhizopus* showing sporangia. Identify the mycelial vegetative hyphae and the upright SPORANGIOPHORES, which bear the terminal spherical SPORANGIA. By what processes do SPORES develop? Are these spores mitospores or meiospores?

b. Examine the prepared slide of *Penicillium* showing conidia (see also exercise 18, section C2). Identify a CONIDIOPHORE, that is, a branch hypha bearing terminal chains of CONIDIA. Are conidia mitospores or meiospores?

c. Examine the prepared slides of sections through CLEISTOTHECIAL fruiting bodies of *Penicillium* and APOTHECIAL fruiting bodies of *Peziza*. Describe and contrast the structure of a cleistothecium and an apothecium. What is the structure of a perithecium? In each slide, identify the ASCI and the ASCOSPORES (see also exercise 18, section C2, and Chap. 9, "The Science of

Biology"). When in the life cycle, and how, do the asci form? How do ascospores develop in an ascus? Is an ascospore a mitospore or a meiospore?

d. Examine the prepared slide of a section through a whole mushroom of *Coprinus* (see also exercise 18, section C3). Describe the structure of the fruiting body and locate the BASIDIA and the BASIDIOSPORES. What are GILLS? What is the adaptive advantage of fruiting bodies in sporulation? When in the life cycle, and how, do basidia develop? How do basidiospores form on a basidium? Is a basidiospore a mitospore or a meiospore?

C. protozoa

1. Fission

a. Study the prepared slide of *Paramecium* showing cell division. In what region of the cellular body does a CLEAVAGE FURROW form? By what processes do the micronuclei and the macronuclei divide? Does the original gullet become the gullet of one of the offspring organisms or do BOTH offspring develop a new gullet? In what respects is fission in ciliates such as *Paramecium* different from fission in zooflagellates?

b. Carefully and slowly examine a rich living culture of *Stentor coeruleus* under a dissecting microscope and see if you can find a dividing organism. Such organisms are generally longer and larger than nondividing ones, and in the contracted state they are darker in appearance and quite cylindrical in shape. To be successful in such a search, THE CULTURE MUST REMAIN UNDISTURBED, with the organisms remaining attached to the bottom and side walls of the glass container. If you locate a dividing organism, call the instructor; he will attempt to isolate it with a medicine dropper having a narrow, finely drawn-out capillary end.

Observe the newly formed membranelles developed around roughly the middle of the dividing ciliate. Move the mirror of your microscope and see if you can locate the dividing macronucleus. When division is nearing completion, note the transverse constriction dividing the body into anterior and posterior offspring. Note also the newly formed gullet and contractile vacuole in the posterior offspring and the newly formed holdfast on the anterior offspring. Permit other members of the class to view the specimen and observe it yourself at roughly 15-min intervals, until fission is completed.

2. Conjugation

a. Examine the prepared slide of conjugating pairs of *Paramecium bursaria.* At which body region are the mating partners joined? What is the fate of the macronucleus during conjugation? Describe the processes taking place in a micronucleus during conjugation. Are paramecia separately sexed or hermaphroditic? What is the structure of the gametes? Does the organism REPRODUCE by means of gametes and fertilization?

b. For a demonstration of the mating reaction, two rich cultures of *Paramecium aurelia* are set out. One culture contains organisms of one mating type; the other culture, organisms of the other, complementary mating type. Clean a blank slide and put on it a drop containing many paramecia of one mating type. Then, USING A DIFFERENT MEDICINE DROPPER, add a drop containing many organisms of the other mating type. Adjust the slide under the microscope and watch for several minutes without disturbing the slide; conjugating pairs should be forming. What are the conditions necessary to make paramecia of opposite mating types conjugate?

IV analysis

1. Define REPRODUCTION and SEXUALITY, and distinguish these two processes (*a*) functionally, (*b*) structurally. What are the necessary conditions for reproduction?

2. In organisms where the adult is haploid, meiosis occurs after fertilization; in organisms where the adult is diploid, meiosis occurs before fertilization. Cite evidence in support of these generalizations, and show how these conditions are adaptively significant.

3. Define ISOGAMY, ANISOGAMY, OOGAMY, and give an example of each. Define MALE, FEMALE, HERMAPHRODITE, MATING TYPE. Distinguish between MATING and FERTILIZATION.

4. Among the life cycles studied, list examples of (*a*) reproduction with sex, (*b*) reproduction without sex, (*c*) sex without reproduction.

5. What is the life cycle of *Protococcus*? How, in the absence of spores, does an organism dis-

perse geographically; and how, in the absence of sex, does it adapt to changing conditions?

6. Describe the reproductive repertoire of (*a*) schizophytes, (*b*) cyanophytes. In organisms without sex, how is adaptation accomplished?

7. Describe the course of an (*a*) haplontic, (*b*) diplontic, (*c*) diplohaplontic, life cycle. Name three organisms exemplifying EACH of these cycles.

8. What is a spore? What is the adaptive advantage of reproduction by sporulation? Citing specific examples, describe different ways in which spores may be formed.

9. Define the nature of (*a*) vegetative, (*b*) sporulative, (*c*) gametic, reproduction. Describe various methods by which each of these forms of multiplication can be accomplished among Protista.

10. What different types of life cycles and reproductive patterns are encountered among (*a*) green algae, (*b*) stoneworts, (*c*) brown algae? Describe the reproductive structures of (*a*) *Fucus*, (*b*) *Chara*, (*c*) *Ectocarpus*.

11. Review the methods of vegetative reproduction encountered among fungi. How are sporulation and sexuality executed in *Saprolegnia* and *Rhizopus*? Describe the life cycles of these two phycomycetous fungi and show how each life cycle is particularly adapted to the respective ways of life of the fungi.

12. Describe the life cycle of an ascomycetous fungus. Define PLASMOGAMY, KARYOGAMY. What is the adaptive advantage of fruiting bodies? What is the characteristic structure of the three types of fruiting bodies found among Ascomycetes?

13. Describe the life cycle of a basidiomycetous fungus. In what basic respects is such a cycle different from that of Ascomycetes?

14. Describe the detailed nature of the sexual process in *Paramecium*. How does conjugation here differ from conjugation in *Spirogyra*? Define CONJUGATION, SYNGAMY, BINARY FISSON, MULTIPLE FISSON. Give a specific example of each of the last three.

15. Review the reproductive repertoire of protozoa as a whole. What different forms of each of the methods of reproduction are encountered?

exercise 41 reproduction: bryophytes, tracheophytes

I materials

Each student

microscope
hand lens
dissecting instruments
blank slide

Each 1 or 2 students

prepared slides of:

moss gametophyte, longitudinal sections through tips with antheridia and archegonia
Marchantia, section of gemma cup
Marchantia, section through antheridia
Marchantia, section through archegonia
Psilotum, section through sporangium
Lycopodium, section through strobilus
Selaginella, section through strobilus
Equisetum, section through strobilus
fern, section of leaf with sorus
fern, whole mount of prothallium
fern, section of gametophyte showing antheridia and archegonia
fern, whole mount of gametophyte with attached sporophyte

Class stock

moss, living or preserved gametophytes with sex organs
Marchantia, living or preserved thalli with gemma cups
Marchantia, living or preserved thalli with antheridial and archegonial receptacles
Lycopodium, preserved strobili
Selaginella, preserved strobili
Equisetum, preserved strobili
fern, potted sporophyte with sori
fern prothallia, potted

II introduction

The life cycle of Metaphyta is diplohaplontic, an alternation of dissimilar sporophyte and gametophyte generations occurring universally. In all cases, also, the sporophyte is diploid and produces meiospores meiotically. The gametophyte is haploid and produces gametes mitotically. The dominant generation in bryophytes is the gametophyte, and in tracheophytes, the sporophyte. The latter has been more completely adaptable to terrestrial conditions, and tracheophytes consequently are the most successful Metaphyta on land. In early tracheophytes and ferns, the gametophyte is still an independent plant requiring moist conditions, and the sperms produced still require liquid water for fertilization. This circumstance restricts the adaptive possibilities for life on land. Indeed, the success of these tracheophytes, though greater than that of bryophytes, remains limited. Full reproductive independence from free water has been achieved only by the later tracheophytes, the seed plants. The propagation of these plants will be studied in the succeeding exercise.

III directions

A. bryophytes

1. Mosses

a. Review the structure of a moss gametophyte, as outlined in exercise 19, section A2. Ascertain once more the position of the SEX ORGANS and then study the prepared slides of sections through gametophyte tips bearing ANTHERIDIA and ARCHEGONIA (see also Chap. 25, "The Science of Biology"). Note the arrangement of the stalked antheridia on the gametophyte tip. In a large antheridium, identify the external sterile layer, or JACKET, and the interior SPERMATOGENOUS TISSUE. What is the structure of a mature SPERM? How does it move and under what conditions does it meet an egg? Note the arrangement of archegonia on a gametophyte tip. In such a stalked female sex organ, identify the EGG in the interior and the flask-shaped tissue in which the egg is located. The wider bottom part of this tissue, around the egg, is the VENTER; it is continuous with the NECK above. In a mature archegonium note the hollow NECK CANAL, through which a sperm may travel toward the egg.

b. Review the structure of a moss sporophyte, as outlined in exercise IV.3, section A3. Show how such a sporophyte develops from a fertilized egg and how it gives rise to new gametophytes. Then describe the entire diplohaplontic life cycle of mosses, with attention to haploid and diploid phases, the timing of meiosis, and adaptations to the bryophyte way of life (see also Chap. 25, "The Science of Biology").

2. Liverworts

a. Review the structure of a *Marchantia* gametophyte, as outlined in exercise 19, section B1. Then examine fresh or preserved thalli bearing GEMMAE CUPS and the prepared slide of a section through such a cup. Describe the structure of the cup and of the GEMMAE within it. What is the function of gemmae and under what conditions is this function carried out?

b. Examine fresh or preserved specimens of stalked RECEPTACLES of *Marchantia* bearing sex organs (see also exercise 19, section B2a). The stalks are known as GAMETOPHORES. What is the shape of an antheridium-containing and an archegonium-containing receptacle? Where in a receptacle are antheridia and archegonia located? Study the prepared slides of sections through antheridia and archegonia. In an ANTHERIDIUM, identify JACKET and SPERMATOGENOUS TISSUE. In an ARCHEGONIUM, identify EGG, VENTER, NECK, and NECK-CANAL CELLS (present in the neck of immature archegonia). How does the structure of the sex organs compare with that observed in mosses? How does fertilization take place?

c. Review the structure of a *Marchantia* sporophyte, as outlined in exercise 19, section B2b. Show how such a sporophyte develops and how it gives rise to new gametophytes. Describe the entire life cycle of a liverwort and compare it with that of a moss.

3. Hornworts

Review the structure of the gametophyte and sporophyte of *Anthoceros*, as studied in exercise IV.3, section C. Describe the life cycle of this plant and compare it with that of other bryophytes.

B. tracheophytes

1. Psilopsida

Review your observations on the sporophyte of *Psilotum* (exercise 20, section A), and recall the appearance and position of the SPORANGIA. Then examine the prepared slide of a section through a sporangium and locate the SPORANGIAL WALL (see also Chap. 25, "The Science of Biology"). How many cell layers are present here? Note the three SPORE CHAMBERS and the SPORES. How are these produced?

In your text review the structure of the psilopsid gametophyte and describe the entire life cycle of such plants (see also Chap. 10, "The Science of Biology"). How does such a cycle differ from that of bryophytes?

2. Lycopsida

a. Review your observations on the sporophyte of *Lycopodium* (exercise 20, section B1), and recall the external appearance and position of the spore-producing cones, or STROBILI. Then examine a preserved strobilus and the prepared slide of a section through a strobilus. Locate the VASCULAR TISSUE, the APEX, and the SPORANGIA situated on the surfaces of sporangial leaves, or SPOROPHYLLS. In a sporangium, note the SPORES and describe their shape. Is this shape related to the process which produces spores?

Review the structure of a gametophyte of *Lycopodium,* and describe the life cycle of these plants (see also Chap. 10, "The Science of Biology").

b. Review your observations on the sporophyte of *Selaginella* (exercise 20, section B2), and recall the appearance and position of the strobili. Examine a preserved strobilus and then a prepared slide of a longitudinal section through a strobilus (see also Chap. 25, "The Science of Biology"). Note the two types of sporangia, namely, the microspore-producing MICROSPORANGIA and the megaspore-producing MEGASPORANGIA. How do the spores differ in the two types of sporangia? How is each type of spore produced?

Review the structure of a gametophyte of *Selaginella,* and compare the life cycle of the plant with that of *Lycopodium.*

3. Sphenopsida

Review your observations on the sporophyte of *Equisetum* (exercise 20, section C), and recall the external appearance and position of the strobili. Examine a preserved strobilus and also the prepared slide of a section through a *sporophyll.* Note the stalk, or SPORANGIOPHORE, and the two SPORANGIA borne on it. In a sporangium examine the SPORES. What are the appendages on the spores? How do they aid in spore dispersal?

Review the structure of a gametophyte of *equisetum,* and describe the life cycle of the plant (see also Chap. 10, "The Science of Biology").

4. Pteropsida: Ferns

a. Review the general structure of a fern sporophyte and the specific structure of a SORUS, on the underside of a fern leaf (see exercise 20, section D). With a razor blade or scalpel, slice off a sorus from a living fern (without damage to the leaf) and put it into a drop of water on a blank slide. Gently spread the material with forceps and examine under the microscope. The SPORANGIA will appear as stalked transparent capsules. Note the ANNULUS around each sporangium and the SPORES within. By what processes are spores formed? How are spores released? What does a spore develop into?

b. If available, examine living fern gametophytes (PROTHALLIA) grown in pots (see also Fig. 41.1). Describe the shape of the plantlets. Then study a prepared whole mount of such a gametophyte. Note the RHIZOIDS on the underside, the parenchymatous BODY, and the SEX ORGANS. Antheridia are spherical, archegonia are flask-shaped. Both types of organs may be present on the same gametophyte. If so, where is each type located? Study prepared slides of sections through ANTHERIDIA and ARCHEGONIA. In an antheridium, identify JACKET and SPERMATOGENOUS TISSUE. In an archegonium, identify EGG, VENTER, NECK. How does the structure of these organs compare with that seen in bryophytes? How does fertilization occur in ferns?

c. With hand lens and microscope, examine the prepared whole mount of a young sporophyte attached to a gametophyte. Identify the body parts of the sporophyte. What structure of the sporophyte attaches this plant to what structure of the gametophyte? What is the later fate of each plant? Review the entire life cycle of ferns, with attention to haploid and diploid phases and adaptations to the terrestrial way of life (see also Chap. 25, "The Science of Biology").

IV analysis

1. Define SPORANGIUM, ANTHERIDIUM, ARCHEGONIUM, GAMETOPHYTE, SPOROPHYTE. Check again the definition of GAMETE and SPORE.

2. Describe different forms of vegetative reproduction encountered among Metaphyta. What is reproduction by posterior decay?

3. Describe the structure and development of an (*a*) antheridium, (*b*) archegonium, in Metaphyta. Can you interpret the structural similarity of the sex organs in many metaphytan groups on (*a*) a functional, (*b*) an evolutionary, basis?

4. Contrast the life cycles of liverworts and

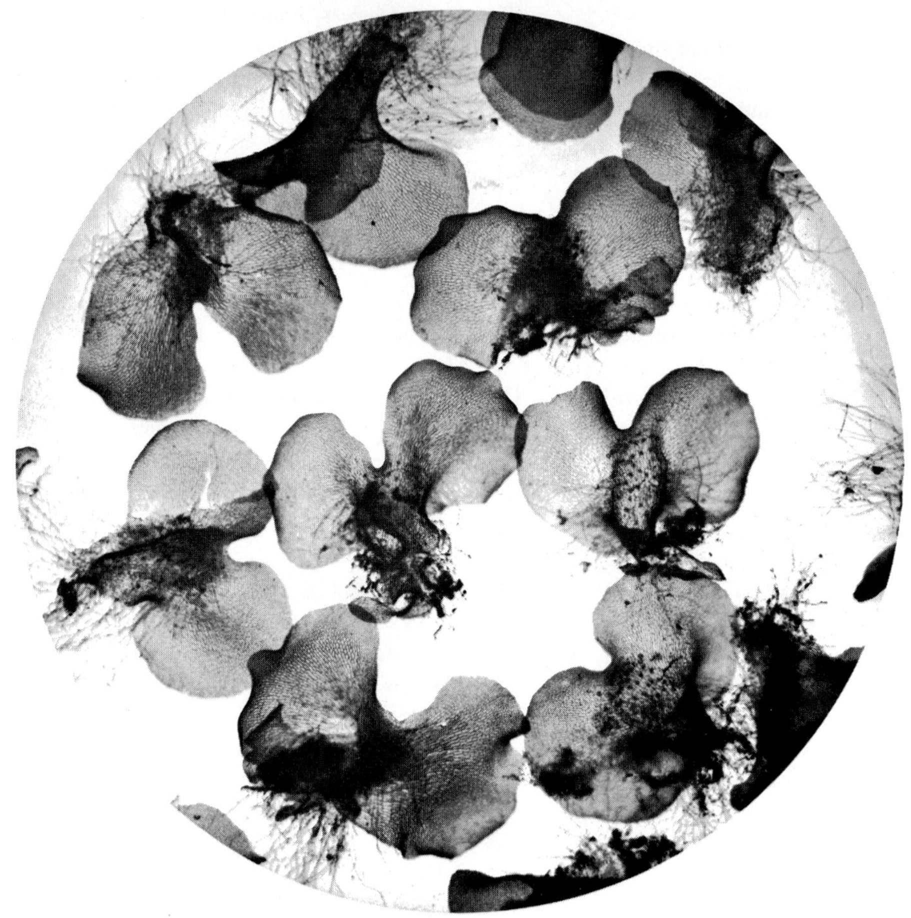

Fig. 41.1 Fern gametophytes (prothallia). Identify the parts of such a plant. (Courtesy of General Biological Supply House, Inc.)

mosses. Which type of plant is reproductively more advanced? Discuss.

5. In bryophytes generally, which life-cycle phase is the dominant, "main" phase? What conditions attest to this? Which is the haploid and which the diploid phase, and what event terminates each?

6. Review the general pattern of the life cycle in bryophytes and tracheophytes, and describe the functions of the two alternating phases.

7. Which protistan groups have diplohaplontic life cycles, and in which of these groups are the sporophyte and gametophyte generations structurally (*a*) similar, (*b*) dissimilar?

8. How may (*a*) oogamy, (*b*) dissimilar alternating generations, have evolved in Metaphyta? Can these evolutionary developments be related to the life of Metaphyta under terrestrial conditions?

9. What is the adaptive advantage of the stalked condition of bryophyte sporophytes? Would a longer stalk be even better?

10. What prevents the development of large size in bryophytes? How is attainment of large size made possible in ferns? Why then have fern gametophytes remained small?

11. Which life-cycle phase is dominant in ferns? What conditions attest to this? What powerful adaptive advantage tends to maintain the phase dominance evident in ferns?

12. In what respects is the reproductive mechanism of bryophytes and ferns "inefficient"? How have early land ANIMALS solved similar reproductive problems?

13. In general, is the haploid or the diploid condition genetically more advantageous? Discuss. In the light of this, what is the adaptive advantage of the timing of meiosis in bryophytes?

14. Describe the life cycles and the structure of the gametophytes in psilopsids, lycopsids, and sphenopsids. In what respects is the reproduction of *Selaginella* unusual?

15. Inasmuch as fern archegonia are on the underside of the gametophyte, how can the developing sporophyte grow upward? Is the position of the archegonia adaptively advantageous here?

exercise 42 reproduction in seed plants

I materials

Each student

microscope
hand lens
dissecting instruments

Each 1 or 2 students

prepared slides of:

pine, longitudinal section of microstrobilus
pine, median section of ovule with megaspore mother cell
pine, median section of ovule with megagametophyte and eggs
pine, section of ovule with pollen tubes
pine, section of ovule with immature embryo
lily, section of anther with mature pollen
lily, section of ovary showing ovules with megaspore mother cells
lily, section of ovary showing (series of) ovules at stage of double fertilization
lily, section of fruit showing seeds with early embryos

Class stock

pine, fresh or preserved micro- and megastrobili
flowers, fresh, for dissection
lily, series of sections showing transformation of megaspore mother cell into eight-nucleate megagametophyte
fruits and seeds, assorted types, for inspection and dissection

II introduction

Seed plants are HETEROSPOROUS, that is, two types of spores are produced, one type small and called MICROSPORE, the other type large and called MEGASPORE. A MICROSPORANGIUM produces microspores, and a MEGASPORANGIUM (or OVULE) produces a MEGASPORE MOTHER CELL which matures into (usually one) functional megaspore. Meiosis occurs during the maturation of both microspores and megaspores.

The spore cell within the wall of the microspore subsequently develops into a small male gametophyte, or MICROGAMETOPHYTE, which does NOT become an independent plant; it remains non-green and confined within the microspore wall. The whole structure now constitutes a POLLEN GRAIN. It eventually escapes from the microsporangium and is transferred by wind or by animals to a megasporangium. This transfer process represents POLLINATION.

Similarly, the functional megaspore, always retained within the megasporangium, develops into a small, nongreen female gametophyte, or MEGAGAMETOPHYTE, which produces eggs. After pollination, the microgametophyte forms an elongated POLLEN TUBE, which carries two sperm nuclei at its tip. This tube grows through the wall of the megasporangium and eventually into the megagametophyte, where a sperm nucleus fuses with an egg nucleus. This is FERTILIZATION and results in the formation of a diploid zygote. Note that seed plants have become reproductively independent of free external water by virtue of pollination and pollen tubes. The latter effect a kind of "internal fertilization" rather reminiscent of equivalent processes in animals.

After fertilization, the wall of the megasporangium hardens and together with all its contents is then known as a SEED. The zygote within forms a sporophyte embryo, and after seed dispersal and seed germination, the embryo becomes a mature sporophyte. In gymnosperms, seeds are "naked"; that is, they are not surrounded by other tissues. In angiosperms, the megasporangia are enclosed within an OVARY, and after the megasporangia have become seeds, the ovary enlarges and develops into a FRUIT. The latter, containing the seeds within it, aids in seed dispersal in fairly obvious ways. The name "angiosperm" (hidden seed) implies the existence of fruit tissue around the seeds.

Life cycles of gymnosperms and angiosperms will be studied in this exercise. Whenever you come to examine a given stage of such cycles, fix in your mind the events of preceding and succeeding stages; do not lose sight of the continuity of the cycle and of the significance of a given stage within a larger pattern of processes.

III directions

A. gymnosperms

1. Reproductive Organs

Examine fresh or preserved specimens of a MICROSTROBILUS and a MEGASTROBILUS of the pine. In each, note the structure and arrangement of the cone leaves, or SPOROPHYLLS. Where does a living microsporophyll bear MICROSPORANGIA and a living megasporophyll bear MEGASPORANGIA? With the aid of your text, review the basic sequence of events in the life cycle of seed plants to provide a conceptual framework for the material to follow (for example, see Chap. 25, "The Science of Biology").

2. Microspores and Microgametophytes

With a hand lens, examine the prepared slide of a longitudinal section through a mature microstrobilus of the pine (see also Chap. 25, "The Science of Biology"). Note the axial STEM, the MICROSPOROPHYLLS, and the position of the MICROSPORANGIA. Under high power, focus on a microsporangium and study the POLLEN GRAINS within. In one of the grains, identify the membranous external WINGS and the interior cells. The largest cell, taking up most of the space between the wings, is the TUBE CELL. Less readily identifiable are a small GENERATIVE CELL and the remnants of two degenerated PROTHALLIAL CELLS, situated just inside the thickened part of the wall of the pollen grain, in the rounded portion where wings are not present. By what sequence of processes does such a pollen grain mature? What part of it represents the microgametophyte? What is the later fate of the tube cell and the generative cell?

3. Megaspores and Megagametophytes

a. Study the prepared slide of a median section through a pine ovule showing the MEGASPORE MOTHER CELL (see also Chap. 25, "The Science of Biology"). Identify this cell in the center and, surrounding it, the tissue of the OVULE. The inner portions of this tissue constitute the MEGASPORANGIUM, the outer portions, the INTEGUMENT. Note that the integument is extended on one side into two flaps, the MICROPYLAR ARMS. The MICROPYLE is the canal between these arms. What is the fate of the megaspore mother cell? What is pollination, and how is this process accomplished? What events occur during pollination?

b. Study the prepared slide of a median section through a pine ovule showing the megagametophyte with eggs (see also Chap. 25, "The Science of Biology"). Identify the INTEGUMENT, the MICROPYLAR ARMS, the wall of the MEGASPORANGIUM, the tissue of the MEGAGAMETOPHYTE, and the large, food-filled EGGS. If the section passes through an egg in the median plane, two small NECK CELLS may also be identified, on the side where the cavity in which the egg lies opens to the surface of the megagametophyte. Together with the egg, the neck cells represent a highly reduced archegonium. How is this stage of megagametophyte development reached from the condition seen in section a above?

4. *Fertilization and Seed Formation*

a. Study the prepared slide of a section through a pine ovule showing POLLEN TUBES. Identify the visible portions of these tubes and also the parts of the ovule, similar to those seen in section 3b above. What structures give rise to pollen tubes? What events occur in fertilization? What structures function as male gametes and how do they form? What events occur after fertilization?

b. Study the prepared slide of a section through a pine ovule showing an immature embryo (see also Chap. 25, "The Science of Biology"). Identify the SEED COAT, the tissue of the MEGAGAMETOPHYTE, the sporophyte EMBRYO (with COTYLEDONS and early STEM-ROOT tissues), and the SUSPENSOR, which attaches the embryo to the inner surface of the seed coat. How has this stage of seed development been reached from the condition seen in 4a above? What events occur in later seed development? How is the seed dispersed, and how does it germinate?

c. Review the entire life cycle of the pine, and correlate all stages studied above with the sequence of events in this cycle (see also Chap. 25, "The Science of Biology").

B. angiosperms

1. *The Flower*

With instruments and hand lens, dissect and examine a fresh flower. Identify the following parts: the RECEPTACLE, the expanded basal portion to which all other flower parts are attached and which joins the flower to the stem; the outermost floral leaves, individually called SEPALS, collectively called CALYX; the inner floral leaves, individually called PETALS, collectively called COROLLA; the STAMENS, each consisting of a FILAMENT and a terminal ANTHER; the central PISTIL, consisting of three parts, namely, the expanded basal portion, or OVARY, the long, slender STYLE, and the free tip, or STIGMA. How many of each of these parts are present? On this basis, classify the flower as a monocot or a dicot.

2. *Microspores and Microgametophytes*

Study the prepared slide of a section through a lily anther with mature pollen grains (see Fig. 42.1). Note the MICROSPORANGIA (how many?) and the POLLEN GRAINS within each. In one of the grains, identify the large TUBE CELL and the smaller GENERATIVE CELL (entirely or almost entirely surrounded by tube-cell cytoplasm). What is the subsequent fate of these cells? Describe the events of pollination (see also Chap. 25, "The Science of Biology").

3. *Megaspores and Megagametophytes*

a. Study the prepared slide of a cross section through a lily ovary with ovules showing megaspore mother cells (see also Chap. 25, "The Science of Biology"). Note the OVARY WALL and the pairs (how many?) of OVULES and their attachment. In one of the ovules, identify MEGASPORE MOTHER CELL, MEGASPORANGIUM, INTEGUMENT, and MICROPYLE. What is the subsequent fate of the megaspore mother cell?

b. If available, study a sequence of prepared slides showing the transformation of the lily megaspore mother cell into an eight-nucleate MEGAGAMETOPHYTE. Consult your text to review the course of the nuclear divisions and fusions leading to this eight-nucleate stage.

c. Study the prepared slide showing DOUBLE FERTILIZATION in the lily. First review the events preceding and occurring during fertilization. Then locate, in one or in several of the ovule sections on the slide, a megagametophyte in which two centrally located POLAR NUCLEI are about to fuse with one sperm nucleus, forming a pentaploid ENDOSPERM NUCLEUS; and a megagametophyte in which an egg nucleus at one end is about to fuse with a sperm nucleus, forming a diploid ZYGOTE NUCLEUS. What are the subsequent fates of the endosperm and zygote nuclei?

4. *Seeds and Fruits*

a. Study the prepared slide of a section through the fruit of the lily, showing seeds with early embryos. Identify the tissue of the FRUIT (what tissue has given rise to it?) and the SEEDS. In one of the seeds, identify the SEED COAT (what tissue has given rise to it?), the ENDOSPERM tissue, the EMBRYO, and the SUSPENSOR, which attaches the embryo to the inner surface of the seed coat. What structural parts of the embryo can you identify?

b. Examine assorted fruits available for study. First classify the fruits according to whether they are FLESHY or DRY; whether they can be split along natural suture lines (DEHISCENT) or not (INDEHISCENT); whether they are SIMPLE, formed from one ovary, AGGREGATE, formed from two or more ovaries of the same flower, or MULTIPLE, formed from several flowers; and whether they are TRUE, derived from ovary tissue alone, or FALSE, derived from other flower parts in addition to ovary tissue.

In each of the fruits identify the following parts, using instruments and hand lens as necessary: STEM ATTACHMENT; OVARY TISSUE; degenerated STIGMA and STYLE; SEEDS, seed arrangement, seed number, and seed attachment. On the basis of the arrangement and the number of seeds, classify each fruit as belonging to the DICOT or the MONOCOT subclass of angiosperms. Open the seeds and identify the SEED COAT, the small EMBRYO sporophyte, the COTYLEDONS, and the ENDOSPERM.

c. Examine the class stock collection of seeds showing structural adaptations aiding seed dispersal. Determine HOW dispersal is facilitated in each of these seeds.

IV analysis

1. Define MICROSPORANGIUM, MEGASPORANGIUM, POLLEN GRAIN, OVULE, OVARY, SEED, FRUIT, POLLINATION, FERTILIZATION.

2. Review the GENERAL pattern of the seed-plant life cycle, with attention to haploid and diploid phases and the timing and location of meiosis and fertilization.

3. Describe the detailed processes leading to the formation of a mature pollen grain in the (*a*) pine, (*b*) lily.

4. Describe the detailed processes leading to the formation of a mature megagametophyte in the pine. Then describe the events of pollination and pollen-tube formation. What is pollination fluid?

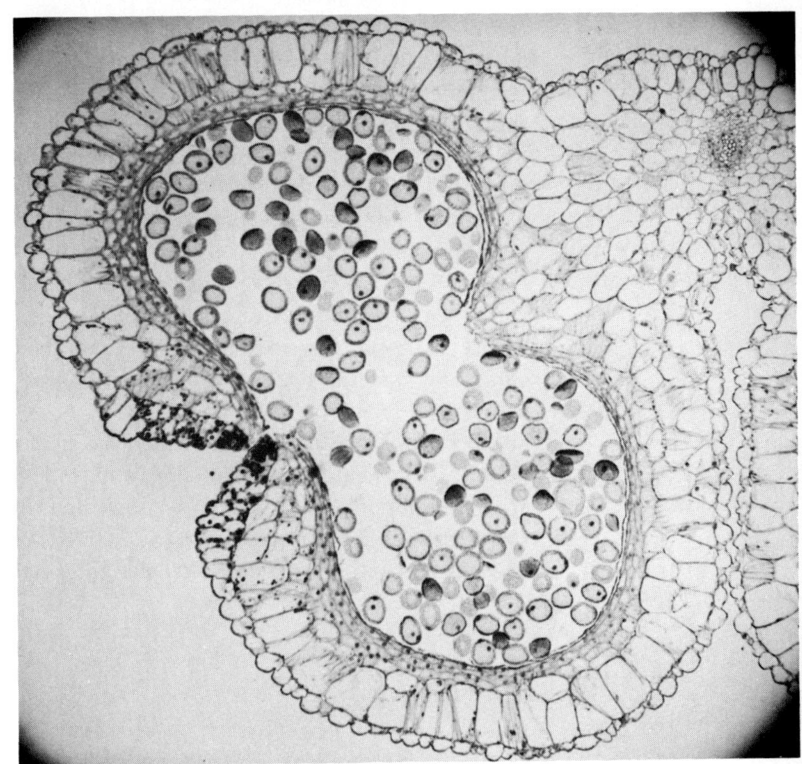

Fig. 42.1 Section through half of a lily anther. Label the parts. (Courtesy of General Biological Supply House, Inc.)

5. Describe the events of fertilization and seed formation in the pine. How many seasons elapse between the beginning of cone growth and the formation of seeds? How much time elapses between pollination and fertilization? Describe the transformation of a zygote into an early embryo.

6. Describe the structure of a flower. What are the detailed processes leading to the formation of a mature megagametophyte in (*a*) the lily, (*b*) most other angiosperms? How does pollination occur? What is double fertilization? How does an endosperm develop, and what is its function?

7. How do the megagametophytes of gymnosperms and angiosperms differ structurally? Cite evidence that the (*a*) megagametophyte, (*b*) sex organs, of seed plants have undergone evolutionary reduction.

8. Summarize in detail the differences in the reproductive patterns of gymnosperms and angio-

sperms, and show how each difference is adaptively significant.

9. Which of the following tissues are haploid and which diploid: flower petal, microsporangium wall in pine, stigma, pollen tube; fleshy part of apple, ovule wall of lily, seed coat? What is the ploidy of the starchy tissue of a corn kernel? What is the name of this tissue?

10. Describe how a bee would aid in pollination when it visits snapdragon flowers. Are bees partial to given flower colors? Where do bees obtain raw material for honey, and how is honey made?

11. Given the structural and functional potential of a flower, make some intelligent guesses as to how self-pollination could be prevented by simple devices developed through evolution. Then find out how self-pollination is actually prevented in normally cross-pollinating plants.

12. Give an example of each of the following fruit types: dry, fleshy, dehiscent, indehiscent, simple, aggregate, multiple, true, false.

13. When seeds lie dormant for years, do they respire, use up food, and excrete wastes? How are normal and dormant states different? What conditions promote seed germination? HOW do these conditions affect the seed?

14. How are seedless fruits produced? How can plants with seedless fruits reproduce or be perpetuated commercially?

15. What is common and parallel in the reproduction of seed plants and well-adapted terrestrial animals? Outline the mammalian life cycle, with attention to haploid and diploid phases, and compare with flowering plants.

exercise 43 development: animals

I materials

Each student

microscope
dissecting instruments
hand lens
medicine dropper
2 small petri dishes
finger bowl
starfish cleavage, all stages, slide
frog-embryo series, 12 or more stages (unfertilized to neurula), preserved, in stoppered vial

Class stock

frogs, live adult male
frogs, pituitary-injected adult females, ready to be stripped of eggs (see Appendix)
frog tadpoles, living series
raw unfertilized chicken eggs
hard-boiled chicken eggs, longitudinal halves with shell
chicken eggs, fertilized, incubated at 41°C for 2, 3, and 5 days prior to lab, total to equal number of students
human fetuses, preserved series
pig or other mammalian uteri with fetuses, as obtainable locally
binocular dissecting microscopes
Ringer solution, room temp, and warmed to 40°C

II introduction

In this exercise you will examine the development of four animals: starfish, frog, chicken, and man. You will find that the basic pattern of the developmental sequence is the same for all four. This is not too surprising, however, since all four are enterocoelomates and the last three mentioned are vertebrates. But you will also find that the details of development vary from type to type, sometimes considerably. Most of these variations can be interpreted in an adaptive sense; the four animals chosen represent four different ways of life, hence their reproductive and developmental machinery (as also other aspects of their biology) may be expected to vary accordingly. Starfish and frogs, for example, represent water developers, chicken and man, land developers. This difference alone is correlated with dozens of major and minor adaptations. As another example, in the series starfish–frog–chicken–man, time intervals between fertilization and hatching (or birth) are ½, 10, 21, 281 days, respectively; here again, important adaptations are in evidence which make such time differences possible and necessary.

A dual lead theme, therefore, emerges for the work in this exercise: (1) what is the basic pattern of enterocoelomate development; and (2) what is the adaptive role of reproductive and developmental features found uniquely among each of the animals studied?

III directions

A. fertilization and cleavage

This part of the exercise is an experimental illustration of two of the developmental steps common to all vertebrates (and most other animals and plants as well). Time is required before results can be studied; hence the experiment must be set up at the very beginning of the laboratory period.

1. Watch while the following is done: the instructor piths an adult male frog, dissects out the testes, and macerates these organs in a dish of Ringer solution. The resulting SPERM SUSPENSION is kept standing for about 10 min (that is, until the sperms become motile). The instructor then strips eggs from an ovulating female frog into the sperm suspension. This female had been injected 2 days previously with whole macerated frog pituitary glands. What is the endocrine mechanism promoting ovulation?

Note the appearance of the eggs as they come from the cloaca of the frog. Are they sticky? As the egg mass lies in the sperm suspension, the instructor will subdivide the mass into small portions, each consisting of about 10 eggs. You then ready a clean petri dish, and with medicine dropper and forceps transfer one of the egg portions into your dish together with a quantity of sperm suspension.

2. Examine the contents of the dish with a hand lens and under the low power of your microscope (adjusted for DIRECT top illumination of the microscope stage; also screw off the lowest lens of the low-power objective to obtain a less magnified view). You will be observing FERTILIZATION in progress. Note the SPERMS; details will not be visible, but movement of the sperms will be readily noticed as light reflects off them. Observe the eggs. Note the JELLY layers surrounding each egg; how many are there? Jelly layers are very thin when the eggs are released by the female, but they swell considerably and fairly rapidly thereafter, as the protein of the jelly absorbs water from the environment. On the egg surface, note the dark and light PIGMENTED areas. What is their geometrical arrangement? After the eggs have been in sperm suspension for about 10 min, add Ringer solution in sufficient amount JUST to cover the eggs. Record the approximate time of fertilization.

3. Proceed with other parts of the exercise until about 20 to 30 min after fertilization. Then inspect the eggs, and note that most or all of them have rotated within their jelly coats so that the dark side is uppermost. If an egg has not turned in this way it can be assumed to have remained unfertilized. With forceps gently detach the egg jellies from the glass bottom to which they may be stuck, and flip the egg mass over to turn the light areas uppermost. Observe after a few minutes: what has happened? Most of the egg YOLK (yellowish in color) is located in the light half of the egg, and yolk is heavier than clear cytoplasm; hence the rotation of the eggs. Inspect the jelly coats, and estimate if they have swelled since the first inspection.

4. During the ensuing 2 hr proceed with other parts of the exercise. Then watch for the FIRST CLEAVAGE DIVISION. It occurs 2¼ hr after fertilization. Note the developing CLEAVAGE FURROW, progressively extending longitudinally around the egg until a left and right cell is clearly marked off. By gentle manipulation with forceps and scissors, try to strip the jelly coats from one of the eggs. Jelly-free eggs give a much clearer view of division. Approximately half an hour after the first cleavage, a SECOND CLEAVAGE DIVISION occurs. It again cuts the egg longitudinally, at right angles to the first furrow. A four-cell-stage embryo is so formed. Note the TENSION LINES on the surface of the egg as it is constricted by the cleavage furrow.

Subsequent cleavage divisions subdivide the embryo into smaller and smaller cells (and correspondingly more of them), until a BLASTULA is formed. If conditions permit, cover your dish loosely with a glass plate and inspect the developing embryos with a hand lens daily over a period of a week.

B. early starfish development

In the slide provided, all stages of early starfish development are included. Survey the slide until you find a given stage as described, then study in detail (see also Chap. 26, "The Science of Biology").

1. Unfertilized Egg

This is a round, evenly stained, and fairly homogeneous mass. Estimate its diameter (see exercise 13), and later compare with the size of other egg types studied. From the even staining and the size, do you estimate much yolk to be present? Are there jelly or other membranes surrounding the egg?

2. Two-, Four-, and Eight-cell Stages

From the pattern of cellular arrangement in these stages, determine how the first three cleavage divisions subdivide the egg: longitudinally or transversely? Are these divisions mitotic or meiotic? Does the total mass of living matter increase during cleavage? How are the cells held together? Are all cells of the same size? Specify.

3. Morula and Blastula

Find clusters of 16 or more cells, so-called MORULA-stage embryos. As cleavage continues, the cells become arranged into a single-layered hollow sphere, the BLASTULA. Find such a stage also. How have cell size and cell number changed since earlier stages? How does the diameter of a blastula compare with that of an unfertilized egg? Is there evidence of ciliation on the surface of the blastula? Note that starfish embryos HATCH at the blastula stage (some 10 to 12 hr after fertilization).

4. Gastrula

Find an embryo in which one side of the cell layer appears pushed in, or INVAGINATED, at one point. The invagination process is GASTRULATION, and the resulting embryo is a GASTRULA. Two cell layers are now present, the outer ECTODERM and the inner ENDODERM. A third layer of cells, the MESODERM, will soon develop as an outgrowth from the endoderm and will be situated between ectoderm and endoderm. These three GERM LAYERS represent the structural building blocks from which all tissues and organs of the adult will be formed. Note the cavity within the endoderm. This is the beginning of the gut, the ARCHENTERON. The opening connecting the archenteron with the outside is the BLASTOPORE, which will later be the anus. Is the embryo still spherical as in the blastula stage?

The gastrula does not become an adult starfish directly. Rather, it first develops into a LARVA, some 2 days after fertilization. The larva is ciliated on the surface (as was the blastula after hatching), and it may be considered to represent a digestive system surrounded with appropriate tissues to house this system. After a period of feeding and growth, the larva METAMORPHOSES into an adult starfish.

C. frog development

Eggs, sperms, and the process of fertilization in this animal have already been observed above. Subsequent stages of development can be studied by examining preserved embryos, found in a stoppered vial. Pour the contents of this vial into a petri dish, study the embryos as described, and when finished return embryos AND preserving fluid to the vial.

In examining the various stages use a hand lens and the low power of the microscope (adjusted as above for direct stage illumination, with the lowest objective lens removed). In a quick, initial survey make preliminary stage identifications, then study in detail as follows.

1. One-, Two-, Four-, and Eight-cell Stages

Estimate the diameter of the unfertilized egg. From this datum and your observations above on egg rotation of the living egg, do you estimate that much or little of the egg substance is yolk? Compare with observations on starfish; compare also hatching times: are any correlations apparent? From the arrangement of the cells, determine how the first three cleavage divisions subdivide the egg (see also Fig. 43.1). Are all cells of the eight-cell stage of the same size? Is the eight-cell stage larger than the unfertilized

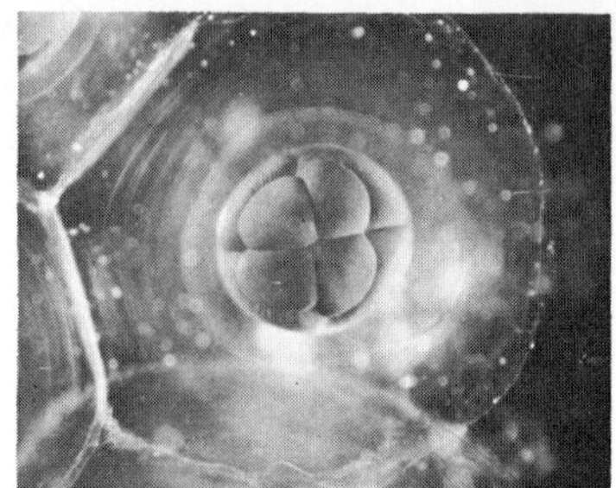
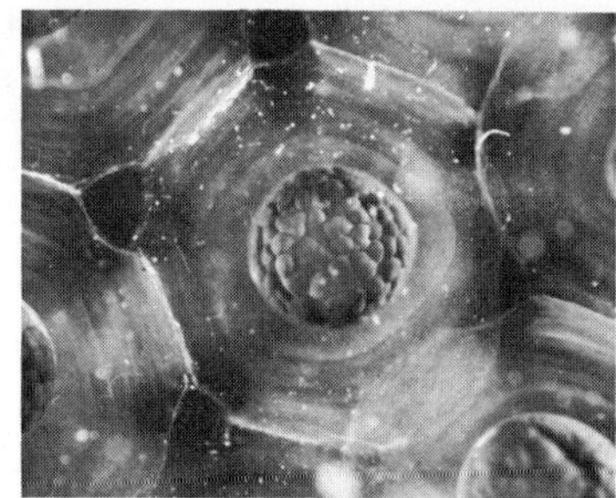

Fig. 43.1 Two-cell stage, eight-cell stage, and early blastula in frog development. (Courtesy of Carolina Biological Supply Co.)

egg? What is the function of the jelly layers of the egg? Is the dark pigment of adaptive value?

2. *Blastula*

Examine early and late blastula stages. In the frog a typical morula stage does not form. Considering that at the morula stage the center of the embryo is filled with cells, why would it be difficult for such a stage to arise in the frog? How many cells do you estimate a late blastula to contain? How many cleavage divisions would produce that number of cells? Is the frog blastula hollow, like that of the starfish? How has the dark pigmented area changed since earlier stages?

3. *Gastrula*

At this stage, all the embryo surface is pigmented brown-black, except for a small, circular, sharply defined yellow area in one region. This area is the YOLK PLUG. It is found near the "posterior" end of the embryo, and it progressively decreases in size (see also Fig. 43.2). Embryos in the yolk-plug stage are undergoing gastrulation. This process in the frog is much more complicated than in the starfish. Why do you think a simple inpushing in one region, as in a starfish embryo, cannot occur in the frog? In this animal, instead, cells around the rim of the yolk plug roll in and under, producing an inner endodermal layer. A mesoderm arises almost simultaneously from the newly formed endodermal cells. The rim of the yolk plug in a late gastrula corresponds to the rim of the blastopore, and the yolk plug itself projects out from the archenteron. Can individual cells be made out on the ectodermal surface of the gastrula? Is this stage larger than that of the unfertilized egg?

4. *Neurula*

The yolk plug eventually disappears from view, being covered over by pigmented cells, and the embryo becomes slightly elongated. In view of the disappearance of the yolk plug, do you estimate the cells of the ectoderm or of the endoderm to divide more rapidly? The initial elongation of the embryo coincides with the blocking out of the early nervous system. Find stages where a flat, roughly pear-shaped area is marked off at one side of the embryo, the so-called NEURAL PLATE. This will be the dorsal side of the future frog. At subsequent stages, an ectodermal fold to each side of the midline grows up from the side edges of the neural plate, and these NEURAL FOLDS eventually meet and fuse along the midline. This encloses a NEURAL TUBE underneath an outer layer of ectoderm. Find embryos at such NEURULA stages. The anterior end of the neural tube (in the expanded region of the earlier neural plate) will later become brain, and the posterior end, spinal cord (see also Fig. 43.3).

5. *Hatching and Larval Stages*

Development proceeds rapidly, and by the hatching stage, some 10 days after fertilization, a self-supporting TADPOLE larva has formed. Hatching involves the emergence of the tadpole from the jelly layers. How is this accomplished? All through the tadpole phase, frogs are herbivorous (they are carnivorous as adults). Tadpoles breathe by means of gills, located underneath gill covers on the side of the head (as in fish). Adult frogs breathe through lungs: these organs mature during the tadpole phase.

As available, examine tadpoles of various ages. Note the change of surface pigmentation with age, the manner of locomotion, and, in late tadpoles, the small but rapidly growing hind legs. What gross structural changes take place during the metamorphosis of the tadpole into a froglet? What functional changes take place at this time? How long after hatching does metamorphosis occur?

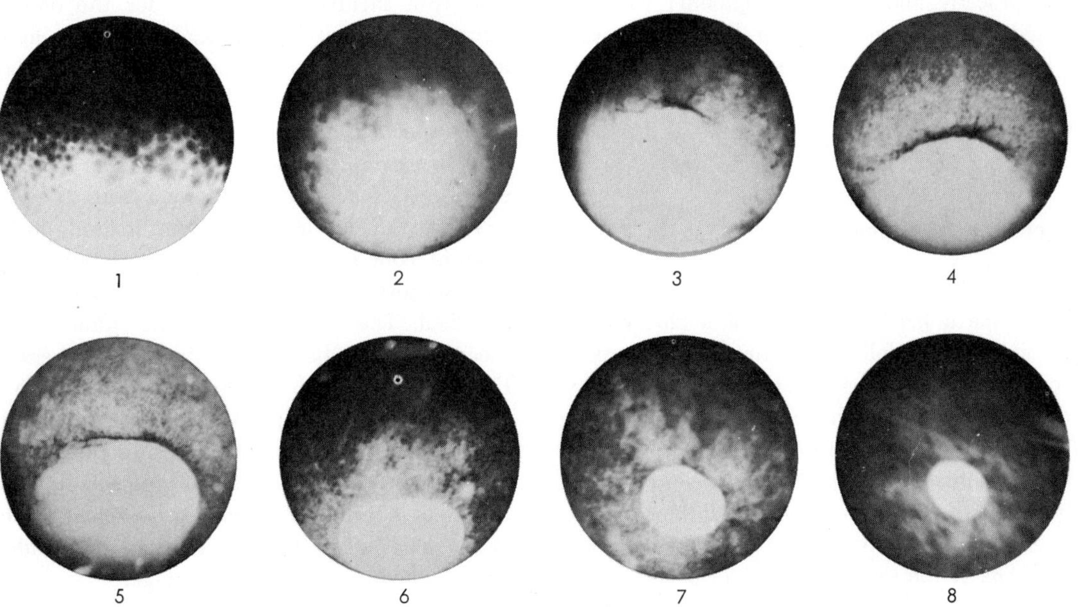

Fig. 43.2 Progressive stages of gastrulation in frog development. 1, 2, *late blastulae;* 3, 4, *inrolling of ectoderm beginning (dark lines along upper boundary of yolk);* 5 *to* 8, *inrolling and ectodermal overgrowth continuing, delimiting a yolk plug which decreases in size gradually. (Courtesy of Dr. Roberts Rugh, from "Experimental Embryology," Burgess Publishing Co., Inc., Minneapolis, 1948.)*

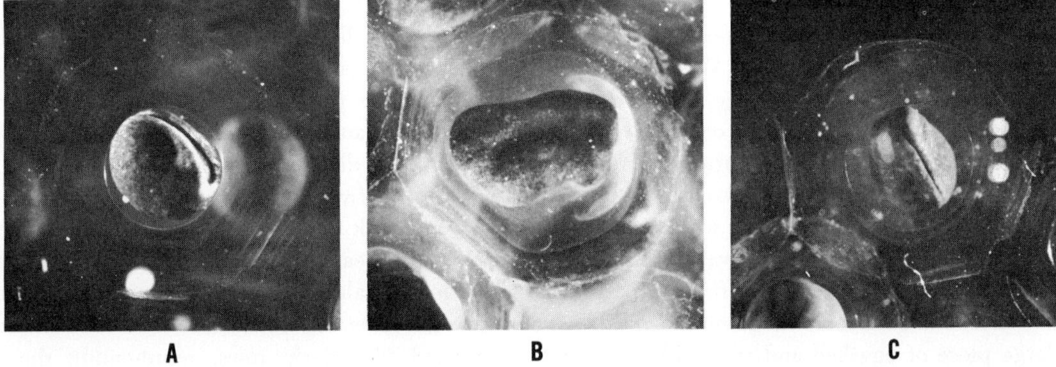

Fig. 43.3 Early neurula (A), *later neurula* (B), *and tailbud* (C) *stages in frog development. (Courtesy of Carolina Biological Supply Co.)*

6. Interpretation

Compare your observations on starfish and frog in detail. Determine first what aspects of development appear to be part of a basic pattern. Then determine how the residual aspects could be interpreted in adaptive terms, that is, how additional features (of mating, of fertilization, of egg structure, of early and later development) could be related to the requirements of the specific ways of life of starfish and frog. Check your understanding further by answering pertinent questions in the Analysis section.

D. chicken development

1. The Unfertilized Egg

Examine a hard-boiled half of a chicken egg and identify the following: SHELL, AIR SPACE at blunt end, MEMBRANES under the shell, ALBUMEN, YOLK. Next examine the contents of a raw egg (opened carefully into a dish of water so that the yolk stays intact). On the broken shell of this egg note again the white membranes and the air space. Carefully test the albumen with a probe, and note that some of the egg white is thicker and denser than the remainder. These thicker masses are the so-called CHALAZAE, two spirally wound strands of albumen, one in the blunt and one in the narrow half of the egg. On top of the yolk mass examine the BLASTODISC, a small white spot containing the clear cytoplasm of the egg cell and the egg nucleus.

What parts of the chicken "egg" come from the ovary, that is, how much of what is familiarly called "egg" is actually the egg cell? Where is the rest of the "egg" produced? When? What accounts for the characteristic egg shape? Compare true egg size and relative yolk content in chicken and frog; compare also the duration of development: what correlation is apparent? What is the function of albumen? What structures of the chicken egg do not have equivalents in the frog egg, and what is their adaptive function?

Remove the membranes from the inside of a large piece of eggshell and try to blow cigarette smoke through the shell. Can it be done? What does this test tell you about the functional properties of the shell?

2. Embryonic Stages

Five, three, and two days before this laboratory period, appropriately marked fertilized chicken eggs were put into an incubator held at 41°C and were kept there up to laboratory time. Enough eggs were used to provide one (of any stage) for every student. When the instructor hands you a still-warm incubated egg, look for the number written in pencil on the eggshell. This figure indicates that the embryo within is so many days old. Your neighbors will have eggs of the other stages specified above, so that three students will have one complete series between them. For this exercise, each such trio will form a team.

Treat your egg as follows: cup it firmly in the palm of your hand, and by means of small snips with scissors cut a fairly large oval window into the shell. Then gently lift off the cutout in one piece, severing the egg membranes if necessary. Determine first if a living embryo lies on top of the yolk mass. If only a white spot is found, the egg failed to develop. Such failures often occur in a certain percentage of cases, especially under less than optimal laboratory conditions. If your egg is dead, bring into your team another student with a living egg of equivalent stage.

For better observation of the embryo, you may (but need not) put your egg into a finger bowl with warmed Ringer, cut around the "waist" of the shell, and remove the shell halves, so that the unbroken yolk and the embryo lie free in the saline solution. The instructor may mount good preparations under dissecting microscopes. Otherwise use a hand lens for study.

a. Two-day embryo. An embryo at this stage is already well beyond gastrulation. The huge amount of yolk in the chicken egg crowds the cytoplasmic portion of the egg cell into a flat blastodisc, and developmental processes therefore occur in a discoidal pattern, not a spherical one as in the frog (see also Fig. 43.4). The embryonic disk is well visible in the 2-day embryo. Note the beating HEART; anterior to it the HEAD, with EYES already partially formed; the SOMITES along the embryonic trunk, blocks of tissue arranged in orderly rows, representing the forerunners of the body musculature. Identify the VITELLINE BLOOD VESSELS, emerging from about the middle of the trunk and ramifying over the yolk within a circular area. These vessels carry food materials from the yolk mass to the embryo.

b. Three-day embryo. Note that the embryo now lies on its side. The head is very large, and it exhibits two pronounced bends which make it curve back on itself. The eyes thus come to lie at the level of the heart. Just behind the heart identify the ANTERIOR LIMB BUD, a bulge of tissue which would give rise to the wing on that side. A POSTERIOR LIMB BUD may similarly be found near the tail end. Reidentify the somites. What changes have occurred since the 2-day stage in the circular area of blood vessels around the embryo?

c. Five-day embryo. In this stage many fine details are difficult to make out in a gross examination. It may help to wash the embryo through several changes of clean warmed Ringer. The most obvious advances over earlier phases are increase in embryo size and in vascularity. Note the rich network of blood vessels applied against the inside of the shell. What function do they particularly serve in this position? In the posterior third of the embryo note the ALLANTOIS, an easily identified, transparent, fluid-filled sac. It is one of the EXTRAEMBRYONIC MEMBRANES and functions as an embryonic urinary bladder. Metabolic wastes accumulate in it, and it becomes progressively larger as the yolk mass becomes smaller. Another extraembryonic membrane, the AMNION, surrounds the whole embryo, but this structure has probably collapsed as the egg was cut open and it may be difficult to identify.

When your examinations are completed, dispose of eggs and embryos as directed by the instructor.

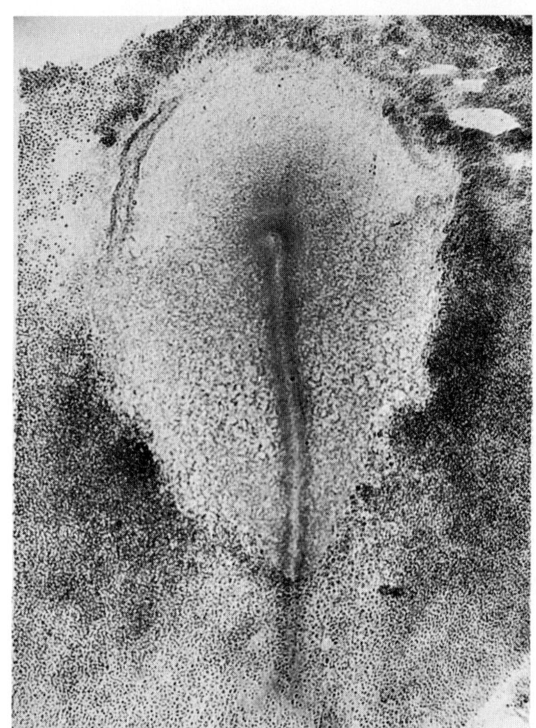

Fig. 43.4 Whole mount of 13- to 16-hr chicken embryo. The light oval area is the blastodisc atop the yolk mass. The longitudinal furrow is the so-called primitive streak, along which ectoderm rolls in and under to form an endodermal layer. The stage thus corresponds to that of gastrulation. (Courtesy of Ward's Natural Science Establishment, Inc.)

E. mammalian development

Most mammals develop within the uterus of the female, and a PLACENTA provides mechanical attachment, exchange of respiratory gases, and supply of nutrients between mother and embryo. In view of this, do you expect the mammalian egg to be relatively large or small, that is, to be rich or poor in yolk? The general sequence of development is characteristically vertebrate, but details vary considerably from those examined in other forms. This is in large measure a result of the new placental mechanism. After a certain stage of development (8 to 10 weeks in man), the mammalian embryo is known as a FETUS.

1. Human Fetuses

Examine the series of preserved fetuses set out as demonstrations. Correlate approximate fetal size and weight with developmental age. At what stage is the fetus recognizably mammalian? At what stage is it recognizably human? The series may include uteri cut open to show early embryos. If so, note the region of placental attachment and identify visible extraembryonic membranes.

2. Other Mammalian Fetuses

Study these as available, noting particularly the

appearance of placentae, regions of placental attachment in uterus, umbilical connections between placenta and fetus, and appearance of fetuses.

3. *Interpretation*

Compare your observations on chicken and mammalian development, and compare both with those on starfish and frog. Determine in particular what developmental features of the land vertebrates are specific adaptations to terrestrial life. Estimate also the advantages and disadvantages of development by means of (*a*) shelled eggs as in birds, and (*b*) placental mechanisms as in most mammals. Check your understanding here further by answering pertinent questions in the Analysis section.

IV analysis

1. Where is the egg at the time of fertilization in each of the four animal types studied? How do sperms get to the eggs? Define EXTERNAL and INTERNAL fertilization, and review the adaptive significance of the latter.

2. What is the detailed pattern of developmental processes common to all vertebrates and related groups? List item by item, from mating to emergence of adult.

3. What is the mechanism which ensures that only one sperm enters an egg? What is the significance of the gastrula? List the adult tissues the three embryonic germ layers will produce. HOW do adult tissues arise from a germ layer?

4. In the four animal types studied, relate egg size, yolk content, and duration of development. What generalization can be made? How useful is this generalization, considering for example that ostriches hatch in 7 weeks?

5. Show how the relative yolk content of eggs influences developmental patterns. Account for the observation that a morula stage is found in starfish and man, but not in frog or chicken.

6. What is the adaptive advantage of a larva? Show how this applies to starfish and frog, and why a larva is evidently unnecessary in birds and mammals. What is the adaptive advantage of larval forms in insects?

7. Contrast structure and methods of executing basic vital functions in frog tadpoles and adults. Describe what structural and functional transitions take place at the time of metamorphosis.

8. What is the adaptive advantage of a placental mechanism over a shelled egg? Discuss also the reverse of this.

9. What parts of a (*a*) frog egg, (*b*) chicken egg, emerge from the ovary, and how are the other parts formed? Is a chicken egg fertilized before or after a shell is present? Describe what produces the characteristic shape of a bird egg.

10. What are the functions of the jelly coats of frog eggs? What is the adaptive significance of the pigmentation of frog eggs? Starfish eggs are fairly translucent. Is this condition advantageous, or would a pigmented condition as in frog eggs be better?

11. Describe the properties an eggshell must necessarily possess if it is to serve as enclosure for a terrestrially developing embryo. What is the metabolic source of the pigments often found on the eggshells of birds? What would happen if a developing chicken egg were placed into water?

12. Are extraembryonic membranes present in reptiles? Name and describe the position and function of these membranes in birds and mammals.

13. Discuss whether the evolutionary development of extraembryonic membranes can be considered a necessary prerequisite for the successful invasion of the land by vertebrates. What other adaptations were required to make terrestrial life possible?

14. How does a breakfast egg differ from the ones you studied? How are double-yolked eggs produced?

15. Show how problems of terrestrial reproduction are solved in land animals not studied in this exercise, for example, insects, spiders, worms.

part 8 adaptation

exercise 44 gene transmission: probability

I materials

Each student

hand lens
dissecting instruments
genetic corn, 3:1 and 9:3:3:1

Each group of 4 students

2 paper bags, each with 100 white and 100 black beans
Drosophila, culture bottle with F_2 of vestigial-winged female × wild-type male (see section C3 and Appendix)
Drosophila, culture bottle with F_2 of vestigial-winged female × white-eyed male (see section C3 and Appendix)

Class stock

ether-anesthesia bottles for fruit flies
camel's-hair brushes
Drosophila, males and females of wild-type, vestigial-winged, and white-eyed flies, stocks for identification

II introduction

In the first part of this exercise, some of the fundamental laws of probability will be examined, particularly as they apply to the biology of inheritance. In the second and third parts, breeding experiments with corn and fruit flies will be studied and interpreted. The overall objective of the exercise is to allow you to become thoroughly familiar with the meaning of the two laws of Mendel, the LAW OF SEGREGATION and the LAW OF INDEPENDENT ASSORTMENT, and with the biological mechanisms underlying them.

In many cases (and in the cases studied in this exercise), visible traits are expressions of DOMINANT genes, RECESSIVE genes, or of both. Four possibilities exist in which dominant and recessive genes affecting a given trait may be combined pairwise during fertilization:

1. Paternal dominant and maternal dominant, giving a HOMOZYGOUS DOMINANT condition
2. Paternal recessive and maternal dominant, giving a HETEROZYGOUS condition
3. Paternal dominant and maternal recessive, also giving a HETEROZYGOUS condition
4. Paternal recessive and maternal recessive, giving a HOMOZYGOUS RECESSIVE condition

Which of these possibilities is actually realized depends on the genetic constitution of the parents and on the number of offspring produced. For example, a parental mating of $Aa \times AA$ cannot produce homozygous recessive offspring; the gametes of one parent will be 50% A and 50% a, the gametes of the other parent will all be A, and no combination here can give an aa offspring. But the parental mating above CAN produce either heterozygous (Aa) or homozygous dominant (AA) offspring (verify this). What the offspring will actually be like will depend on the number produced; a SINGLE offspring could be either Aa or AA, and more than this cannot be predicted from the information available. If there are MANY offspring, by contrast, half are statistically likely to be Aa, the other half AA.

Note how the mathematics of probability and the biology of inheritance are intimately connected here. It is the function of this exercise to analyze these two sets of principles more fully, and to illustrate their combined effect on living organisms.

III directions

A. probability and genetic ratios

Students will work in pairs, each team using one of the paper bags containing 100 white and 100 black beans.

1. *Probability of Single Events*

Mathematically, the probability (P) of some event (x) is always a NUMBER between 0 and 1. This number is arrived at by dividing the number of favorable outcomes (m) of the event by the number of total possible outcomes (n):

$$P_x = \frac{m_x}{n_x}$$

If every possible outcome is a favorable outcome, that is, if $m_x = n_x$, then $P_x = 1$, or event x is CERTAIN to occur. If no possible outcome is a favorable outcome, then $P_x = 0$, or event x is an IMPOSSIBILITY. "Probability" lies between these extremes, and the larger the value of P_x, the more certainly may event x be EXPECTED to be favorable.

Note the emphasis on the word "expected"; probability values are purely theoretical, mathematical measures of EXPECTATIONS. Actual, practical realization of the expectations requires that events occur many times. The more often an event occurs, the more closely will the number of favorable outcomes approach the number predicted by the P value. Thus, probability predictions are most unreliable where they concern one-time occurrences but become the more reliable as the number of occurrences increases. These principles are illustrated in the following tests.

a. Pick out from the paper bag four beans, one at a time and at random. To ensure this, shake up the bag before each selection. PUT BEANS BACK after EACH draw to keep the size of the bean population constant. RECORD the number of white and black beans picked.

b. Pick out 10 beans, one at a time, as above. Again RECORD the number of white and black beans drawn.

c. Pick out 20 beans, one at a time, as above. Again RECORD the number of white and black beans drawn.

d. Add up the totals for white and black beans from (a), (b), and (c), and RECORD.

e. Calculate the RATIOS of white and black beans, separately for the data recorded in (a), (b), (c), and (d); divide the smaller number (regardless of whether it represents white or black) into the larger number, and carry the division to two decimals. Compare the four values so obtained; what pattern is apparent?

f. On the basis of the theoretical consideration that $P_x = \frac{m_x}{n_x}$, what is P_{white} and P_{black}, that is, the probability of drawing a white bean and that of drawing a black one? Determine the numerical value of the ratio $P_{\text{white}}/P_{\text{black}}$, and compare this ratio with the four values obtained in (e). Which of the four comes closest to the theoretical value of $P_{\text{white}}/P_{\text{black}}$? Which of the tests above thus provides the most reliable measure of "bean-picking" probability?

2. *Probability of Joint Independent Events*

The probability of several joint independent events occurring together is arrived at by multiplying the probabilities of the individual events: $P_{x,y,z,\ldots} = P_x \times P_y \times P_z \times \cdots$. Thus the probability of throwing two sixes with two dice is

$P = \frac{1}{6} \times \frac{1}{6} = \frac{1}{36}$, $\frac{1}{6}$ being the individual probability of throwing a six with any one die.

This rule governing the simultaneous occurrence of two events has an important bearing on the mathematics of gene transmission from one to the next generation of organisms. At fertilization an egg combines randomly with a sperm. For any given genetic trait, the sperm may contain either a dominant OR a recessive gene, and the egg also may contain either a dominant OR a recessive gene. Thus, the probability of the sperm carrying a dominant gene is ½, and the probability of the egg carrying a dominant gene is also ½. Hence the probability of the zygote obtaining TWO dominant genes will be ½ × ½, or ¼; in a large population of offspring, and under the conditions here cited, 25% of the offspring may statistically be predicted to carry two dominant genes. Analogous arguments hold for recessive and heterozygous gene combinations. These principles are illustrated in the following tests.

a. Pick out from the paper bag two beans at a time, 12 times, at random. Shake the bag before each draw and return the beans drawn after inspecting them. RECORD the color of the bean pairs drawn (ww, wb, bb).

b. On the basis of the relation $P_{x,y} = P_x \times P_y$, calculate the theoretical probability of drawing ww, wb, and bb color pairs, and compare the ratio of these calculated values with that actually obtained in the tests. Is a wb pair in the same mathematical category as a bw pair? Explain.

c. Pick out from the paper bag three beans at a time, 16 times, at random. Shake the bag after each draw, and return the beans drawn after inspecting them. RECORD the color combinations drawn (www, wwb, wbb, bbb).

d. Calculate the theoretical probabilities of drawing the above color combinations, and compare the ratio of the calculated values with that actually obtained. How many mathematical categories do the combinations wbb and wwb represent? Without actually carrying out the test, can you predict from theoretical considerations what ratio of combinations would be obtained if you picked four beans at a time, many times?

B. inheritance in corn

Each kernel on an ear of corn is a seed, capable of growing into a whole new plant. A complete ear is the result of many individual fertilizations and represents a compact population of potential offspring suitable for studies in heredity.

You are supplied with two ears of corn, each having kernels of different types of colors. The instructor will tell you how to name each type. These colors are gene-determined traits, and your task is to find out how the traits are inherited.

For each ear, find answers to the following:

1. Total number of kernels on ear.
2. Number of kernels of each different color type.
3. Percentage of kernels of each different color type.
4. Arranged in order of abundance, what typical Mendelian ratio do these percentages exemplify?
5. How many gene pairs appear to be involved in this instance of inheritance?
6. Which traits are dominant and which recessive?
7. Expressed in symbolic form, what is the probable genotype of each color type?
8. Reasoning backwards, what was the genotype of the parents which produced this ear of corn? What was the phenotype of the parents?
9. What could have been the genotypes and phenotypes of the grandparents of this ear of corn?
10. What Mendelian law is this instance of gene transmission governed by? Show how the law applies specifically.

C. inheritance in fruit flies

The fruit fly *Drosophila* has been used for decades as a favorite organism in genetic studies. The animal can be bred easily; sexually mature offspring can be obtained in 3 weeks; chromosome number is small ($2n = 8$); giant chromosomes exist in the salivary glands (see exercise 39), and precise microscopic investigation of experimental effects on *Drosophila* chromosomes is feasible. In the course of years, mutations have appeared in the stocks of flies kept in various laboratories, and the inheritance of two such MUTANT TRAITS will be analyzed here. The mutations to be studied (and most others also) are

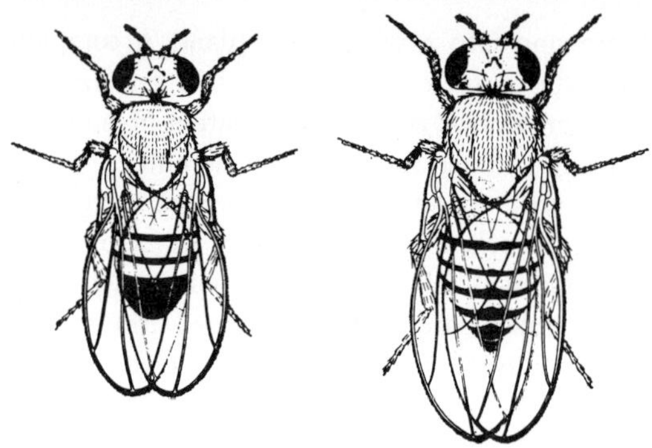

Fig. 44.1 Diagram of male (left) and female (right) fruit fly.

recessive; that is, the wild-type normal condition is dominant.

1. Handling of Flies

Flies are usually grown in half-pint milk bottles containing food medium at the bottom. Larvae and pupae generally become well surrounded by food, and adult flies are found in the free space above the food. In investigating a given genetic problem, a small number of desired parental flies is introduced in a new culture bottle containing food, and the bottle is capped and left undisturbed for about 1 week. During this time mating takes place and fertilized eggs are deposited by the females. Parent flies are removed at the end of the week, the bottle is recapped, and nothing further is done for another week or two. By the end of this time offspring larvae have developed into adults and the trait characteristics of these adults can now be studied.

Fly populations are examined under ether anesthesia. The culture bottle containing the flies is inverted over another bottle which has been well saturated with ether vapor. Narcotized flies fall into the vapor bottle, and from there the organisms may be spread on a sheet of white paper for counting and examination. This is done with a hand lens or the unaided eye, depending on how easily traits can be identified. Camel's-hair brushes (or needles) are used to shift the flies about on the paper. The examination is carried out as rapidly as possible, so that the flies remain well anesthetized throughout. When the work is done the organisms are returned to their culture bottle, where they are allowed to recover.

To ensure your proper handling of flies, the instructor will give additional oral directions as necessary.

2. Identification of Genetic Characters

Male and female flies of three types will be studied: wild-type, vestigial-wing, and white-eye. WATCH carefully as the instructor anesthetizes sample stocks of these fly types and deposits them on separate sheets of paper. Obtain about five or six flies from each of these samples, bring them to your workplace, and with hand lens and brush IDENTIFY and study the traits described below. You should become proficient in typing the flies rapidly and surely.

a. Wild-type males and females. Wild-type flies represent the genetic norm for *Drosophila.* Since the experiment below will involve wing and eye traits, fix in your mind their wild-type appearance. Wings reach just beyond the tip of the abdomen, and the eyes are red in color. It will also be important to distinguish the sexes. Males (indicated by the symbol ♂) are slightly smaller than females (designated by the symbol ♀). The tip of the abdomen in the male is broader and more rounded than in the female and is pigmented almost solid black. In the female the tip of the abdomen carries transverse stripes. There are other external sex differences, but the ones mentioned should suffice to allow you to make a reliable sex distinction (see Fig. 44.1).

b. Vestigial wing. A gene for wing development is located on the second chromosome of *Drosophila.* The recessive mutant condition produces a highly reduced "vestigial" wing, very easily distinguished from the wild-type wing. The recessive gene may be designated *vg*, and the dominant wild-type gene, *Vg* (or also "+"). Identify male and female vestigial-winged flies, and compare with the wild type of each sex.

c. White eye. A gene controlling eye color is located on the first chromosome, that is, the sex (*X*) chromosome of *Drosophila.* The recessive mutant condition produces white eye color (due to the absence of any pigmentation), easily distinguished from the red of the wild type. The recessive gene may be designated *w*, and the dominant wild-type gene, *W* (or also "+"). Identify male and female white-eyed flies, and compare with the wild type of each sex. Visualize what white-eyed AND vestigial-winged flies would look like. Keep in mind also that white eye, being produced by genes on the X chromosomes, is a SEX-LINKED recessive condition. Hence, in symbolic representation, a white-eyed female would be written X_wX_w, a white-eyed male X_wY, and normal-eyed females and males XX and XY, respectively.

Return all sample flies to the instructor.

3. Test Design

Six weeks in advance of the laboratory, two sets of *Drosophila* mating cultures (P generation) were started. Into each of about six culture bottles of one set were put five vestigial-winged, otherwise normal virgin females, and five wild-type males. This mating (cross I) can be represented symbolically by:

CROSS I P: $vgvg \times VgVg$
female male

Into each of about six culture bottles of a second set were put five vestigial-winged, normal-eyed virgin females, and five normal-winged, white-eyed males. This mating (cross II) can be represented symbolically by:

CROSS II P: $vgvgXX \times VgVgX_wY$
female male

The flies were allowed to mate and lay eggs into the culture bottles. One week after starting the cultures the parental flies were removed. F_1 generations soon hatched out subsequently.

Three weeks in advance of the laboratory the pair of culture bottles which you will study was started. Five male and five female F_1 flies were put into each of your two bottles, to produce F_1 (brother-sister) matings for cross I, and F_1 (brother-sister) matings for cross II. A week thereafter the F_1 adults were removed. F_2 populations soon hatched out in each bottle, and these are the ones on your desk, to be studied below.

(The instructor will have prepared two like sets of F_2 flies for each cross, so that the sets can be used alternately on successive days of laboratory. A fly population used today should be allowed to recover for 48 hours before being used again.)

4. Experimental

Four students will work together as a team. Each team has available one F_2 culture bottle of cross I and one F_2 culture bottle of cross II. All four members of the team first deal with cross I, as follows:

Anesthetize the flies in the bottle, as described above and following the oral directions of the instructor. Pour the narcotized flies on a sheet of white paper, and with a brush divide the population into four roughly equal piles of flies. Each member of the team now types the flies in one pile.

Examine the flies one by one; the unaided eye will probably suffice, but use hand lens if necessary. For each fly RECORD the SEX and the appearance of the WINGS. Record in Data Sheet 15, page 000, the total number of flies in each trait category of your pile. When all four piles have been counted, calculate the cumulative totals and record these also.

When done, return all flies of cross I to the culture bottle, cap it, and proceed to cross II.

Anesthetize the F_2 flies of cross II as above, divide the narcotized population into four piles, one for each team member, and proceed to type each fly. Greater care will be required here than in cross I since a greater number of trait categories will have to be looked for. Each fly is to be examined for SEX, for EYE COLOR, and for WING CONDITION. Thus, theoretically there will be eight trait categories. Record in Data Sheet 15 the total number of flies of each category found. When all four piles have been counted, calculate the cumulative totals and record these also.

Return all flies of cross II to the culture bottle and cap it.

5. Interpretation

CROSS I:

a. Calculate the PERCENTAGE of flies in each of the four categories. Record.

b. From (a), determine the following percentage RATIOS:

(1) Wild-type males : vestigial-winged males.
(2) Wild-type females : vestigial-winged females.
(3) All wild-type flies : all vestigial-winged flies.

c. Is there a significant difference between these ratios? Do you conclude that inheritance of the vestigial wing is influenced by the sex of the animal?

d. What Mendelian ratio is exemplified by the

F_2 of cross I? How does this experiment illustrate the law of segregation?

e. On the basis of all information, work out the genotypes of the P, F_1, and F_2 generations, and state what the phenotypes of these animals are.

CROSS II:

a. Calculate the PERCENTAGE of flies in each of the trait categories. Record.

b. From (a), determine the following percentage RATIOS:

(1) All male flies : all female flies (regardless of eye or wing condition).
(2) Normal-winged males : vestigial-winged males (regardless of eye color).
(3) Normal-winged females : vestigial-winged females (regardless of eye color).
(4) All normal-winged flies : all vestigial-winged flies (regardless of sex or eye color).
(5) Normal-eyed males : white-eyed males (regardless of wing condition).
(6) All normal-eyed flies : all white-eyed flies (regardless of sex or wing condition).
(7) All wild type : all white eye : all vestigial winged : all white eye AND vestigial winged (regardless of sex).

c. From these ratios and those determined for cross I, is the inheritance of the vestigial wing influenced by the simultaneous inheritance of (*a*) eye-color traits, and (*b*) sex?

d. Is the inheritance of white eye influenced by the simultaneous inheritance of (*a*) wing traits, and (*b*) sex?

e. How is sex inherited? How does sex influence the inheritance of white eye?

f. What Mendelian ratio is exemplified by the F_2 of cross II? How does this experiment illustrate the law of independent assortment?

g. On the basis of all information, work out the genotypes of the P, F_1, and F_2 generations, and state what the phenotypes of these animals are.

IV analysis

1. In flipping a coin, what is the probability of throwing seven heads in succession? Five heads and two tails? One head and six tails?

2. What is the probability that three children born to a couple will all be girls? Is this more or less probable than getting two girls and one boy, or two boys and one girl, or three boys?

3. If a paper bag contains 50 white beans and 100 black beans, what is the probability of drawing (*a*) 2 white beans together, (*b*) 1 white and 1 black bean together, (*c*) 2 black beans together?

4. Write down the color combinations of beans you obtained when you picked two and three beans simultaneously. Work out by trial-and-error arithmetic what the combinations would be if four beans were picked. Then work out the expansion $(a + b)^n = \cdots$, where n is taken successively as 1, 2, 3, 4. Compare the coefficients of this expansion with the color ratios of beans. What is apparent? The expansion $(a + b)^n$ is known as the BINOMIAL THEOREM.

5. How and where can the binomial theorem be applied to the biology of inheritance? If two parents heterozygous for three traits produced offspring, could the binomial theorem be used to predict the genotypes and phenotypes of these offspring?

6. Review the test design and the results of crosses I and II above, work out all genotypes if not already done, and show what can be concluded from the various percentage ratios obtained in the F_2's.

7. State the first law of Mendel in full, and in your own words fix its meaning precisely. How is this law important and useful? What biological processes make this law a necessary consequence? Show how (*a*) the inheritance of kernel color in corn, and (*b*) crosses I and II, follow this law.

8. State the second law of Mendel in full, and in your own words fix its meaning precisely. How is this law important and useful? What biological processes make this law a necessary consequence? Show how (*a*) the inheritance of kernel color in corn, and (*b*) cross II, follow this law.

9. Does Mendel's second law apply where two (or more) gene pairs are located on the same chromosome pair? Discuss. Under what conditions does this law hold?

10. Do Mendel's laws apply where reproduction does not include a sexual process? Discuss. By what laws or rules does an amoeba inherit traits, and how can such traits change from generation to generation?

11. Define SEX LINKAGE, and show how sex-

linked traits are inherited. Use your evidence from cross II. How is sex itself determined, and how is sex inherited?

12. In given populations of organisms, the following phenotype ratios are found: (*a*) 15:1, (*b*) 9:6:1. What can be concluded about (1) the number of gene pairs involved in producing the phenotype traits; (2) the genotypes of the F_1 and P generations; (3) the manner of interaction of the genes involved?

13. A tall, red-flowered, large-fruited plant is mated with a short, white-flowered, large-fruited plant. The following offspring are obtained: 79 tall, white, large; 75 tall, red, large; 88 short, white, large; 81 short, red, large; 22 tall, white, small; 27 tall, red, small; 24 short, white, small; 30 short, red, small. What are the genotypes of the parents and offspring?

14. What F_2 would be obtained from the following *Drosophila* mating (followed by brother-sister mating in the F_1): white-eyed female × wild-type male? Note that this is the reciprocal of the cross: wild-type female × white-eyed male, carried out as part of the exercise above. Compare the F_2's of these two reciprocal crosses.

15. Assume that right-handedness in man is dominant over left-handedness, and that dark hair is dominant over blond hair. Suppose a right-handed blond man whose father was left-handed marries a left-handed woman from a family in which all members have been dark-haired for as many generations as can be remembered. What will the children of this marriage be like?

appendix: reagents and supplies

A. reagents and media

Commonly used solutions of inorganic salts (such as $CuSO_4$, NaCl, Na_2CO_3) should be made up in bulk lots as concentrated stocks. Portions can then be diluted for use as required.

1. *Acetocarmine Stain*

Stir carmine powder into boiling 45% acetic acid until a saturated solution is formed. Cool and filter. For long-term storage add some rust scrapings.

2. *Acids*

The concentration characteristics of the common concentrated mineral acids as purchased are as follows:

	normality	*weight, per cent*
conc. HCl	12	36
conc. H_2SO_4	36	96
conc. HNO_3	16	71
conc. acetic acid (glacial)	17	99.5

A sufficiently accurate 1 *N* (3%) HCl solution, for example, can be prepared by diluting the concentrated acid 12 times. It is advisable to maintain ready-made stocks of frequently used standard dilutions (for example, 1 *N*, 1/10 *N*, and 10%), particularly for HCl and acetic acid.

3. *Agar, Alkaline Gel*

To make 1 liter, dissolve 30 g agar in a mixture of 987.5 ml distilled water, 10 ml methyl red solution, and 2.5 ml 0.1 *N* NaOH.

4. *Agar, Nutrient*

For bacterial cultures, standard nutrient agar may be purchased ready-made (for example, Difco). The nutrients are 3 g beef extract and 5 g peptone for every 15 g of agar.

5. *Auxin*

The hormone can be either naphthaleneacetic acid (NAA) or indoleacetic acid (IAA). Dissolve 100 mg of hormone in 2 ml of 95% absolute ethyl alcohol. Then add this solution to 100 g of hydrous lanolin paste and mix thoroughly. Use directly or store covered in the refrigerator.

6. *Bases*

A 1 N solution of NaOH contains 40 g solid alkali per liter of water (4% solution). Make up and maintain bulk stocks of concentrated NaOH with a normality of 12 N to 14 N. Also maintain stocks of frequently used dilutions, for example, 10% solutions (2.5 N).

A 1 N solution of KOH contains 56 g solid alkali per liter of water (5.6% solution). For CO_2 absorption in exercise VI.3, make up 22 or 23 N KOH (125 g alkali/100 ml water). See also 20, below.

7. *Benedict's Reagent*

To make 1 liter, mix 173 g Na-citrate and 100 g Na_2CO_3 with 800 ml distilled water. Warm to dissolve, then cool and filter; add distilled water to make 850 ml. Then dissolve 17.3 g $CuSO_4$ in 100 ml distilled water and stir slowly into first solution. Bring up to 1 liter with distilled water.

8. *Buffers*

If required buffers are not being purchased ready-made, make up an $M/15$ monobasic potassium phosphate solution (9.08 g KH_2PO_4 in 1 liter of water) and an $M/15$ dibasic sodium phosphate solution (9.47 g Na_2HPO_4 in 1 liter of water). Mix the two in the following proportions to obtain 100 ml of buffer of the indicated pH:

pH	$M/15$ KH_2PO_4	$M/15$ Na_2HPO_4
5.3	97.5 ml	2.5 ml
7.0	39 ml	61 ml
8.0	5 ml	95 ml

These mixtures will suffice whenever buffers of pH 5 and 7 are specified. The pH 8 mixture may actually also substitute for pH 9 buffers. If a precise pH 9 buffer is desired, mix together 50 ml of 0.2 M H_3BO_3, 50 ml of 0.2 M KCl, 21.5 ml of 0.2 M NaOH, and dilute to 200 ml with distilled water.

9. *Diphenylamine Reagent*

To make 1 liter, mix 486 ml glacial acetic acid and 14 ml conc. sulfuric acid. Then add 5 g diphenylamine, stir, and dilute with 500 ml of distilled water.

10. *Ethylene Glycol Solution*

A 0.3 M solution is isotonic to mammalian blood; add 17 ml (19 g) of ethylene glycol to 1 liter of distilled water.

11. *IKI Reagent*

To make a 1-liter lot, add 20 g potassium iodide to 1 liter of distilled water and stir to dissolve. Then add 4 g iodine crystals and again stir; dissolution will take place slowly. Keep the reagent in dark stoppered bottles.

12. *Limewater*

Add an excess of $Ca(OH)_2$ to distilled water, stopper, and shake well. Let stand overnight. Then decant the supernatant limewater and keep it tightly stoppered.

13. *Methyl Cellulose Suspension*

Stir successive small amounts of water into a given quantity of methyl cellulose until a suspension of desired viscosity is obtained. For best results the mixture should be just stiff enough to support a glass rod upright.

14. *Methylene Blue*

If not used as a stain, the dye is made up as an aqueous solution in the concentration specified in a given exercise. For use as a stain, make up a 1.5% stock solution of dye powder in 95% ethyl alcohol. Then dilute 1 part of stock with 9 parts of water for class use.

15. *Millon Reagent*

The reagent is made by dissolving 1 weight-part of mercury in a 2 weight-parts of conc. nitric acid and diluting with water. This reagent should be purchased ready-made.

16. *Ninhydrin Reagent*

Ninhydrin is triketohydrindene hydrate, or

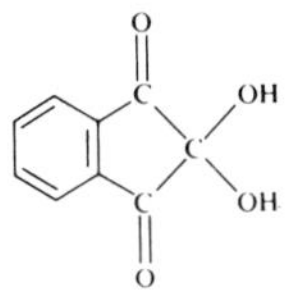

The reagent is a 0.1 or 0.2% solution of the

compound in acetone (and is consequently HIGHLY FLAMMABLE).

17. Orcinol Reagent

Orcinol is dihydroxymethylbenzene, or

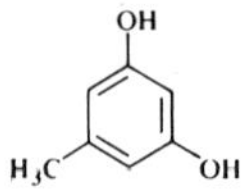

To make the reagent, mix 70 ml distilled water and 30 ml conc. HCl, Dissolve in this 0.1 g orcinol and 0.05 g $FeCl_3$.

18. Phenol Reagent

To 70 ml distilled water add 30 ml conc. HCl. Stir, then dissolve in this 0.5 g carbolic acid (phenol, or hydroxybenzene, C_6H_5OH). A somewhat better reagent for testing ketose sugars uses RESORCINOL; see 21, below.

19. Phloroglucinol Reagent

Make up a 1% solution of phloroglucinol in water and mix with an equal volume of conc. HCl.

20. Pyrogallol Solution

Make up an approximately 22 *N* KOH solution by dissolving SLOWLY 160 g of solid alkali pellets in 130 ml of distilled water. Then add 10 g of resublimed pyrogallic acid and stir. This makes about 200 ml of pyrogallol. Use fresh and keep well stoppered. The KOH solution without pyrogallic acid is used for the CO_2 absorption tests.

21. Resorcinol Reagent

To 70 ml distilled water add 30 ml conc. HCl. Stir, then dissolve in it 0.05 g resorcinol. This compound is dihydroxybenzene, $C_6H_4(OH)_2$. In testing for ketose sugars, this reagent is preferable to acid phenol solutions (see 18, above).

22. Ringer Solutions

Stocks can be made up in concentrated form or as mixed weighed powders.

for frogs and turtles

NaCl, 7 g
KCl, 0.15 g
$CaCl_2$ (anhydrous), 0.15 g
$NaHCO_3$, 0.1 g
distilled water to 1 liter

for chickens and mammals

NaCl, 9 g
KCl, 0.4 g
$CaCl_2$ (anhydrous), 0.24 g
$NaHCO_3$, 0.2 g
distilled water to 1 liter

B. biological supplies

1. Prepared Slides and Preserved Materials

All are obtainable as specified from biological supply houses. Fetal pigs for dissection should be 11 to 13 in. long, at least single-injected, embalmed or formaldehyde-preserved, and are best procured in individual plastic bags.

2. Monera, Protista, Living

a. Bacterial cultures (including *Bacillus megatherium*) and yeasts may be obtained from the American Type Culture Collection, 2112 M Street, N.W., Washington, D.C.

b. Algae are available both from biological supply houses and from the Algal Type Culture Collection, Dept. of Botany, Indiana University, Bloomington, Ind.

c. Most of the common protozoa (including stocks of *Paramecium* for demonstration of the mating reaction) can be procured from biological supply houses. Directions for maintaining such cultures usually come with the organisms. Rich long-term mass cultures of *Amoeba, Pelomyxa, Paramecium, Stentor*, and other protozoa may be started from such supply-house stocks. Put organisms in original water medium into small (50 ml) dishes; add one barley grain per dish and a small amount of boiled tap water. Note that *Pelomyxa* requires paramecia as food. Keep cultures in the dark, lightly covered. Replenish medium from time to time with boiled tap water and change barley grain once every week. Subculture as desired, using initially some of the water medium of the parent culture and adding small amounts of boiled tap water over a period of days.

3. Plant Material, Living

a. To grow BEAN SEEDLINGS about 6 in. tall,

allow 3 to 4 weeks growing time after planting seeds.

b. To grow germinating RADISH SEEDS with rootlets and root hairs, put seeds into a thoroughly moistened clay dish, cover lightly with wet filter paper, invert a beaker over the covered seeds, and allow about 5 to 7 days growing time. Keep moist throughout.

c. To grow grass seeds, fast-germinating varieties (such as Red Top) should be used. These are obtainable in any seed store.

d. Light-sensitive lettuce seeds (for example, variety Grand Rapids) may be procured from the Educational Division, MacAlister Scientific Corporation, 243 Broadway, Cambridge, Mass.

e. If not available locally, other required living plant material may be purchased as specified from biological and botanical supply houses.

4. *Animal Material, Living*

a. Stock cultures of *Drosophila* mutants for genetic exercises are obtainable from biological supply houses. The latter also supply the necessary bottles and glassware, as well as food media and instructions for using these materials. Mutant stocks other than the ones specified in exercise VIII.1 may well be used, and the exercise can readily be adapted accordingly.

b. To induce ovulation in frogs, use large females received fresh from hibernation (from January to May they may be kept at 4°C in the refrigerator; animals to be used for induced ovulation should not be reared or stored at room temperature, or the eggs deteriorate). Frog pituitary glands are injected in the abdominal cavity 2 days before eggs are wanted, according to the following dose schedule:

Sept. to Jan.:	10 male or 5 female glands
Feb.:	8 male or 4 female glands
Mar.:	5 male or 3 female glands
Apr.:	4 male or 2 female glands

One ovulating female will supply enough eggs for a large class. Detailed directions of procedure may be found in "Experimental Embryology," by Roberts Rugh, Burgess Publishing Co., Inc., Minneapolis, 1948. NOTE: mammalian pituitary extracts should not be used to induce ovulation in frogs.

c. Embryological materials (including series of preserved embryonic stages of frogs) are obtainable from biological supply houses.

Data Sheet 1. Observations on unknowns

	Visible diagnostic features	*Probable classification*
1		
2		
3		
4		
5		
6		
7		
8		
9		
10		
x		
x		
x		

Data Sheet 2

Expt. 1 Phosphatase			
Test tube	*Contents*	*IKI negative after (min)*	*Benedict's result*
1			
2			
3			
4			
5			
6			

Expt. 2 Catalase				
	0 time, 1 min	*3-min time, 4 min*	*6-min time, 7 min*	*9-min time, 10 min*
$KMnO_4$, mm				

Plot:

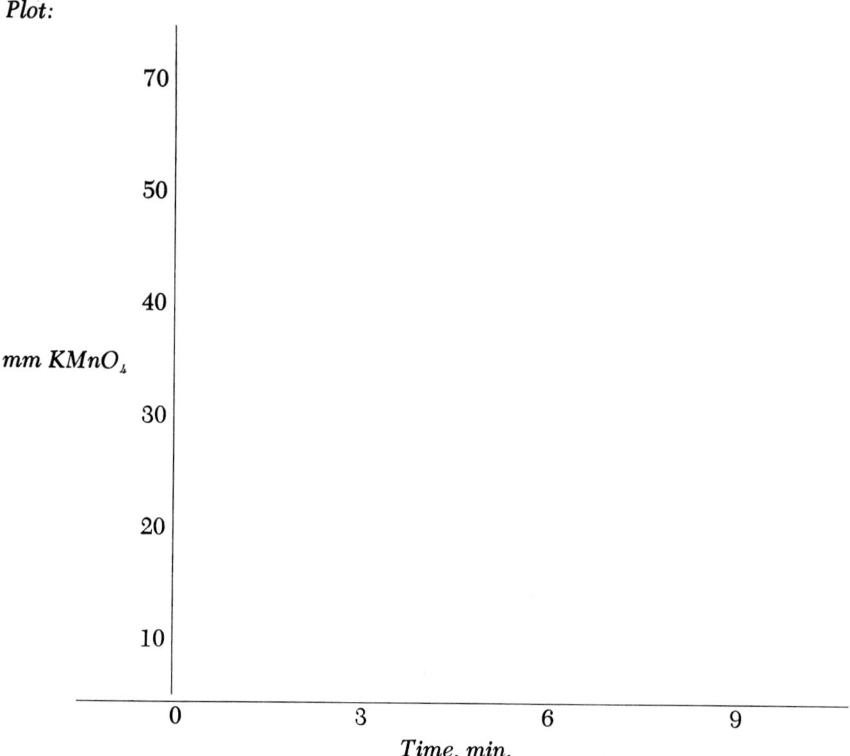

Data Sheet 3

Expt. 3	*Enzyme extract*			
	Full strength	*¾ strength*	*½ strength*	*¼ strength*
mm $KMnO_4$, 4 min				

Expt. 4 H_2O_2	H_2O_2			
	full strength	*½ strength*	*1/10 strength*	*1/20 strength*
mm $KMnO_4$, 4 min				

Expt. 5			
	10°C	*Room temp*	*37°C*
mm $KMnO_4$, 4 min			

Expt. 6			
	pH 5	*pH 7*	*pH 9*
mm $KMnO_4$, 4 min			

Expt. 7				
	Control	*Trypsin-treated*	*NaN_3-treated*	*NaF-treated*
mm $KMnO_4$, 4 min				

Data Sheet 4

Expt. A2: Diffusion rate

Position of diffusion front, mm	0	5	10	15	30	60	90	120	*minutes*
Tube 1									
2									
3									
4									

Position of diffusion front, mm

80
70
60
50
40
30
20
10

0 5 10 15 30 60 90 120 *minutes*

Expt. D: Permeability

	1	2	3	4	5
Hemolysis time, sec					

	Isotonic ethylene glycol		
	10°C	*Room temp*	*37°C*
Hemolysis time, sec			

Expt. E1: Heartbeat

	Room temp	*0°C*	*10°C*	*20°C*	*30°C*
Rate of heartbeat					

Rate of heartbeat

0 10 20 30

Temperature, °C

Expt. E2: Ciliary movement			
	10°C	*Room temp*	*30°C*
Cork motion, cm/min			

Data Sheet 6

	Pond surface	*Pond bottom*	*River shore*	*Tide pool*	*Ocean beach*
Number of objects, high-power average					
Types of nonliving material					
Number of living objects, high power					
Number of motile and nonmotile forms					
Number of different motility types					
Number of shapes among organisms					
Number of size classes among organisms					
Number of colors among organisms					
Number of translucent and opaque forms					
Notes on internal architectures					
Number of species					
Other features, pH					

	Soil I	*Soil II*	*Soil III*	*Soil IV*	*Soil V*
Geographic source, name of soil if known, and pH					
Particle types, relative proportions					
Particle shapes, relative proportions					
Predominant particle size, comparative					
Other microscopic characteristics					
Air-holding capacity, volume %					
Water-holding capacity, volume %					
Mineral-holding capacity, comparative					
Living organisms, comparative, and pH of diluted sample					

Data Sheet 8

Duration of experiment, min:

Internal diameter of transpirometer tube, mm:

Transpirometer	*1*	2	3	4	5	6	7	8	9	10
Experimental condition										
Distance between watermarks, mm										
Total water volume transpired, ml										
Water transpired, m/hr										

Test	Contents	Results
B1 1		
2		
3		
4		
5		
6		
B2 7		
8		
9		
10		
11		
12		
13		
C1 14		
15		
16		
17		
18		
C2 19		
20		
21		
22		
23		
24		
25		
26		
27		
D1 28		
29		
30		
31		
32		
D2 33		
34		
35		
36		
37		
38		
39		
40		

Data Sheet 10

Test	*Contents*	*Initial gas reading, cm^3*	*Terminal gas reading, cm^3*	*Net gas volume, cm^3/hr*
1				
2				
3				
4				
5				
6				
7				
8				
9				
10				
11				
12				
13				
14				

	1	2	3	4	5	6
Contents						
Decoloration time						

Data Sheet 12

	Breathing rate per min	*Breath holding at inspiration*	*Breath holding at expiration*
After normal breathing			
After forced ventilation			
While and after re-breathing same air			
After exercise			

	Lips	Finger tip	Palm of hand	Back of hand	Inner wrist surface	Outer wrist surface	Inner forearm near elbow	Outer forearm near elbow
1/16 in.								
1/8 in.								
1/4 in.								
1/2 in.								
1 in.								

Data Sheet 14

	Normal frog	*Decerebrated frog*	*Spinal frog*
Posture			
Breathing			
Eye reflex			
Croak reflex			
Righting reflexes			
Balance reflexes			
Swimming reflex			
Jumping reflex			

Cross I

F_2 of P: ____________ X ____________

	Pile 1	Pile 2	Pile 3	Pile 4	Totals
Wild-type male					
Vestigial-wing male					
Wild-type female					
Vestigial-wing female					
Totals					

Cross II

F_2 of P: ____________ X ____________

	Pile 1	Pile 2	Pile 3	Pile 4	Totals
Wild-type male					
Normal-eye, vestigial-wing male					
White-eye, normal-wing male					
White-eye, vestigial-wing male					
Wild-type female					
Normal-eye, vestigial-wing female					
White-eye, normal-wing female					
White-eye, vestigial-wing female					
Totals